HUMAN BIOLOGY

A GUIDE TO FIELD METHODS

IBP HANDBOOK No. 9

HUMAN BIOLOGY
a guide to field methods

Compiled by

J. S. WEINER
Convenor

and

J. A. LOURIE
Scientific Co-ordinator

SECTION IBP/HA
(Human Adaptability)
21 Bedford Square, London WC1, England

INTERNATIONAL BIOLOGICAL PROGRAMME
7 MARYLEBONE ROAD, LONDON NW1

BLACKWELL SCIENTIFIC PUBLICATIONS
OXFORD AND EDINBURGH

*The programme of work leading
to the publication of this
handbook has been supported
in part by grants to the
International Council of
Scientific Unions made by the
Ford and Nuffield Foundations*

Printed in Great Britain by
BURGESS AND SON (ABINGDON) LIMITED
ABINGDON, BERKS
and bound by
THE KEMP HALL BINDERY, OXFORD

CONTENTS

Foreword

by

E. B. Worthington

The purpose of this series of books is to provide in a handy and low-cost form the kind of information and guidance which is needed by biologists all over the world so that they can participate effectively in the International Biological Programme. Such is the need today for guidance, especially in methods of research, that many of the volumes, including this one, are likely to have a value long after the Programme itself has drawn to a close in 1972.

Human Adaptability (HA) is the subject of one of the seven sections into which the IBP is divided. Together they are intended to provide a world plan of research concerned with "the biological basis of productivity and human welfare". Section HA is somewhat different from the rest because it deals particularly with one species, *Homo sapiens*. The other sections deal not with one particular species so much as with whole ecosystems such as marine, freshwater, terrestrial, which are sub-divided into biomes such as grassland, woodland, desert or into groups of problems such as those associated with herbivorous mammals or biological control. HA was one of the first sections to get organised and it produced the first Handbook in this series (No. 1 Guide to the Human Adaptability Proposals, by J. S. Weiner, August 1965). That was a slender volume of some 70 pages and the contrast with this much more comprehensive book is a measure of the Section's activity during the past three years.

Although this Handbook, like others in the series, is to some extent provisional, it is able to be precise in describing many methods of research. In some other sections the object is not to *standardise* methodology—for the subjects covered are evolving rapidly, and to standardise could discourage improvement—but rather to recommend methods to those who want them. In human adaptability research there are many methods of measurement and of experimentation already widely used and proved, and the job has been to select those which are most likely to give inter-comparable results when applied to different human groups living in environments which range from the Poles to the Equator.

The subject has advanced to a point when large quantities of data, sometimes resulting from relatively simple measurements, are needed for statistical and computer treatment in order to derive conclusions which may be far-reaching in their applications. Side by side with the preparation of this volume of methodology, therefore, work has been proceeding on the establishment of a human adaptability data centre at which the information collected, much of it in standard form, can be stored, retrieved and processed.

This book results from a large number of consultations and technical meetings between many of the world's leading anthropologists and physiologists. Thereafter certain individuals were deputed to write up the results in the form of chapters. To all of those whose names appear as having contributed, and to many others whose names may not do so, sincere thanks are extended by the Special Committee for the IBP. But the biggest task of all inevitably fell to the Editors of the whole volume. Of these the senior Editor, Professor J. S. Weiner, needs little introduction. With degrees from the University of Witwatersrand, St. George's Hospital, London, and London and Oxford Universities, with much teaching and research experience in Oxford, in Southern Africa and at the London School of Hygiene and Tropical Medicine, where he is now Professor of Environmental Physiology, he is clearly very well qualified for this task. But perhaps more important, as Convener of the HA International Section of IBP since its inception, he is in the best possible position to judge what is desirable and what is possible at various levels of scientific sophistication in a world programme of this sort. The junior Editor, Mr. J. A. Lourie received his degree in Physiology and Diploma in Human Biology at Oxford, and assisted Professor Weiner as Scientific Co-ordinator of the Section during 1967 and 1968. He is now engaged on field research, and I hope will be putting his Handbook's advice to the test.

Preface

Some 50 separate procedures are described in this Handbook covering a wide range of enquiry essential to the biological study of human populations. A primary consideration in the selection and presentation of each procedure is its suitability for field conditions. This raises two issues of major importance. Firstly it should be pointed out that many of the procedures require quite sophisticated equipment and in some cases a portable electricity supply. This, of course, adds to the expense and organizational difficulties of an expedition. Nevertheless, unless equipment of this sort is taken into the field it will not be possible to make the kind of study which is essential for understanding many of the adaptive properties of human populations. In any case the equipment described has successfully been used by some expeditions already. A second and closely related point requires special emphasis—the procedures described in this Handbook are only to be carried out by properly trained investigators, well versed in the technique before they go into the field. This Handbook is not a simple cook-book for the amateur explorer. Even apparently simple techniques, such as anthropometry, require a good deal of training under expert supervision.

The techniques described in this Handbook are based on contributions made by some 100 human biologists, expert in their own fields. Nearly all the techniques have been the subject of discussions at scientific conferences, seminars or working groups (listed below), and they have been submitted by the contributor himself or by the Convener of the Human Adaptability Section to other authorities in the particular field. It can be claimed, therefore, that a large measure of agreement has been reached in formulating the procedures in the Handbook. It should, however, be stressed that these methods are to be regarded only as *recommendations* as the basis for projects within IBP. It is hoped that the great majority of investigators will find it possible to include these procedures in their investigations even if they decide to use additional or alternative methods, appropriate for any special objectives they have in mind. In this way one of the major aims of IBP—a high degree of comparability between studies of different populations—will be achieved.

The names of the scientists who have contributed particularly to each procedure are given in the list of acknowledgements below. Many others have helped in one way or another at meetings and discussions. To all named and unnamed the Editors tender their gratitude.

Acknowledgement should be made here of the encouragement given to the HA Section, at the very inception of the IBP, by the International Union of Physiological Sciences, which recognised the need for intensive consideration of methodology as an important preliminary to launching the HA programme. The IUPS, at the suggestion of the (then) General Secretary, Professor Wallace Fenn, not only set up a Commission on Physiological Anthropometry in 1963, but made available financial help for the work of this Commission. Its members (listed below) were able to take part in many of the working parties and other meetings concerned with methodology. Through the Commission, the IUPS made a major contribution to the organisation of the three day Methodology Seminar in Kyoto in September 1965, at the time of the 23rd International Physiological Congress. The proceedings of this Seminar were published under the joint auspices of the IUPS and the Japanese HA Committee (ref. 1).

During the discussions on methods, it soon became apparent that a number of special investigations were needed in order to make objective decisions on the comparative merits of alternative methods and, where feasible, for their inter-calibration. These investigations have been an important feature of the preparatory phase of the IBP and the results obtained by the multi-national teams assembled for this purpose represent a very tangible achievement by IBP. Cold tolerance methods were investigated by a four nation team at the Department of Physiology (ref. 1), Lexington University, Kentucky, under the enthusiastic leadership of Professor Loren Carlson. A six nation team carried out comparative studies of heat tolerance methods at the Laboratories of the Occupational Health Research and Training Facility, Cincinnati, through the generous co-operation of Drs. D. H. K. Lee and Austin Henschel (ref. 2). A ten nation team made comparative studies of tests of working capacity in the Department of Applied Physiology, Toronto University, with the enthusiastic co-operation of Professor Shephard. The results have been fully used in the present Handbook and a number of papers have also been published in the scientific press (ref. 4). Inter-calibration and field testing of equipment have been carried out in a number of instances with the requirements of the HA programme in mind, and this information has also been incorporated into the Handbook.

A good deal of help has been given in the compilation of this Handbook by the panel of honorary HA Consultants (whose names are appended). The Consultants have also during the preliminary phase of IBP answered numerous enquiries on problems of methodology.

Special acknowledgment is due to Miss G. Garrard (HA Co-ordinator in 1968), who assisted the Editors with unflagging enthusiasm and efficiency, to Miss D. Ainsworth for invaluable secretarial help throughout the preparation of this Handbook, and to Mrs. K. J. Collins for carrying out the major typing of the manuscript.

The Editors also gratefully acknowledge the co-operation of Mr. D. E. Lee, who assisted with the figures and reproductions for the Handbook, and of Mr. S. P. Prestidge, for providing a number of the photographs.

Finally, the Convener of the HA Section, as Senior Editor of the Handbook, is well aware that inaccuracies may well have crept in or been overlooked when editing or re-drafting the material. For this he apologises in advance to both contributors and readers. The Handbook in its present form should be regarded as a provisional document and should be under constant revision as a result of field experience and of improvement in methods and instruments. All suggestions and criticisms will be welcomed in the hope that they can be incorporated in a future edition.

Working Parties and other Meetings concerned with HA Methodology (1962–1968)

(references in brackets are to HA documents)

(1) Conference on Project D—Human Adaptability (IBP):
    Ciba Foundation, Dec. 4th–6th, 1962 (HA 5).

(2) Anthropometry of Growth and Physique:
    Ciba Foundation, Aug. 6th, 1963 (HA 22).

(3) Working Party on Assessment of Cold Tolerance:
    Rauland, Oslo, Nov. 1st–4th, 1963 (HA 18).

(4) Working Party on Physiological Indices of Fitness:
    Rauland, Oslo, Nov. 4th–5th, 1963 (HA 19).

(5) Working Party on Assessment of Heat Tolerance:
    Ciba Foundation, November 11th–12th, 1963 (HA 20).

(6) Research Group on Cold Tolerance:
Lexington, U.S.A. 1963 (ref. 1.)

(7) Wenner-Gren Symposium:
Burg Wartenstein, Austria, June 11th–24th, 1964 (ref. 3).

(8) Human Adaptability and its Methodology:
IUPS/Japan: IBP Symposium, Kyoto, Japan, Sept. 13th–17th, 1965 (ref. 1).

(9) Natural Selection and Transmissible Disease:
Ciba Foundation, June 21st–22nd, 1965.

(10) Research Group on Heat Tolerance:
Cincinnati, May–June, 1966 (ref. 2).

(11) Research Group on Methods of Measurement of Working Capacity:
Toronto, Canada, 1967 (HA 89) (ref. 4).

(12) HA/UM Meeting on Methods in Human Nutrition:
Paris, March 28th–30th, 1967 (HA 76).

(13) Working Party on Psychological Methods in the Field:
Ciba Foundation, Sept. 1967 (IBP News No. 10).

(14) Working Party on Sampling and Data Processing:
Utrecht, Holland, Jan. 3rd–5th, 1968 (HA 103).

References

(1) Human Adaptability and its Methodology. Ed. H. Yoshimura and J. S. Weiner.
Japan Society for the Promotion of Science, 1966.

(2) Comparative Methodology for Heat Tolerance Testing. A. Henschel.
U.S. Department of Health, Education and Welfare, 1967.

(3) The Biology of Human Adaptability. P. T. Baker and J. S. Weiner.
Oxford University Press, 1966.

(4) (a) The Maximum Oxygen Intake. R. J. Shepherd, C. Allen, A. J. S. Benade, C. T. M. Davies, P. E. di Prampero, R. Hedman, J. E. Merriman, K. Myhre and R. Simmons.
Bull. Wld Hlth Org., 1968, **38**, 757–764.

(b) Standardization of Submaximal Exercise Tests.
R. J. Shephard, C. Allen, A. J. S. Benade, C. T. M. Davies, P. E. di Prampero, R. Hedman, J. E. Merriman, K. Myhre and R. Simmons.
Bull. Wld Hlth Org., 1968, **38**, 765–775.

TECHNICAL INTRODUCTION

I. AIMS AND USE OF THE HANDBOOK

    (1) Arrangement of Sections

    (2) Need for training

    (3) Organisation of HA field-work

II. SPECIFICATION OF THE INDIVIDUAL AND THE GROUP; BASIC IDENTIFICATION SHEETS

    (1) Description of the population group and sample selected

    (2) Identification of the individual (including age ascertainment)

    (3) Description of the individual

    (4) Selection of sample size

TECHNICAL INTRODUCTION

I. AIMS AND USE OF THE HANDBOOK

The aim of this Handbook is to provide, in a form suitable for use in the field, instructions on the whole range of methods required for the fulfilment of human biological studies on a comparative basis.

Certain of these methods can be used to carry out the rapid surveys on growth, physique, and genetic constitution. They are also appropriate for the pursuit of intensive multidisciplinary investigations. Finally, procedures are laid down whereby the requisite background information about the group, sample, and subject under study may be obtained. This concerns in particular the full identification of the group, sample, and subject, medical and nutritional status, socio-demographic characteristics, an analysis of habitual activity patterns, and a description of the environment.

(1) Arrangement of Sections

As far as practicable, for each procedure, an attempt has been made to provide information under the following headings:

(i) An **Introduction** which includes a brief general description and rationale of the procedure, a list of the observations to be made, and, most important, a note on desirable sample sizes and composition.

(ii) **Technique.** This part includes detailed instructions for carrying out any tests required relative to the ' observations to be made '. (Cross-references are made to Sections in the Handbook on ' General Medical Examination ', ' Nutritional Assessment ', and other major topics, so instructions for carrying these out are not specified in every Section.) In this part, details of Equipment and its availability are also included as necessary, but no attempt has been made to provide exhaustive lists of instruments.

(iii) **The Data Collecting Sheet.** This is a form to be filled in for each individual studied, giving minimal personal details and all the essential data obtained by means of the procedure. Full specification of the group and the individual is provided for in the Basic Identification Sheets (see below).

A few of the Data Sheets (those relating to growth, morphology and work capacity) are in the form of coded proformae suitable for computer processing and tabulation. These forms are also to be used as primary data collecting sheets in the field. The great majority of the Data Sheets, however, are presented in a form suitable for recording in the field, but for computer use transfer and encoding of the data would be necessary.

(2) Need for Training

None of the procedures described in this Handbook is to be undertaken by untrained personnel. The methods, even where these are described in great detail, demand a thorough acquaintance with their underlying principles, as well as the technical details and use of the instruments. Even the simple techniques, such as those of anthropometry and anthroposcopy, cannot give reliable results unless the observer has practiced the methods thoroughly, and has an appreciation of the inherent errors and limitations of the technique. Facilities for training in all the requisite techniques certainly exist, although it is appreciated that to take advantage of these may in some cases be difficult on financial grounds. Many institutions will of course accept students for post-graduate training in the main branches of human biology leading to a research degree. Arrangements can also sometimes be made for students to obtain instruction in special short-term courses on particular techniques.

(3) Organisation of HA field-work—approach to local populations

The detailed formulation for research and its execution is naturally the responsibility of the team concerned, and they will undertake the necessary discussions with those countries whose cooperation in a particular region is desirable. Wherever possible, a preliminary visit should be planned so that proper arrangements can be made with the authorities concerned (administrative, customs, etc.), and a full explanation of the aims and conduct of the proposed investigation can be given to the communities and the local authorities concerned. Their full cooperation must in all cases be ensured. In this connection, research teams in the field will be under special obligations to maintain a high ethical approach to the local populations. Permission to test subjects in the field should be sought not only from individuals and administrative leaders, but also from community and tribal leaders. The presence of a team of investigators should ensure that the local inhabitants benefit not only in the long term from the research carried out, but at the time of the investigation also in the form of medical, dental, and other services, which the team should be well qualified to render.

It is appropriate here to draw the attention of team leaders to their responsibility for providing medical and first-aid equipment for the use of their team members. This is especially important where the field research team does not include a qualified medical man. Team leaders are urged to consult the excellent guides published in various languages on this topic, e.g. ' A Traveller's Guide to Health ', by J. M. Adam; Hodder and Stoughton, London, 12/6.

II. SPECIFICATION OF THE INDIVIDUAL AND THE GROUP

(1) Description of the population group and sample selected

For each technique described in the Handbook, sufficient information is to be recorded to make possible the clear identification of both the subject of the examination and the population group to which he belongs. In general, this minimal information comprises the following particulars: name, subject number, age, sex, ethnic and tribal origin (or nationality), and place and date of examination.

In addition to this minimal record, and for the purposes of the many different objectives of any multidisciplinary study, it is clearly essential that a special effort be made to obtain as complete an identification as possible of the community, and all the subjects involved in the study. This detailed specification of the group and the individual would in some investigations be done naturally as part of the course of the demographic analysis. In all cases, however, it seems highly desirable to record these particulars in the basic identification sheets given below.

(2) Identification of the individual

The key data for subsequent recognition of the subject comprise the subject's name, family and group affinities, as well as his age and sex. In many pre-literate groups, language difficulties will make this a problem. There are therefore many occasions when additional measures should be taken to ensure reliable re-identification. The following suggestions may be considered.

(a)　Marking the subject

A useful method is to write the subject's serial number with silver nitrate on the fingernail. In some census-taking, a rubber numbering-stamp has been used. Silver nitrate has the advantage of remaining legible for several weeks.

(b)　Photographs

A ' Polaroid ' camera makes it possible to produce photographs at the first examination of the subject. (In some cases subjects can be promised that when they return for subsequent examination they will be given their photograph.)

(c)　Fingerprints

Where these are taken as part of an investigation (see **B12**), they can naturally be used for re-identification of the subjects.

(d)　Distinguishing features

The medical examination of a subject (see **F1**), and anthroposcopic examination (see **B15**) gives an opportunity of recording features that may be useful for subsequent re-identification.

(e)　Other

Some investigators provide the subject with a metal stamped number-plate, worn as a necklace or bracelet. This method is by no means reliable, since subjects may lose these, or even interchange them.

Age Ascertainment

Where the chronological age is known, this should be recorded as the ' decimal age ', according to the table given in Section **A1,** p.32.

Many persons living in the developing regions of the tropics, however, are ignorant of their exact age, or occasionally may employ a system of age classification different from the western method. The reason for this is that precise age may have little significance unless it has a recognised social value, e.g. in relation to legal responsibility, admission to school, pension rights, etc. Among some peoples, functional or physiological age-groups are recognised, e.g. ' big enough to be able to herd goats ', or ' capable of carrying a younger sibling ', or ' marriageable '.

Often transitions from one group to another are recognised by special ceremonies and by the wearing of different clothes, decorations or hair-style thereafter. These include initiation rites in some communities, e.g. the elaborate ceremony and short hair-cut carried out before a girl can enter the marriageable group among the San Blas Indians of Panama.

For adults, all that may be possible is to consider the two sexes in broad age-groups—young adults, adults, old adults. However, differentiation may sometimes be difficult in groups where the scalp hair is shaved, where there is no ' middle-aged ' obesity, and where facial wrinkles are less prominent against a darker complexion, or, conversely, where women age rapidly with continuous child-bearing and too much work. A long-term local calendar of important events may have to be constructed, based on events in the preceding years, including agricultural, climatic and political occurrences, as well as natural or man-made disasters. Jelliffe (WHO Monograph **53,** 60–61 1966) cites an example constructed by Tukei for the age assessment of Baganda children. However, such a calendar takes weeks to prepare and pre-test in the field, while its use in survey circumstances is laborious, time-consuming, and often least satisfactory with the unsophisticated communities for which it is intended. Also, these calendars will plainly have to be specific for different communities.

More exact age assessment is desirable in the anthropometry of young children (see **A1**). When dealing with infants and pre-school children, ages should, if possible, be known to the nearest month. For school-children, assessment of ages to the nearest three months should be attempted.

In field-survey circumstances, age assessment in young children may be attempted in various ways. Documentary evidence may, though rarely, be forthcoming, including birth-certificates, horoscopes, and baptismal certificates. Careful prior enquiries must always be made, and, wherever possible, the parents must be encouraged to bring these vital papers at the time of examination.

The skeletal age from hand and wrist X-rays should be taken whenever the facilities are available. When the exact chronological age is known, the skeletal age assigned to the X-ray will give valuable information about the relative rates of growth both between individuals in a given study and between studies in different countries. When chronological age is not known, the skeletal age assessment is helpful. The technique to be adopted is given in **A4.** A small X-ray machine is quite suitable for this purpose (see **A4**).

Sometimes, the mother may not know the child's age, but may be able to recite the month of birth, and occasionally the day as well. If this is so, the mother will often recall details of the youngest child only, not those of the older siblings. If dates are known, they should be recorded as given, and the ages calculated later. The presence of older or younger siblings, or a pregnant mother, may provide further useful information in guiding age assessment of the individual child, although in some groups it is difficult for the observer in a prevalence survey to discover whether the children do in fact belong to the particular women.

In some communities, the period of the year in which the child was born can be recognised by the name given, e.g. ' born during millet-harvesting ', or as belonging to a certain ritual age-set; or there may be a local lunar calendar—thus it may be possible to obtain information in relation to Muslim lunar months.

As approximate supporting evidence, or as an alternative method, the child's deciduous dental eruption should be noted. However, times of dental eruption can vary greatly in normal children, and further work is needed to establish local standards, because some presumed genetic differences in tooth-eruption timing have been noted in different parts of the world. The eruption of the permanent dentition should also be recorded, but the significance must be interpreted cautiously, in view of the individual variation.

Methods of assessing the age-range approximately from dental eruption are described in detail in Section **A1** (para. 4 'Dental examination').

(4)   Selection of Sample Size*

(a)   For a single population

An intelligent choice of the sample size for a particular survey involves many considerations among which are the number and types of parameters to be estimated, the cost per sampling unit, and the resources in manpower and funds available. Patently, these particulars will vary from survey to survey; however, a rough framework can be constructed within which general and responsible decisions with respect to sample size can be made. The purpose of the Tables to follow is to provide some simple numeric guidelines to approximate sample sizes. It must be borne in mind that the values set out in Tables 1 to 3 involve a series of assumptions which may not hold in specific instances; among these are the following:

* Prepared by W. J. Schull; consultation with M. J. R. Healy and S. Mandel.

(1) **sampling is simple, random and without replacement**

(2) **the population sampled is infinitely large** and

(3) **the sample size in each instance is to provide a confidence interval of half-range d with probability 0·05.**

Two cases are considered, namely, the estimation of a proportion, and the estimation of the mean of a normally distributed variable.

The sample size when sampling for proportions

Consider the estimation of the proportion of individuals in a population with some particular attribute, for example, blue eyes. This proportion, though not precisely known to the investigator, is generally known to him to an order of magnitude at least; that is to say, he will often know that blue eyes are quite rare (say, less than 1 in 1,000 persons), somewhat infrequent (1 in 100 to 1 in 1,000 persons), fairly common (1 in 10 to 1 in 100), or very common (more than 1 in 10). If blue eyes are known to be more infrequent than 1 in 100, simple random sampling would invariably be much too inefficient and other sampling methods appropriate to the estimation of rare events should be used. To assume random sampling is, therefore, tantamount to assuming that the investigator's interest centres on only those attributes whose frequencies are at least 1 in 100. Even within these limits it is clear that if the population proportion is to be known exactly the entire population must be examined. This is impracticable and generally unnecessary, for the investigator usually does not require this element of exactness. His requirements are related, of course, to the uses to which the estimate or estimates are to be put, and these may vary from investigator to investigator and with the proportion itself. The Tables attempt to take both of these factors into account.

Imagine, now, that in a particular population blue eyes are thought to be fairly common, that is, the proportion lies between 0·01 and 0·10. A hypothetical investigator wishes to know how large a sample must be drawn so that the estimate, **p**, derived therefrom will fall in an interval defined by the population proportion, **P**, plus or minus some quantity of his choosing, **d**, with a predictable frequency. Alternatively stated, how large must the sample be so that

$$\text{Prob} \left(\mid p - P \mid \leqslant d \right) = 1 - \alpha$$

where d is the half-range (half of the interval) and $(1 - \alpha)$ is the confidence probability. The sizes set out in the tables to follow assume $P = 0·05$.

The half-range, d, is the permissible level of error in the estimate. Otherwise stated, any estimate which lies in the interval

$$P \pm d$$

will be considered a " good " estimate. If it is assumed that the sample estimate, p, is normally distributed, then we know that

$$\text{Prob} \left(p \varepsilon \left(P \pm t\sigma_p \right) \right) = 1 - \alpha$$

where t is the normal deviate which defines an interval enclosing $1 - \alpha$ of the area subsumed by the normal curve, and σ_p is the standard error of the estimate. The latter can be shown to be

$$\sigma_p = \sqrt{\frac{pq}{n}} = \sqrt{\frac{N-n}{N-1}} \sqrt{\frac{PQ}{N}}$$

where n is the sample size, N is the size of the population sampled, $q = 1 - p$ and $Q = 1 - P$. Finally, we can solve the relationship

$$d = t\sigma_p$$

for n. The values set out in Tables 1 and 2 have been so calculated, save that the fraction $(N - n)/(N - 1)$ has been taken to be one as would be true if N was infinitely large. To provide estimates of sample size for more than one degree of precision, and for varying proportions, the half-ranges have been expressed as a series of fixed percentages to be added to or subtracted from the population proportion.

To illustrate the use of the Tables, consider the specific case to which reference has already been made. Assume that an investigator will be content if the estimate of the population proportion lies within five per cent (absolute) of the " true " value. The latter he takes to be 0·10; thus, any estimate between 0·05 and 0·15 is acceptable. He enters Table 1 in the row which corresponds to the population proportion, 0·10, and then finds the column which describes the acceptable half-range, namely five per cent. The sample size is read from the intersection of the row and column; a sample of 140 is found to be sufficient.

It should be noted that a rough approximation to sample sizes associated with half-ranges not encountered in Table 1 (or samples in Table 2) can be obtained by linear interpolation.

Recall, now, that one of the assumptions upon which these sample sizes are based is that the population sampled is infinitely large. Obviously, this rarely obtains; populations are generally finite, and may, in fact, be quite

TABLE 1

The sample size required to estimate a proportion at varying levels of precision.

Population proportion	Acceptable half-range expressed as a percentage						
	1	2	3	5	7	10	20
0·01	390	0	0	0	0	0	0
0·02	790	200	0	0	0	0	0
0·03	1160	290	130	0	0	0	0
0·04	1520	380	170	0	0	0	0
0·05	1860	470	210	74	0	0	0
0·06	2210	560	250	88	0	0	0
0·07	2540	640	290	110	51	0	0
0·08	2860	720	320	120	58	0	0
0·09	3180	800	360	130	64	0	0
0·10	3490	880	390	140	71	34	0
0·15	4900	1230	550	200	99	48	0
0·20	6150	1540	690	250	130	61	15
0·25	7210	1810	810	290	150	72	18
0·30	8070	2020	900	330	170	80	20
0·35	8740	2190	980	350	180	87	21
0·40	9220	2310	1030	370	190	92	23
0·45	9510	2380	1060	390	200	95	23
0·50	9610	2410	1070	390	200	96	24

An estimate within the interval defined by the population proportion, plus or minus the stated half-range, is assumed to be acceptable. The probability that the estimate will lie outside this interval is 0·05. Simple random sampling is assumed, and the estimate of the population proportion is taken to be normally distributed.

TABLE 2

Approximate sampling errors of proportions.

Sample sizes

Reported proportion	50	100	200	500	1000
0·01	0·000–0·037	0·000–0·029	0·000–0·023	0·001–0·018	0·003–0·016
0·02	0·000–0·058	0·000–0·047	0·000–0·039	0·007–0·032	0·011–0·028
0·03	0·000–0·077	0·000–0·063	0·006–0·053	0·015–0·044	0·019–0·040
0·04	0·000–0·094	0·001–0·078	0·012–0·067	0·022–0·057	0·027–0·052
0·05	0·000–0·110	0·007–0·092	0·019–0·080	0·030–0·069	0·036–0·063
0·06	0·000–0·125	0·013–0·106	0·027–0·092	0·039–0·080	0·045–0·074
0·07	0·000–0·140	0·019–0·120	0·034–0·105	0·047–0·092	0·054–0·085
0·08	0·004–0·155	0·026–0·133	0·042–0·117	0·056–0·103	0·063–0·096
0·09	0·010–0·169	0·033–0·146	0·050–0·129	0·064–0·115	0·072–0·107
0·10	0·016–0·183	0·041–0·158	0·058–0·141	0·073–0·126	0·081–0·118
0·15	0·051–0·248	0·080–0·219	0·100–0·199	0·118–0·181	0·127–0·172
0·20	0·089–0·310	0·121–0·278	0·144–0·255	0·164–0·235	0·175–0·224
0·25	0·129–0·370	0·165–0·334	0·189–0·310	0·212–0·287	0·223–0·276
0·30	0·172–0·427	0·210–0·389	0·236–0·363	0·259–0·340	0·271–0·328
0·35	0·217–0·482	0·256–0·443	0·283–0·416	0·308–0·391	0·320–0·379
0·40	0·264–0·535	0·303–0·496	0·332–0·467	0·357–0·442	0·369–0·430
0·45	0·312–0·587	0·352–0·547	0·381–0·518	0·406–0·493	0·419–0·480
0·50	0·361–0·638	0·402–0·598	0·430–0·569	0·456–0·543	0·469–0·530

For most items the chances are 95 in 100 that the value being estimated lies within the tabulated range.

TABLE 3

The sample size required to estimate a mean at varying levels of precision.

Coefficient of variation	Acceptable half-range as proportion of mean.				
	0·01	0·02	0·05	0·10	0·25
0·1	390	96	15	0	0
0·2	1540	390	61	15	0
0·3	3460	870	140	34	5
0·4	6150	1540	250	61	9
0·5	9610	2410	390	96	15
0·6		3460	560	140	22
0·7		4710	760	190	30
0·8		6150	990	250	39
0·9		7780	1250	320	49
1·0		9610	1540	390	61
2·0			6150	1540	250
3·0				3460	560

An estimate within the interval defined by the mean, plus or minus the half-range, is assumed to be acceptable.

small. The element of approximation introduced by the assumption of infinite population size becomes important, however, only if the sample itself represents a substantial portion of the population, say, twenty per cent or more. Under the latter circumstances, a correction for the finiteness of the population is advisable. The appropriate correction involves division of the sample size given in Table 1 by the quantity $(1 + c)$ where **c** is the proportion of the population represented by the entry in Table 1. For example, suppose the population of interest numbered only 500 persons. A sample of 140 would thus constitute 28 per cent of the population; correction for finite population size in the manner just stated would lead to a sample of 140/1·28 or about 110.

Often the size of a particular sample is pragmatically determined, that is to say, it is the maximum number of observations which can be obtained with the funds or in the time available. An investigator may, in these circumstances feel that he has little choice of the sample size, but he may still be interested in " How much precision can be bought with this sample?". Table 2 is designed to provide a response to this query. Thus, for example, if an investigator knew that 200 observations would be available, and he wished to determine the probable precision of an estimate of a population proportion of 0·10, say, he need merely enter the Table in the column designating the sample size and the row corresponding to the reported proportion. In this instance, there would be 95 chances in 100 that the sample estimate would be in the interval 0·058 to 0·141.

The sample size when estimating means

As in the estimation of sample proportions, a judgment must be made by the investigator about the level of error which he deems tolerable. Once this is determined, and let us suppose the error permissible in the estimate of the population mean, μ to be $t s_{\bar{y}}$, then he wishes to know how large the sample must be so that

$$\text{Prob} \left(\left| \bar{y} - \mu \right| \leqslant t_\alpha \, s_{\bar{y}} \right) = 1 - \alpha$$

where $\bar{y}$ is the mean of the sample, μ the mean of the population, $s_{\bar{y}}$ is the standard error of the sample mean, and t_α is the normal deviate subsuming $(1 - \alpha)$ of the area of the standard normal curve. We know that the standard error of the mean, $s_{\bar{y}}$, is merely

$$s_{\bar{y}} = S/\sqrt{n}$$

where S is the square root of the population variance, and n is the sample size. Classical statistical inference asserts that

$$\bar{y} - t_\alpha \sqrt{\frac{N-n}{N}} \, \frac{S}{\sqrt{n}} \leqslant \mu \leqslant \bar{y} + t_\alpha \sqrt{\frac{N-n}{N}} \, \frac{S}{\sqrt{n}}$$

or alternatively

$$|\bar{y} - \mu| \leqslant t \sqrt{\frac{N-n}{N}} \, \frac{S}{\sqrt{n}}$$

since $(\bar{y} - \mu)$ can always be expressed as a multiple of μ say $d\mu$, we have

$$d\mu \leqslant t \sqrt{\frac{N-n}{N}} \, \frac{S}{\sqrt{n}}$$

or solving for n, one finds

$$n = \frac{\left(\dfrac{t}{d}\right)^2 \left(\dfrac{S}{\mu}\right)^2}{1 + \dfrac{1}{N} \left(\dfrac{t}{d}\right)^2 \left(\dfrac{S}{\mu}\right)^2}$$

Again, since N is presumed to be infinite

$$n = \left(\frac{t}{d}\right)^2 \left(\frac{S}{\mu}\right)^2$$

If $t = 1 \cdot 96$ (that is, $\alpha = 0 \cdot 05$), then

$$n = \left(\frac{1 \cdot 96}{d}\right)^2 \left(\frac{S}{\mu}\right)^2$$

Thus, to determine the sample size needed to provide an estimate of the mean of a normally distributed variable requires some notion not only of the probable size of the mean but also of the variability inherent in the distribution of which it is the central value. That is to say, some notion of the coefficient of variation, the ratio of the standard deviation to the mean, is needed if the sample size is to be estimated.

Table 3 provides estimates of the sizes of samples needed to estimate a mean with the stated precision when the coefficient of variation varies from $0 \cdot 1$ to $3 \cdot 0$. Thus, for example, suppose an investigator wished to estimate the mean stature of a population of males to a precision of $0 \cdot 05$ reckoned in terms of the coefficient of variation. Imagine the coefficient of variation to be $0 \cdot 5$. Table 3 is then entered in the row corresponding to a coefficient of variation of 0·5, and the column representing a half-range of 0·05. A sample of 390 would be required. Observe that since this implies

$$20 \sim \left(\frac{2S}{d\mu} \right)$$

$$d\mu \sim \frac{S}{10} \; ;$$

the mean would be estimated with a precision (a half-range in terms of the mean) of about a tenth of the standard deviation of the population. As in the previous case, that is, the estimation of the requisite sample size when sampling for proportions, an adjustment is possible for finite population size, and proceeds along identical lines.

(b) For comparison of two populations

The standard procedure for deciding the appropriate sample size to obtain a given chance of discriminating between the means of two normal populations is set out in " Biometrika: Tables for Statisticians ", Cambridge University Press (1954), p. 25 and Table 10. Where the comparison is between two proportions for the two populations, the procedure to be followed is described in most statistical textbooks, e.g. E. S. Keeping "Statistical Inference " (1962), p. 116, Van Nostrand Co.

DESCRIPTION OF THE POPULATION GROUP AND SAMPLE SELECTED

Date of study:

Names of team members:

Names of other observers:

Sponsoring institution:

---

1. Name of population group: ....

2. Geographical location: ....
   (For a full environmental description a data sheet is provided in **H1**)

3. Has data sheet for **H1** (environmental description) been filled in?: yes/no.

4. Basis of identification of group: (give details)

   (a) Linguistic: ....

   (b) Religious: ....

   (c) National: ....

   (d) Ethnic: ....

   (e) Socio-cultural: ....
       (Use the following classes: hunting/food-
       gathering/nomadic/pastoral/horticultural/simple
       agricultural/advanced agricultural/rural/urban/
       industrial.)

   (f) Socio-economic: ....
       (State occupational and social index used.)

5. Brief description of other neighbouring groups, and others within the geographical
   region of the group studied:

6. Approximate number of people in the group studied:

7. Has the demographic analysis (**G1**) been carried out?: yes/no

8. Is there any evidence of lack of homogeneity within the group studied (e.g.
   economic, linguistic, etc.)?: yes/no

   If yes, specify briefly:

9. Is the sample representative of the entire group?: yes/no
   If not, specify the sectors represented in the sample:

10. Describe method used for obtaining the sample:

11. Basis for excluding members of the group from the sample:—
    (a) On the basis of health? yes/no
        If yes, specify:

    (b) If other, specify:

12. Describe final size and composition of sample:

    (a) Number of males:. . . . . Age range:. . . . .

    (b) Number of females: . . . . Age range:. . . . .

    (c) Other details of sample composition:
        (Use categories in (4) above)

13. Has nutritional assessment (**E1**) of group been carried out?: yes/no
    Has nutritional assessment (**E1**) of sample been carried out?: yes/no

14. Has medical examination (**F1**) of group been carried out?: yes/no
    Has medical examination (**F1**) of sample been carried out?: yes/no

15. Has information been obtained on the habitual activity (**C5**) of the group or the sample?: yes/no

16. Indicate the main lines of investigation carried out on this sample:

DESCRIPTION OF THE INDIVIDUAL

Date of study:

Names of team members:

Name of investigator filling in this sheet:

Sponsoring institution:

Has data sheet for description of group and sample been filled in (see above)?: yes/no

---

Subject's name:

Subject no.:

Age:

How age assessed?:
   documentary/chronological/skeletal/dental/other (e.g. local diary—specify)

Sex:

Occupation:
   If school-boy, state Boarding/Day

Civil status: married/single/divorced/living as married/widowed

Has demographic analysis (**G1**) been carried out?: yes/no

If **G1** not carried out, record the following:

   Village of residence:

   Village of birth:

   Religion:

   Tribe:

	Name	*Birthplace*	*Residence*	*Alive/dead*
Father's				
Mother's				
Sibs'				

(State if sibs are full, half, or adopted, and give birth-rank)

INDIVIDUAL IDENTITY SHEET

Subject's name:

Place of examination:

IBP/HA Project Ref. No.   1 ☐☐☐☐
Study No.   5 ☐☐
Serial No.   7 ☐☐☐
Sex (M=1; F=2)   10 ☐
Presumed age (years)   11 ☐☐
Examination date
   (yrs. + 3 decimals–see Table)13 ☐☐☐☐☐
Procedure category   18 ☐☐

Code for accuracy of age assessment:

0—Birthdate known.
1—To 1 month.
2—To 3 months.
3—To 1 year.
4—To 5 years.
5—To 10 years.
6—subadults/young adults/
   middle-aged/elderly.

Code for method of age assessment:
0—Documentary.
1—Interrogation.
2—Dental.
3—Skeletal.
4—Menarche.

Accuracy of age assessment ⎫ (use code)   20 ☐
Method of age assessment   ⎭   21 ☐

Father's I.D. No.   22 ☐☐☐☐☐
Mother's I.D. No.   27 ☐☐☐☐☐

Place of residence:
Place of birth:
Ethnic information (use own code)
(Tribe, clan, etc.):   ☐☐
National registration number:
   ☐☐☐☐☐☐☐☐☐

Procedures carried out (tick as appropriate)

A │1│2│3│4│5│
B │1│2│3│4│5│6│7│8│9│10│11│12│13│14│15│
C │1│2│3│4│5│6│7│8│
D │1│2│3│4│5│6│7│8│9│10│11│12│
E │1│2│3│4│
F │1│2│3│4│5│6│
G │1│2│
H │1│

Signature of investigator:

A. GROWTH AND PHYSIQUE STUDIES

by

J. M. TANNER, J. HIERNAUX AND SHIRLEY JARMAN

A1   Anthropometry

A2   Puberty rating

A3   Photogrammetry

A4   Radiographic measurements

A5   Body density by underwater weighing

A1 ANTHROPOMETRY

I. INTRODUCTION

   (a) General

   (b) Observations to be made

   (c) Sampling

II. TECHNIQUES

   (a) Measurements

      1. Basic List

      2. Full List

      3. Other measurements

      4. Dental examination

   (b) Instruments

III. DATA COLLECTING SHEETS

I. INTRODUCTION

(a) General:

For the collection of comparable data on the growth and physique of different populations from all over the world, it is essential that all studies carried out should follow carefully the same recommendations. Those given below are **not** meant, however, to be exclusive: many workers will want to add further measurements or measurements of particular interest to themselves. It is hoped many will do this; but only on condition that they complete the basic list.

In the preparation of this Section the IBP/HA growth sub-committee has done its utmost to anticipate the requirements of field-workers engaged in studies of growth and physique. More than a hundred copies of the draft were sent out to anthropologists, paediatricians and others, so that their suggestions and criticisms could be taken into account in the finalisation of the present recommendations. The authors wish to thank most sincerely all those who have given them the benefit of their advice and experience.

Specialists in this field of research will notice that in a few of the measurements, for example Stature, the techniques given here depart somewhat from the more traditional methods. We have taken this step only when long years of practice have shown the newer method to be substantially more reliable than the traditional one. Some workers will wish to record a measurement using **both** methods and thus provide valuable comparisons.

Several measurements in common use have been omitted from the recommended BASIC LIST. Our aim was to produce a base-line of measurements which could reasonably be carried out under all conditions.

Under many conditions of field-work the collection of subjects takes more time and effort than does the actual measuring. Therefore, we recommend taking a fairly substantial number of measurements (21 in the Basic List), as an excessively simple battery is usually a waste of hard-won opportunity. The Basic List takes between 10 and 15 minutes when done by a team of two persons. The anthropometric measurements are chosen so they can be taken in the same way both under field conditions and in regional laboratories.

Also included in this Section is a longer FULL LIST of 38 measurements for those who may wish to carry out a more complete anthropometric examination. Any team may, of course, add further measurements for its own particular purposes.

Two points relating to research practice may perhaps be mentioned here.

1.   If more than one anthropometrist is assigned to a study, it is essential that the measurers involved should regularly check the repeatability of their measurements, one against the other.

2.   In some areas of the world dates of birth will not be recorded and thus chronological ages of the subjects not known with certainty. When this is so, great efforts should be made to establish accurate or carefully estimated chronological ages by reference to social or historical events contemporaneous with the birth. (See Technical Introduction, p. xviii.) In the majority of cases this can be done, if necessary with suitable professional help. However, when it is completely impossible to obtain the chronological age of a child subject, a radiograph of the hand and wrist (see **A4**) should be taken so that he may be assigned a Skeletal Maturity Score instead. Different populations or different groups can then be compared for height, say, at a given skeletal maturity. The skeletal maturity score can also be used to give a " bone age ", which simply says what age the child would be if he were an average British or American child, according to the standards used.

Professor J. Hiernaux in Brussels, and Professor J. M. Tanner in London, have agreed to act as Honorary Consultants in Growth and Physique to the IBP Studies. They will do their best to help and advise with any problems which participating workers may encounter in the course of their researches in this field.

Professor J. Hiernaux,
Université Libre de Bruxelles,
Institut de Sociologie,
44, Avenue Jeanne,
BRUXELLES 5,
Belgium.

Professor J. M. Tanner,
IBP Growth Bureau,
Institute of Child Health,
30, Guilford Street,
LONDON, W.C.1.,
England.

(b) **Observations to be made**

1. **IBP Measurements—Basic List (21 measurements)**

Stature/Supine length	Biiliocristal diameter
Sitting height/Crown-rump length	Head length
Bicondylar femur	Head breadth
Wrist breadth	Bizygomatic diameter
Calf circumference	Morphological face height
Upper arm circumference (relaxed)	(nasion-gnathion)
Total arm length	Nose height
Biacromial diameter	Nose breadth
Transverse chest	Triceps skin-fold
Antero-posterior chest	Subscapular skin-fold
Height of anterior superior iliac spine	Body weight

In addition to the above:—

2. **IBP Measurements—Full List (17 Additional measurements)**

Suprasternal height	Chest circumference
Height of tibiale	Upper arm circumference
Upper arm length	(contracted)
Forearm length	Supra-iliac skin-fold
Bicondylar humerus	Bigonial diameter
Hand breadth	Mouth width
Ankle breadth	Lip thickness
Foot length	Head height
Lower leg length	Thigh circumference

3. **Other Measurements** (for use in studies other than human growth and physique)

The measurements above are recommended for studies on growth and physique; others are also needed in studies of work capacity, nutrition, etc., as specified in the relevant Section of this Handbook, where reference will be made to the present Section for the appropriate measurement technique. Detailed instructions for taking them are included under " Techniques " below. These additional measurements are the following:

Minimum frontal diameter	Forearm circumference
Upper face height	Wrist circumference
Ear length	Ankle circumference
Ear breadth	Chest skin-fold (juxta-nipple)
Buttocks-knees length	Mid-axillary skin-fold
Head circumference	Abdomen skin-fold
Neck circumference	Biceps skin-fold
Forearm skin-fold	Thigh skin-fold
Abdomen circumference (umbilical level)	Medial calf skin-fold

4. Dental examination.

(c) Sampling

The sample studied depends on the purpose for which the study is made.

For the construction of standard growth curves for a population the most efficient sample design is to measure groups of children aged 0, 1, 2, etc., to 19 years of age, and then a year later re-measure as many of the same children as possible. In this way the first year's survey gives cross-sectional-type percentile standards for body measurements at each year of age, and the increments from the first to the second year give percentile standards for rate of growth. (These latter do not perfectly represent the true situation at adolescence but are an adequate approximation:—see Tanner, Whitehouse and Takaishi, **Arch. Dis. Childh.**, **41**, 454, 613). Because the growth rate is large in the first two years, these data should be supplemented with measurements on either the same or different children at 3, 6, 9 and 18 months. If the same children are measured then rate of growth standards over this period may also be constructed. The samples on each occasion should be large if percentiles are to be estimated; 500 children of each sex is the minimum number which can yield reasonable estimates of the 3rd and 90th percentiles.

Smaller numbers may suffice for studies of nutrition in different groups of the population, or for comparison of groups under different environmental or genetic circumstances. Here a selection of ages may be taken. A WHO meeting has recommended, for nutritional purposes, samples of boys and girls at birth, 6 months (with limits of $\pm$ 1 month); 18 months (limits $\pm$ 2 months), 3 years (limits $\pm$ 6 months); 7 years; then boys at 12, 18 and 20 years, girls at 10, 16, and 20 years; and adults of both sexes at 20–24 years and 25–40 years. In this case the number of persons of each sex at each age interval may vary according to the size of the differences expected between groups; but it should be seldom less than 100. If smaller projects are envisaged, then it is usually better to restrict the number of ages sampled rather than the numbers of children. Ages may for example be 18 months, 3 years, 7 years and 20–24 years.

In longitudinal studies the magnitude of the task of follow-up usually precludes the use of large samples. A minimal longitudinal study might extend over a period of 5 years and be composed of 4 groups of children, the first followed from 0 to 5, the second from 5 to 10, the third from 10 to 15 and the fourth from 15 to 20. In this case about 150 but not less than 100 subjects of each sex should be studied in each group. Proper attention should be given to ensuring that the groups are comparable in ethnic origin, socio-economic status and rural-urban residence.

II. TECHNIQUES

Measurements should be taken on the LEFT side of the body wherever possible; they are listed in a convenient working order. When measuring circumferences, contact with the skin should be continuous along the tape, but the skin should not be pressed inwards.

Marks placed on the subject

Before beginning the measurements, the following marks may be made on the subject with a black or red dermographic pencil:—

(a) **Frankfort plane**—mark a line from the lower border of the left orbit to the upper margin of the external auditory meatus.

(b) **Nasion**—a point at the root of the nose at the level of the union of the frontal and nasal bones, which usually can be felt with the thumb-nail. In case it cannot be felt, a substitute is provided by a horizontal line joining the top border of left and right epicanthal folds.

(c) **Suprasternal point**—the deepest point in the hollow of the supra-sternal notch.

(d) **Sternum**—At estimated union of 3rd and 4th sternebrae.

(e) **Acromion**—the inferior edge of the most external border of the acromion process.

(f) **Horizontal mark on left arm**—half way (measured) between the inferior border of the acromion process and the tip of the olecranon process.

(g) **Radiale**—the external superior border of the radial head.

(h) **Anterior superior iliac spine**—the most prominent medial point of the anterior superior spine of the ilium.

(i) **Tibiale**—the upper point of the inner border of the medial tibial condyle.

(j) **Malleolus**—the most inferior point of the internal malleolus.

(A) MEASUREMENTS

1. BASIC LIST

Stature   (See Fig. A1/1, facing page)

Stadiometer or   The subject should stand on a horizontal platform with
Anthropometer   his heels together, stretching upward to the fullest
                            extent, aided by gentle traction by the measurer on the
                            mastoid processes. The subject's back should be as
                            straight as possible, which may be achieved by rounding
                            or relaxing the shoulders and manipulating the posture.
                            The marked Frankfort plane must be horizontal. Either
                            the horizontal arm of an anthropometer, or a counter-
                            weighted board, is brought down on to the subject's
                            head. If an anthropometer is used, one measurer
                            should hold the instrument vertical with the horizontal
                            arm in contact with the subject's head, while another
                            applies the gentle traction. The subject's heels must be
                            watched to make sure they do not leave the ground.

Supine Length   Measured with the infant lying supine. One measurer
Infant measuring   holds the infant's head in the Frankfort plane and
table   applies gentle traction to bring the top of his head into
                            contact with the fixed headboard. A second measurer

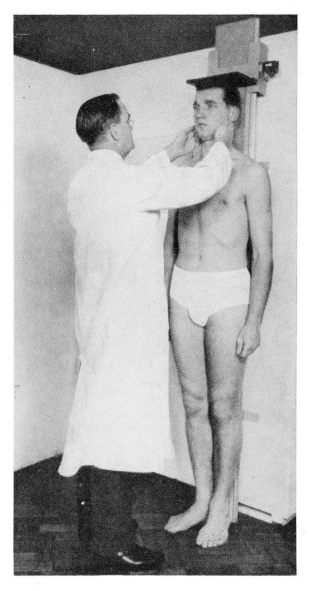

Fig. A1/1 Stature.
(Reprinted from J. M. Tanner, *The Physique of the Olympic Athlete*, Fig. 1.
London: George Allen and Unwin. 1964.)

facing p. 8

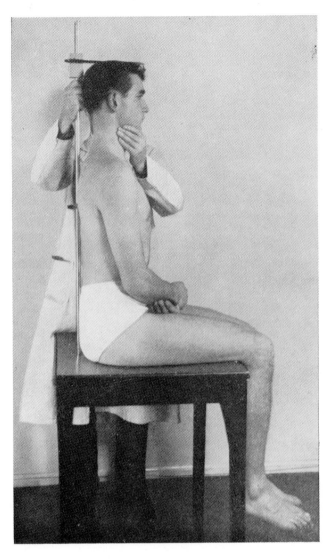

Fig. A1/2   Sitting height.
(Reprinted from J. M. Tanner, *The Physique of the Olympic Athlete*, Fig. 2.
London: George Allen and Unwin. 1964.)

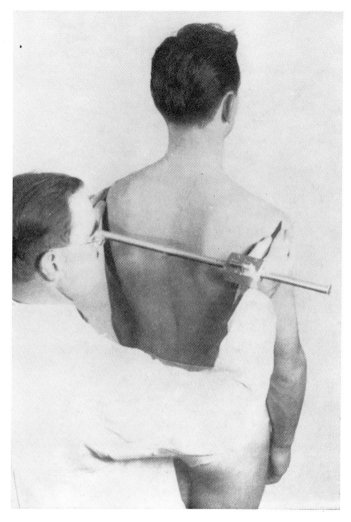

Fig. A1/3 Biacromial diameter.
(Reprinted from J. M. Tanner, *The Physique of the Olympic Athlete*, Fig. 3.
London: George Allen and Unwin. 1964.)

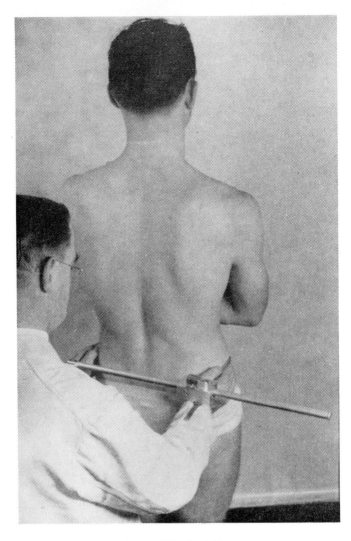

Fig. A1/4   Biiliocristal diameter.
(Reprinted from J. M. Tanner, *The Physique of the Olympic Athlete*, Fig 4.
London: George Allen and Unwin. 1964.)

holds the infant's feet, toes pointing directly upward, and also applying gentle traction, brings the movable foot-board to rest firmly against the infant's heels.

Height of Anterior Superior Iliac Spine
Anthropometer

With the subject standing in the same posture as for Stature, the anterior superior iliac spine is located by palpating with the third finger of the hand holding the horizontal arm of the anthropometer, which is then applied to the point.

Sitting Height
Anthropometer

(See Fig. A1/2, following page 8)
Measured with the subject's back stretched up straight as he sits on a table top with his feet hanging down unsupported over the edge; the backs of his knees should be directly above the edge of the table. Gentle traction is applied under the chin; the muscles of the thighs and buttocks should be uncontracted. The head is held in the Frankfort plane, and the anthropometer is held vertically, in contact with the back at the sacral and interscapular regions.

Crown-Rump
Infant Measuring Table

Measured with the infant lying on his back with his knees bent to a right angle. One measurer holds the infant's head in the Frankfort plane and applies gentle traction to bring it into contact with the fixed head-board. A second measurer supports the infant's legs and brings the movable foot-board to rest against his buttocks.

Bicondylar Femur
Sliding caliper or Anthropometer

The subject sits on a table with his knees bent to a right angle, and the width across the outermost parts of the lower end of the femur is measured. Pressure is exerted to compress the tissues.

Wrist Breadth
Sliding caliper or Anthropometer

Breadth is taken across the styloid processes (oblique to the long axis of the arm), with pressure to compress the tissues.

Calf Circumference
Tape

The subject sits on a table with his leg hanging freely. Maximum circumference is taken horizontally.

Upper Arm Circumference (Relaxed) Tape

The subject's arm hangs relaxed, just away from his side, and the circumference is taken horizontally at the marked level.

Total Arm Length Anthropometer

With the subject's arm and hand fully extended by his side the tip of one arm of the anthropometer is placed at the inferior border of the acromial process. The distance to the tip of the longest finger is measured.

Biacromial Diameter Anthropometer or Spreading caliper

(See Fig. A1/3, following page 8)
To give maximum shoulder width the subject stands with his shoulders relaxed to the point of slumping forward. Standing behind the subject, the measurer feels for the outside edge of the acromial process of the shoulder blade which can be felt as a ridge just above the shoulder joint. He then places the edge of one arm of the anthropometer along the external border of one acromial process and brings the other arm of the anthropometer inwards until its edge rests on the opposite acromial external border.

Transverse Chest Anthropometer or Spreading caliper

The subject stands and the measurement is taken at the end of a normal expiration, at the marked level of the union of the 3rd and 4th sternebrae. The arms of the anthropometer rest on the external surfaces of the nearest rib on each side, in a horizontal plane. Light pressure is exerted.

Antero-Posterior Chest Harpenden anthropometer with recurved arms, or Spreading caliper

The subject stands and the measurement is taken at the marked union of the 3rd and 4th sternebrae in a plane perpendicular to the body axis. The posterior point should be on the tip of a vertebral spine.

Biiliocristal Diameter Anthropometer or Spreading caliper	(See Fig. A1/4, following page 8) The subject stands with his heels together and the anthropometer arms are brought into contact with the iliac crests at the place which gives the maximum diameter. Strong pressure is applied to the anthropometer blades to push aside any fat covering the bone. This measurement is more easily taken with the measurer standing behind the subject.
Head Length Spreading caliper or Harpenden anthropometer with recurved arms	The maximum length in the sagittal plane from glabella (the most salient point between the eyebrows), to the most salient point on the occiput. Pressure is exerted to compress the tissues.
Head Breadth Spreading caliper or Harpenden anthropometer with recurved arms	The maximum breadth in the transverse plane, wherever it occurs. Pressure is exerted to compress the tissues.
Bizygomatic Diameter Spreading caliper	The maximum diameter between the zygomatic arches. Pressure is exerted to compress the tissues.
Morphological Face Height (Nasion-Gnathion) Sliding caliper	With one arm of the caliper held horizontally at the marked nasion, the other arm of the caliper is hooked under the tip of the chin. The teeth should be fully occluded.
Nose Height Sliding caliper	One arm of the caliper is held horizontally at the marked nasion, while the other arm of the caliper is brought down to reach the union of the upper lip with the nasal septum.
Nose Breadth Sliding caliper	The caliper is held horizontally and its arms brought into contact with the outside of the nares, but without pressure.

Skinfold
Thicknesses
Skinfold caliper

The skinfold is picked up between thumb and forefinger and the caliper jaws applied at exactly the level marked. The measurement is read 2 seconds after the full pressure of the caliper jaws is applied to the skinfold; if a longer interval is allowed the jaws may ' creep ' and the reading be inaccurate.

Over Triceps

(See Fig. A1/5, facing page)
The skinfold is picked up at the back of the arm about 1 cm above the level marked on the skin for the arm circumference and directly in line with the point of the elbow, or olecranon process.

Subscapular

The skinfold is picked up under the angle of the left scapula. The fold should be vertical, or pointing slightly downwards and outwards.

Weight
Weighing
machine

Weighing should be done preferably in the nude, or with the subject clothed only in lightweight shorts (which may be provided by the investigator). In the latter circumstance the measurement can be corrected accordingly by adjusting the machine to read zero when a sample garment is placed on it. In all other circumstances, including when trousers are worn, the weight of a representative garment should be entered on the form, for subtraction later. The presence of visible oedema should be recorded.

2. FULL LIST

The techniques given below are for the 17 measurements additional to those described above in the Basic List.

Suprasternal
Height
Anthropometer

With the subject standing in the same posture as for stature, the height of the marked suprasternal point is taken.

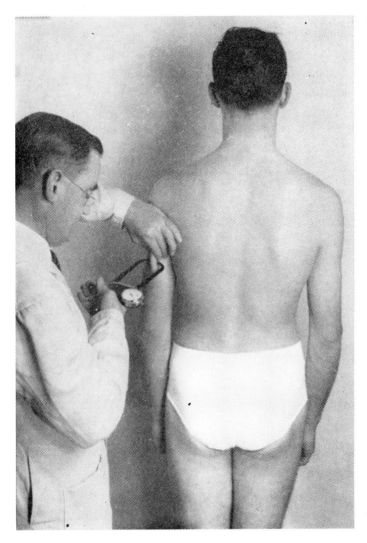

Fig. A1/5   Skin-fold over triceps.
(Reprinted from J. M. Tanner, *The Physique of the Olympic Athlete*, Fig. 10.
London: George Allen and Unwin. 1964.)

facing p. 12

Height of Tibiale
Anthropometer

The subject stands on a flat surface. The anthropometer is held vertically and the distance measured from the standing surface to tibiale.

Lower Leg Length
Anthropometer

With the subject standing in the same position as for Height of Tibiale, the vertical distance from the malleolus to tibiale is measured.

Upper Arm Length
Anthropometer

The external superior border of the head of the radius is marked, and the length from this mark to the inferior border of the acromion process is taken.

Forearm Length
Anthropometer

Measured from the marked head of the radius to the tip of the lateral styloid.

Bicondylar Humerus
Sliding caliper or Anthropometer

The subject's elbow is bent to a right angle and the width across the outermost parts of the lower end of the humerus is taken. This measurement is usually oblique since the inner condyle of the humerus is lower than the outer one. Pressure is exerted to compress the tissues.

Hand Breadth
Sliding caliper

Breadth is taken across the distal tips of metacarpals II-V (which may be oblique); the fingers should be together and in line with the forearm.

Ankle Breadth
Sliding caliper

The subject sits on a table, and the breadth of the ankle is taken across the malleoli, with pressure to compress the tissues. The presence of oedema or tissue indentation should be recorded.

Foot Length
Anthropometer

The subject sits and rests his left foot lightly along the horizontal bar of the anthropometer with the centre of the heel against the arm of the anthropometer; the second arm of the anthropometer is brought into contact with the end of the longest toe, without pressure. If the toe-nail protrudes it must be cut.

Thigh Circumference
Tape

The subject stands with his feet slightly apart and his weight evenly distributed on both feet: the tape is placed round the thigh horizontally with its top edge just under the gluteal fold.

Chest Circumference
Tape

Measured at the marked union of the 3rd and 4th sternebrae, at right angles to the axis of the body, at the end of a normal expiration.

Upper Arm Circumference
(Contracted)
Tape

Taken horizontally at the maximum circumference over the contracted biceps, with the elbow flexed.

Supra-Iliac Skinfold
Skinfold caliper

The skinfold is picked up approximately 1 cm above and 2 cm medial to the anterior superior iliac spine.

Bigonial Diameter
Spreading caliper

The maximum diameter between the angles of the mandible on their external surfaces. Pressure is exerted to compress the tissues.

Mouth Width
Sliding caliper

With the lips closed and the mouth held in a normal position, the distance between the corners of the mouth is measured.

Lip Thickness
Sliding caliper

The caliper is held vertically and put flat on the mouth without pressure; the upper arm of the caliper is brought to the medial point of a tangent between the highest points of the upper lip, while the lower arm of the caliper is brought to the medial point of a tangent between the lowest points of the lower lip. The subject should keep his mouth closed without contracting his lips.

Head Height
Head spanner,
Parallelometer
or
Anthropometer

The subject's head is held in the Frankfort plane. Head height may be measured with an anthropometer. With the instrument held vertically the lower arm is positioned into the left external auditory meatus of the subject, and the upper arm is brought into contact with the top of his head. If a head spanner is used, the lower ends of the curved arms are adjusted to fit into the external auditory meati of the subject, and the central arm brought into contact with the top of his head. If a Schultz's parallelometer is used, its horizontal arm is laid down on the top of the subject's head while its vertical arms are brought into contact with the right and left tragus. The instrument's position is adjusted until the right and left vertical scales give the same value, which is head height.

3. OTHER MEASUREMENTS

Ear Length
Sliding caliper

The maximum length of the subject's ear along its long axis is measured.

Ear Breadth
Sliding caliper

With the fixed arm of the sliding caliper parallel to the long axis of the ear, the maximum breadth of the ear is measured.

Upper Face Height
Anthropometer

The subject stands comfortably with his head oriented in the Frankfort plane. The back of the subject's head should be against a vertical surface. A counter-weighted head-board, as used for the measurement of stature, is brought down on to the top of the subject's head. The anthropometer is then used to measure the vertical distance from the board to the point of contact between the upper and lower lips in the mid-sagittal plane.

Buttocks—Knee Length
Anthropometer

The subject sits erect, his feet resting on a surface so that the knees are bent at about right angles. The horizontal distance from the rearmost point of the left buttock to the front of the kneecap is measured.

Head Circumference
Tape

With the subject seated, the maximum circumference of the head is measured, with the tape passing above (but not including) the brow ridges.

Abdomen Circumference (Umbilical Level)
Tape

The subject stands erect with his abdomen relaxed. The tape is held behind the subject with one edge in the horizontal plane through the centre of the umbilicus. The tape is then wrapped carefully around the subject's torso, using it as an aid in marking the horizontal plane on the sides and back.

Forearm Circumference
Tape

The measurement is taken immediately distal to the elbow joint, with the whole extremity relaxed.

Minimum Frontal Diameter
Spreading caliper

Holding the spreading caliper near its tips, the minimum horizontal diameter across the temporal crests at their points of greatest indentation is measured. Care must be taken that the measurement is made on the crests and not on the temporal muscles.

Neck Circumference
Tape

This measurement is taken in the horizontal plane, just below the level of the thyroid cartilage.

Wrist Circumference
Tape

With the tape passing just proximal to the styloid process of the ulna, the minimum circumference of the wrist is measured.

Ankle Circumference
Tape

With the subject standing, the tape is held slightly above the projections of the ankle bones, and the minimum circumference of the leg is measured.

Mid-Axillary Skinfold
Skinfold caliper

The skinfold is picked up on the mid-axillary line, at the level of the xiphoid process.

Chest (Juxta-Nipple) Skinfold
Skinfold caliper

The skinfold is picked up just lateral to the nipple, at the same level.

Biceps Skinfold
Skinfold caliper

The skinfold is picked up on the front of the arm, directly above the centre of the cubital fossa, at the same level as that at which the triceps skinfold is measured, q.v.

Thigh Skinfold
Skinfold caliper

The skinfold is picked up on the anterior aspect of the thigh, halfway between the mid-inguinal point and the upper border of the patella (with the knee flexed at 90°).

Medial Calf Skinfold
Skinfold caliper

The skinfold is picked up at the level of the maximal circumference of the calf, on the medial border of the leg.

Abdomen Skinfold
Skinfold caliper

The skinfold is picked up at the level of the umbilicus, 2″ to the left of it.

Forearm Skinfold
Skinfold caliper

The skinfold is picked up on the lateral aspect of the forearm at the mid-point of the radius.

4. DENTAL EXAMINATION

Information on tooth emergence has been included in the data sheet under
" Optional Data ". If these data are collected in conjunction with known
chronological ages they will provide valuable new material on the timing
and sequence of the emergence of the teeth in each population group studied.
Tooth emergence is probably less affected by malnutrition than are growth
or skeletal development, so comparative statistics would be particularly
valuable.

Workers undertaking dental studies may find it helpful to read A. A.
Dahlberg and R. M. Menegaz-Bock: " Emergence of the permanent teeth
in Pima Indian children; a critical analysis of method and an estimate of
population parameters ", **J. Dent. Res.**, 37, 1123–1140, 1958.

It is important for persons without formal dental training not to undertake
dental studies without first becoming familiar with the morphology of teeth.
No person should chart the emergence of teeth until he can accurately
recognise each individual primary and secondary tooth and distinguish one
from the other in the mouth with certainty.

Data on tooth emergence may be used to give an estimate of dental " age "
in cases where it is wholly impossible to estimate chronological age by
reference to historical events (see Technical Introduction, p. xx). In such
instances skeletal maturity should also be estimated where possible.

Dental " age " can properly be estimated only by reference to standards
established on the population to which the subject belongs, in similar environmental conditions, and a short time previously. If no such standard exists, the
dental " age " assignment by reference to foreign standards (for example
American or British) can hardly serve for more than to give a rough indication
of chronological age when this is unknown.

In adults, age assessments based upon patterns of tooth wear are to be
avoided, because attrition varies considerably from one group to another,
depending upon diet and other cultural and environmental factors.

Tooth formation assessed from lateral jaw radiographs provides a much
better estimate of dental " age " than does tooth emergence. Workers having
radiographic facilities available in the field may wish to use this more detailed
and accurate method, and they are referred to the papers by C. F. A.
Moorrees, E. A. Fanning and E. E. Hunt: " Formation and resorption of
three deciduous teeth in children ", **Amer. J. Phys. Anthrop.**, 21, 99–108,

1963; and " Age variation of formation stages for ten permanent teeth ",
J. Dent. Res., 42, 1490–1502, 1963.

The collection of tooth data concerned with genetical traits and the effects
of nutrition are dealt with in **B14.**

Recording sheets for Dentition

Data on tooth emergence should be recorded on the sheets for Card 6
(Primary dentition) and Card 7 (Secondary dentition). The Full Heading is
included at the top of each recording sheet and should be filled in.

A recording box is provided for each tooth for both the Primary (20) and
the Secondary (32) dentitions, giving a total of 52 teeth inspected. The
numbers of emerging Primary and Secondary teeth should be recorded at the
end of each sheet, together with the estimated Dental Age, if that is desired.

Dental Ratings

Each tooth is assessed separately, using the following criteria:—
   1—tooth not yet emerged
   2—one or more cusps visible, but not more than one-third of the whole
      crown visible.
   3—more than one-third of crown visible, but tooth not fully erupted
   4—tooth fully erupted (attainment of occlusal level)
   5—tooth exfoliated
   6—tooth misplaced or crowded
   7—tooth failed to develop (agenesis)
   8—tooth extracted.

Five methods in use for the assessment of dental " age ", and standards for
particular **European and American populations** are given as **examples** in
Tables A1/1 to A1/5. These are as follows:—
   1—Primary dentition: age estimated from specific teeth emerged
      (Table A1/1);
   2—Primary dentition: age estimated from number of teeth emerged
      (Table A1/2);
   3—Primary dentition: age estimated from specific teeth exfoliated
      (Table A1/3);
   4—Secondary dentition: age estimated from specific teeth emerged
      (Table A1/4);

5—Secondary dentition: age estimated from number of teeth emerged (Table A1/5);

The emergence of even a single secondary tooth makes it necessary to complete the recording sheet for the secondary dentition; otherwise the population statistics will be invalid.

TABLE A1/1:

Median Ages of Eruption of the Primary Teeth

Upper	Lower	Age
	di_1	0·65
di^1		0·80
di^2		0·95
	di_2	1·03
dm^1		1·25
	dm_1	1·30
	dc	1·51
dc		1·52
	dm_2	2·16
dm^2		2·18

(Data derived from H. C. Sandler: "The eruption of the deciduous teeth", **J. Pediat., 25,** 140–162, 1944. The sample was drawn from white children from lower income groups attending a clinic in the Brownsville and Bushwick Health Districts, Brooklyn, New York, September 1941–February 1942.)

TABLE A1/2:

Age levels for Specified Numbers of Primary Teeth Present

Number of Teeth Present	Age Boys	Girls
1	0·55	0·60
2	0·65	0·70
4	0·82	0·86
6	0·97	1·03
8	1·12	1·18
10	1·27	1·33
12	1·43	1·50
14	1·62	1·70
16	1·85	1·97
18	2·13	2·35

(Data recalculated from H. V. Meredith: "Order and age of eruption for the deciduous dentition", **J. Dent Res., 25,** 43–66, 1946.)

TABLE A1/3:

Mean Age at which the Primary Teeth are shed

		Age	
Upper	*Lower*	*Boys*	*Girls*
	di_1	6·04	5·67
di^1		6·60	6·48
	di_2	7·14	6·75
di^2		7·58	7·25
	dm_1	8·24	7·98
dm^1		8·75	8·48
	dm_2	8·88	8·48
dm^2		9·58	9·37*
	dc	10·17	9·21*
dc		11·09	10·31

*The sequence is reversed in girls for lower canine and upper dm^2.

The sample was drawn from Birmingham (England) schoolchildren aged 5–13. The sample was fully representative of the local population. (Data from: E. M. B. Clements, E. Davies-Thomas, and K. G. Pickett: "Age at which the deciduous teeth are shed." **Brit. Med. J., 1,** 1508-1510, 1957).

TABLE : A1/4

Mean Ages of Eruption of the Secondary Teeth

		Age	
Upper	*Lower*	*Boys*	*Girls*
	M_1	6·21	5·94
M^1		6·40	6·22
	I_1	6·54	6·26
I^1		7·47	7·20
	I_2	7·70	7·34
I^2		8·67	8·20
Pm^1		10·40	10·03*
	C	10·79	9·86*
	Pm_1	10·82	10·18
Pm^2		11·18	10·88
	Pm_2	11·47	10·89
C		11·69	10·98
	M_2	12·12	11·66
M^2		12·68	12·27

*The sequence is reversed in girls for lower canine and upper Pm^1.

(Data from V. O. Hurme: "Ranges of Normalcy in the eruption of permanent teeth," **J. Dent. Child., 16,** 11-15, 1949.)

TABLE A1/5:

Age Levels for Specified Numbers of Secondary Teeth Present

Number of Teeth Present	Age Boys	Girls
2	6·21	5·94
4	6·40	6·22
6	6·54	6·26
8	7·47	7·20
10	7·70	7·34
12	8·67	8·20
14	10·40	9·86
16	10·79	10·03
18	10·82	10·18
20	11·18	10·88
22	11·47	10·89
24	11·69	10·98
26	12·12	11·66
28	12·68	12·27

(Data computed by Moorrees, C.F.A., The Aleut dentition, Harvard University Press, 1957 from V. O. Hurme: "Ranges of normalcy in the eruption of permanent teeth", **J. Dent. Child.**, Second Quarter, 1949.)

Method of assigning Dental " Age "

The dental ratings recorded on the sheets for Cards 6 and 7 are inspected and the dental " age " estimated by reference to the standard times of emergence or exfoliation, or the standard number of teeth emerged, as given in Tables A1/1 to A1/5. The third molars are omitted from the dental " age " assessments because a wide range of variation in their times of tooth emergence from one population to another is known to exist (see E. A. Fanning: " Third molar emergence in Bostonians ", **Amer. J. Phys. Anthrop.**, **20**, 339–346, 1962).

Where European standards (Tables A1/1–5) are inapplicable or doubtful, the appropriate standards to use will be those **established on the same population in sub-samples of children of known chronological age.** For each subject the method used should be recorded in col. 55 (Card 6) or col. 67 (Card 7). In addition the standard used should be recorded in col. 56 (Card 6) or col. 68 (Card 7), as " European " as given in Tables A1/1–5 or " sub-sample " or " other " details should be given.

How to use Tables A1/1–5

As already pointed out these standards cannot be used universally, and are given here merely to illustrate the method.

When dental " age " is assessed by reference to the total number of emerged teeth, this is done by simple selection of the appropriate age in Tables A1/2 or A1/5. For subjects in whom the sequence of emergence varies considerably from the norm, it is usually better to estimate age from the number of emerged teeth.

When dental " age " is assessed by reference to the emergence of specific teeth, or the exfoliation of specific teeth, this is done by reference to the data given in Tables A1/1, 3 and 4. For example, if only one tooth is rated Stage 2 (or Stage 5), then the time given for the emergence, or exfoliation, of that particular tooth will be the estimated dental " age ". Thus, if a boy has the lower canine in the secondary dentition rated Stage 2, and all the other teeth are rated 1, 3, 4, 5, 6, 7 or 8, then the dental " age " for that child is 10·50 years.

If more than one tooth is rated Stage 2 (or Stage 5), then the average of all the possible dental " ages " is taken.

When a child has no teeth in process of emergence, he should be rated half-way between the tooth which presumably was the last to appear, and that tooth which is the next expected to penetrate through the gingiva. For example, in boys there is an interval of about two years between the emergence of the secondary upper lateral incisor (I^2) and the first upper premolar (Pm^1). If a boy falls within this period he should be assigned a dental age of 9·53 years (that is, half-way between 8·67 and 10·40). However, if it can be seen that Pm^1 will soon break through the gum, a better estimate of dental age is 10·40 years, even though this figure is slightly too high.

Should it be necessary to include a crowded or misplaced tooth in the dental age assessment, a correction must be made as such variation will affect its time of emergence. A tooth may be prevented from breaking through the gingiva in its normal position owing to lack of space, in which case it may emerge on the lingual or the buccal side of the dental arch, and its time of emergence will be artificially retarded. On the other hand, if a tooth has been extracted its neighbour, or its successor in the secondary dentition, may emerge earlier than is normal.

There is a hiatus of approximately four years between the completion of the primary dentition and the onset of emergence of the secondary dentition. During this period interpolated ages are not recommended, except when exfoliation of the deciduous predecessors is observed.

Primary Dentition

Studies of the primary dentition show that in some populations boys are advanced over girls in the eruption of the incisors, but that no appreciable sex difference exists in the times of emergence of the remaining primary teeth. An incisor sex difference can be seen in Table A1/2, where the numbers of emerged primary teeth at each age are given; however, in Table A1/1, age at emergence of the specific primary teeth, the sexes have been pooled and the median age given for the emergence of each tooth.

Shedding of the Primary Teeth

The figures given in Table A1/3 are derived from the date of E. M. B. Clements, E. Davies-Thomas and K. G. Pickett: " Age at which the deciduous teeth are shed ", **Brit. Med. J., 1,** 1508–1510, 1957. These authors found that girls shed their primary teeth earlier than boys, and that in both sexes the lower teeth are shed earlier than the upper teeth.

Secondary Dentition

When the secondary dentition begins to appear at about six years of age, girls are slightly ahead of boys. The mean ages of eruption are given separately for girls and boys in Table A1/4.

(B) INSTRUMENTS:

The instrument recommended for taking each measurement is given under the ' Techniques ', above. There may be a choice of instrument for some measurements, depending upon personal preference and financial resources. Ideally the instruments to be used are the following:—

Weighing machine
Stadiometer (and Infant Measuring Table)
Anthropometer
Sliding caliper
Spreading caliper
Skin-fold caliper
Steel measuring tape
Head spanner or parallelometer (for " Full List " only).

A list of manufacturers of these instruments is given below. The accuracy of the instruments should be checked from time to time against a standard Caliper Gauge.

Digital read-out instruments, such as those of the Harpenden range, should be used wherever possible, to reduce visual errors. In difficult field conditions, a number of spare counters should be taken. (These are available from:

Messrs. Veeder-Root,
Prince Henry's Drive,
New Addington, CROYDON, Surrey).

When a sliding caliper is used instead of a spreading caliper, the measurer should take care not to injure the subject, as the tips of the caliper arms are sharp.

All instruments should be calibrated in the metric system.

Weighing Machine
A beam scale with long or short pillar and non-detachable weights should be used. The calibration should be on the measurer's side of the machine. Machines with detachable weights should not be used. Weights should be taken to 0·1 kg. in children and adults, and 10 gm. in babies under 9 months of age. A toddler rail may be added to the machine if required.

HERBERT & SONS LTD.,
Angel Road Works,
Edmonton,
LONDON, N.18.

Approx. nett prices (to health and education authorities): All-purpose weigher (babies, children and adults) (See Fig. A1/6a). £38.0.0.

Lightweight (19 lbs.) personal weigher—£26.0.0. (See Fig. A1/6b).

Lightweight baby weigher—£32.0.0 (See Fig. A1/6c). F.o.b.—£3.0.0.
Insurance—£9.0.0.

Alternative weighing machines are:—

1. **The 'Spido'** This is a bulky, but very accurate machine (see Fig. A1/7, below). The type ' BSW ' weighs 150 kg. by 10 g., is of all-steel construction, and mounted on two wheels. The price is approximately £125 f.o.b.

ALL PURPOSE WEIGHER

for BABIES, CHILDREN and ADULTS

Capacities: 20 stone × 1 oz.   280 lb × 1 oz.

◄ Machine ready to weigh baby.

Machine ready to weigh adult or child.

A

LIGHTWEIGHT BABY WEIGHER ▶

Capacity: 40 lb. × $\frac{1}{4}$ oz.

Reinforced fibreglass case. Cast aluminium platform. Perspex pan 23″ × 15″ × 6$\frac{1}{2}$″.

Tare to balance off blanket.

Carrying weight 19 lb.

C

B

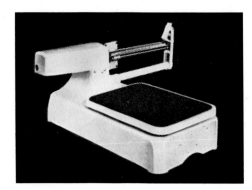

LIGHTWEIGHT ◄ PERSONAL WEIGHER

Available in capacity as detailed in general specification.

Reinforced fibreglass case, with cast aluminium platform, and inlaid rubber mat.

Dimensions:

Height	.. ..	10$\frac{1}{2}$″
Length	.. ..	21″
Width	.. ..	24″
Weight	.. ..	19 lb.

Fig. A1/6

facing p. 24

Fig. A1/7   The 'Spido' weighing machine.

Fig. A1/8   The 'Harpenden' skin-fold caliper.

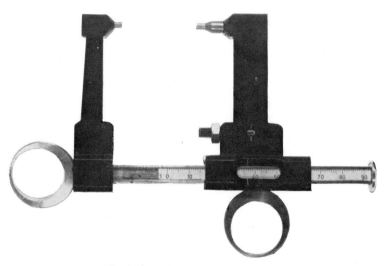

Fig. A1/9   The 'Best' skin-fold caliper.

Amsterdam, including ocean packing, and the machine is available from:

VAN VUCHT'S CONCERN N.V.,
Sarphatipark 31,
AMSTERDAM,
Holland.

2. **Butcher's steel yard** This apparatus is simple and easy to transport, but is normally only accurate to 1/10 kg.

Stadiometer

The Harpenden digital read-out wall-mounted Stadiometer is recommended for use in more permanent anthropometric laboratories. It consists of an upright light alloy frame, provided with adjustable wall brackets for mounting, and a head block which operates via miniature ball-bearing rollers to give a movement which is free yet without crossplay. In field studies stature may be measured with an anthropometer, (see p. 26).

Harpenden Stadiometer,
HOLTAIN LTD.,
Brynberian,
Crymmych,
Pembrokeshire, Wales.

Price: £68.5.0d.
F.o.b.: £10 approx.
Crated: 6' 6" × 1' 7" × 1' 0".
Weight: 110 lbs.

Portable model:
Price: £89.5.0d.
F.o.b.: £7 approx.
Crated: 4' 10" × 1' 8" × 9".
Weight: 100 lbs.

Infant   The Harpenden infant measuring table also has digital
Measuring Table read-out, and is similar in construction to the Harpenden
                    stadiometer. Range is 0 mm to 1200 mm.
                    Harpenden Infant Measuring Table,

HOLTAIN LTD.,
Address as p. 25.

Price: £63.
F.o.b.: £15 approx.
Crated: 4' 5" × 1' 11" × 1' 3".
Weight: 100 lbs.

Anthropometer   The digital read-out Harpenden Anthropometer is
                    recommended; it is easily operated with the tips of the
                    fingers.

HOLTAIN LTD. (address as p. 25), or:

(GPM Anthropological Instruments),

SIBER HEGNER & CO. LTD.,

Talstrasse 14,

8022, ZURICH,

Switzerland.

Also at:—

SIBER HEGNER & CO. INC.,

8 West 30th St.,

NEW YORK,

N.Y. 10001,

U.S.A.

and:—

SIBER HEGNER & CIE.–FRANCE, S.A.,

14, Rue Notre-Dame des Victoires,

PARIS 2eme.,

France.

Approx. price: £89.5.0.

Supplied in carrying case, includes straight and recurved branches, spare counter and beam extensions for measuring heights up to 2 metres. Range 50–570 mm.

(Harpenden Anthropometers are also available on hire from the Eugenics Society, 69 Eccleston Square, LONDON, S.W.1., England).

An alternative lightweight instrument, which consists of four aluminium alloy tubes with special surface treatment which fit into one another to form one rigid rod, is available. Each tube is graduated in mm., on one side from below (0–2100 mm.) The instrument is normally supplied in a canvas bag with a pair of straight crossbars. The net weight is 1.1 kg.

Sliding Caliper

Not absolutely essential, but recommended for several measurements. The Helios caliper is a convenient dial-reading model.

SCHNEIDER AND KERN,
Niedernhall,
WURTTENBERG,
Germany.

BUCK AND RYAN LTD.,
101, Tottenham Court Road,
LONDON, W.1.

England. Approx. price £18.0.0.

Spreading Caliper

No digital read-out spreading calipers are obtainable at present. Olive-tipped branched ends should be used.
A suitable instrument is available from:

SIBER HEGNER & CO. LTD.,
(Address as p. 26).

Approx. price £20.0.0.

Skinfold Caliper

A caliper with rectangular jaws and constant pressure of 10 gm./sq. mm. must be used. Measurements should be recorded to 0·2 mm. or 0·5 mm. The Harpenden Skin-fold Caliper (see Fig. A1/8, after page 24) reads to 0·1 mm. (See J. M. Tanner and R. H. Whitehouse, ' The Harpenden Skinfold Caliper '. **Amer. J. Phys. Anthrop., 13,** 743–746, 1955.)

BRITISH INDICATORS LTD.,
Acrewood Way,
St. Albans,
Herts.,
England.

Approx. price £32.0.0.

A similar caliper is available from Holtain or Siber Hegner (addresses as pp. 25, 26).

The Lange Caliper reads to 0·5 mm., and may be obtained from:—

CAMBRIDGE SCIENTIFIC INDUSTRIES Inc.,
18 Poplar St.,
CAMBRIDGE,
Maryland,
U.S.A. Approx. price: £18.0.0.

An alternative instrument, the " Best " caliper (see Fig. A1/9, after page 24), is obtainable from:
Mr. Hrdlicka,
Vyzkumny Ustar Telovychovny,
PRAGUE 3,
Ujezd 450,
Czechoslovakia. Price: approx. £10.

Steel or Plastic Tape

Steel or plastic tapes should be used, never linen ones which stretch.

Chesterman 2 metre × 1 cm steel tape in bakelite cases

A. COLLIER (BRIXTON) LTD.,
423 Coldharbour Lane,
Brixton,
London, S.W.9. Approx. price: 15/–.

Also from:—

SIBER HEGNER & CO. LTD.,

Addresses as above.

Approx. price: £1.

Head Spanner   For measuring head height only. A parallelometer may be used instead.

Black's Auricular Head Spanner,

SIBER HEGNER & CO. LTD.,

Addresses as p. 26.

Approx. price: £20.

Parallelometer   For measuring head height only.

SIBER HEGNER & CO. LTD.,

Addresses as p. 26.

Approx. price: £65.

Caliper Gauge   All anthropometric instruments should be checked against a standard Caliper Gauge at intervals.

SIBER HEGNER & CO. LTD.,

Addresses as p. 26.

Approx. price: £5.

Additional Anthropometric Instruments   Harpenden digital read-out Sitting Height Table. Approx. price £100.

Harpenden Somatotype Turntable:

    1.   Electrically operated: Approx. price: £100.

    2.   Manually operated: Approx. price: £50.

All available from HOLTAIN LTD.,

Address as p. 25.

A wide range of osteometric instruments is available from:

SIBER HEGNER & CO. LTD.,

Addresses as p. 26.

III.   DATA COLLECTING SHEETS

To facilitate analysis of raw data the recommended measurements have been arranged to fit on to 80-column punched cards, the Basic List on two cards and the Full List on three cards.

Recording the Measurements

The measurements are in millimetres and readings should be taken to the last completed unit on the scale used, e.g. in measuring stature, the figure 162·7 mm is taken if the stature lies anywhere between 162·7 and 162·8 mm. When the data is being worked up statistically the means should be adjusted by adding 0·5 to the final unit.

Skinfolds should be read to the last completed unit, which is 0·2 mm on the Harpenden or Holtain Skinfold Caliper, and 0·5 mm on the Lange Skinfold Caliper.

The record should be made in permanent ink or ball-point pen.

Where a parameter is inappropriate (for example, Menarche for males), or omitted for some unavoidable reason, leave the recording boxes blank.

Layout of Measurement Recording Sheets

Study Number	These 2 boxes are available so that each country may use its own code: for example, Study Number 01 to Study Number 98 Leave 99 for computer use.
Card Number	The measurements fit on to several punched cards and the Card Numbers can be printed on the various recording sheets.
Geographical Area	Each Study has to be assigned to a geographical area. Leave this box blank: it will be filled in by the IBP Office when required.
Sex	1—Male; 2—Female.
Exam Date **Birth Date**	Dates should be recorded in Decimal Years (see Table A1/7 pp. 32, 33. For example, to look up the Decimal Year of, say, 17th July, 1967, first find

figure 17 in the left-hand column and then move along that row to the figures given under the July heading, that is 540. On the recording sheet 17th July, 1967 will be written 67 / 540, the year being recorded before the day and month.

Age

On the recording sheet Birth Date is filled in below Exam Date, so that Age may be obtained by sub-traction, one from the other. For example:—

Exam Date	17th July, 1967	..	67 / 540
Birth Date	1st May, 1950 ..	..	50 / 329
			—————
Age (by subtraction) is thus		..	..	17 / 211
			—————

On the recording sheet Age is rounded off to four figures, in this case 17·21.

Code for Age

Chronological Age should be recorded as accurately as possible. The appropriate code number from the following list should be inserted for each subject.

1—Birth Date known to within one day
2—Birth Date known to within one month only
3—Birth Date known to within three months only
4—Birth Date known to within one year only
5—Birth Date may be inaccurate by more than one year

Number

Each subject must be assigned a separate number, from 001 to 998. Please leave 999 for computer use.

IBP Number

Please leave these two boxes blank; they will be used by the IBP Office, if required.

Health

Code: 1—Apparently healthy
2—Minor chronic or acute illness
3—Definitely ill.

Menarche/Menopause Details for the collection of data on age at Menarche are given under (5) below.

Code: 1—No Menarche

2—Menarche occurred (no menopause)

3—Menopause occurred.

Headings

For both the Basic List and the Full List of measurements only the first of the recording sheets carries the complete Heading. The second and third sheets have a simplified Heading, but it is important to complete this heading also so that data from the different sheets can be collated.

Optional Data

At the end of the Basic List and the Full List of measurements recording boxes have been provided for ratings given for Skeletal Age Assessment, Genital Development, Axillary Hair Development, Pubic Hair Development, Breast Development, and Somatotype. (See **A2, A3,** and **A4.**)

The recording sheet for Section **A4** (Radiographic Measurements) is given as Card 6 below.

None of these assessments forms a part of the recommended base-line, but it is envisaged that many workers will wish to include these data in their growth and physique studies.

TABLE A1/7

Table of Decimal Years

Months of the year are arrayed along the top of the Table, and days of the month in the left-hand column. To look up the Decimal Year of, say, 17th July, 1967, first find the figure 17 in the left-hand column and then move along to the figures given under the July heading, that is 540. Thus, on the Data Sheet 17th July, 1967 will be recorded as 67/540.

		Jan.	Feb.	Mar.	Apr.	May	Jun.	Jul.	Aug.	Sep.	Oct.	Nov.	Dec.
		1	2	3	4.	5	6	7	8	9	10	11	12
1	. .	000	085	162	247	329	414	496	581	666	748	833	915
2	. .	003	088	164	249	332	416	499	584	668	751	836	918
3	. .	005	090	167	252	334	419	501	586	671	753	838	921
4	. .	008	093	170	255	337	422	504	589	674	756	841	923
5	. .	011	096	173	258	340	425	507	592	677	759	844	926
6	. .	014	099	175	260	342	427	510	595	679	762	847	929
7	. .	016	101	178	263	345	430	512	597	682	764	849	932
8	. .	019	104	181	266	348	433	515	600	685	767	852	934
9	. .	022	107	184	268	351	436	518	603	688	770	855	937
10	. .	025	110	186	271	353	438	521	605	690	773	858	940

		Jan.	Feb.	Mar.	Apl.	May	Jun.	Jur.	Aug.	Sep.	Oct.	Nov.	Dec.
		1	2	3	4	5	6	7	8	9	10	11	12
11	..	027	112	189	274	356	441	523	608	693	775	860	942
12	..	030	115	192	277	359	444	526	611	696	778	863	945
13	..	033	118	195	279	362	447	529	614	699	781	866	948
14	..	036	121	197	282	364	449	532	616	701	784	868	951
15	..	038	123	200	285	367	452	534	619	704	786	871	953
16	..	041	126	203	288	370	455	537	622	707	789	874	956
17	..	044	129	205	290	373	458	540	625	710	792	877	959
18	..	047	132	208	293	375	460	542	627	712	795	879	962
19	..	049	134	211	296	378	463	545	630	715	797	882	964
20	..	052	137	214	299	381	466	548	633	718	800	885	967
		1	2	3	4	5	6	7	8	9	10	11	12
21	..	055	140	216	301	384	468	551	636	721	803	888	970
22	..	058	142	219	304	386	471	553	638	723	805	890	973
23	..	060	145	222	307	389	474	556	641	726	808	893	975
24	..	063	148	225	310	392	477	559	644	729	811	896	978
25	..	066	151	227	312	395	479	562	647	731	814	899	981
26	..	068	153	230	315	397	482	564	649	734	816	901	984
27	..	071	156	233	318	400	485	567	652	737	819	904	986
28	..	074	159	236	321	403	488	570	655	740	822	907	989
29	..	077	159	238	323	405	490	573	658	742	825	910	992
30	..	079	–	241	326	408	493	575	660	745	827	912	995
31	..	082	–	244	–	411	–	578	663	–	830	–	997
		1	2	3	4	5	6	7	8	9	10	11	12

Information to be completed for each subject

Name of Population Unit: Study number:

Examined at (place and institution) :

Subject's Name: Subject's Serial Number:

Place of birth:

If at School, please state Boarding . . . .

Day . . . .

If not at School, please check here . . . .

If at Day School, please state : Number of meals at School . . . .

Number of meals at Home . . . .

Distance from Home to School . . . . km/mls*

Father's Name :   Place of birth :

Population Unit :

Occupation :

Mother's Name :   Place of birth :

Population Unit :

Occupation :

Number of Siblings :   Living . . . .

Dead . . . .

Birth Rank :

*Please cross out whichever does **not** apply.

DESCRIPTION OF THE POPULATION UNIT FROM WHICH THE SAMPLE IS DRAWN

(To be recorded separately for each Population Unit.)

1. Name of population unit :

2. Unit's localization and geographical boundaries :

3. If other populations exist within the area of the Unit, then state geographical boundaries, basis of the Unit's identification (e.g. linguistic, religious, social, etc.) and list co-existing groups :

4. Approximate number of people in the Unit :

5. Approximate degree of genetic isolation:

6. Approximate frequency of consanguineous marriages, and attitudes toward them:

7. Is the Sample representative of the entire Unit? If not, which sector of it does the Sample represent?

8. Is there any evidence of a lack of homogeneity within the Unit (e.g. regional differentiation in genetical characters or in environmental factors, affecting growth and physique)? If yes, does the Sample cover representatively all such variation?

9. Method of sampling:

10. Basis for excluding members of the Unit from the Sample (e.g. siblings, foreigners up to a specified level of ancestry, bad health, etc.):

11. List of occupational categories within the Unit, with approximate frequencies:

12. General description of the Unit's diet:

13. General description of the Unit's pathology:

A *Growth and Physique*

Measurement Recording Form for Basic List, Card 1
IBP MEASUREMENTS—BASIC LIST

TUDY NUMBER	1	☐ ☐ ☐
CARD NUMBER	3	☐
GEOGRAPHICAL AREA	4	☐ ☐
SEX (1=Male; 2=Female)	6	
EXAMINATION DATE	7	☐ ☐ ☐ ☐ ☐
BIRTH DATE	12	☐ ☐ ☐ ☐ ☐
AGE	17	☐ ☐ ☐ ☐
Code for Age:	21	☐
SUBJECT NUMBER	22	☐ ☐ ☐
IBP NUMBER	25	☐ ☐
HEALTH: (Code 1, 2 or 3)	27	☐
MENARCHE/MENOPAUSE: (Code 1, 2 or 3)	28	☐
Code: 1=Stature; 2=Supine	29	☐
STATURE/SUPINE LENGTH	30	☐ ☐ ☐ ☐
HT. ANTERIOR SUPERIOR ILIAC SPINE	34	☐ ☐ ☐ ☐
Code: 1=Sit. Ht.; 2=Crown-rump	38	☐
SITTING HEIGHT/CROWN RUMP	39	☐ ☐ ☐ ☐
BICONDYLAR FEMUR	43	☐ ☐ ☐
WRIST BREADTH	46	☐ ☐
CALF CIRCUMFERENCE	48	☐ ☐ ☐
UPPER ARM CIRCUMFERENCE (relaxed)	51	☐ ☐ ☐
TOTAL ARM LENGTH	54	☐ ☐ ☐
BIACROMIAL DIAMETER	57	☐ ☐ ☐
TRANSVERSE CHEST	60	☐ ☐ ☐
ANTERO-POSTERIOR CHEST	63	☐ ☐ ☐
BIILIOCRISTAL DIAMETER	66	☐ ☐ ☐

Codes:

AGE:

1=Birth Date known to within 1 day.
2=Birth Date known to within one month only.
3=Birth Date known to within three months only.
4=Birth Date known to within one year only.
5=Birth Date may be inaccurate by more than one year.

HEALTH:

1=Apparently healthy.
2=Minor chronic or acute illness.
3=Definitely ill.

MENARCHE/MENOPAUSE:

1=No menarche.
2=Menarche occurred (no menopause).
3=Menopause occurred.

Measurement Recording Form for Basic List, Card 2

IBP MEASUREMENTS—BASIC LIST

STUDY NUMBER   1 ☐☐
CARD NUMBER   3 ☐
SEX (1=Male; 2=Female)   4 ☐
AGE   5 ☐☐☐☐
SUBJECT NUMBER   9 ☐☐☐
IBP NUMBER   12 ☐☐

HEAD LENGTH   14 ☐☐☐
HEAD BREADTH   17 ☐☐☐
BIZYGOMATIC DIAMETER   20 ☐☐☐
FACE HEIGHT (Nasion to Gnathion)   23 ☐☐☐
NOSE HEIGHT   26 ☐☐
NOSE BREADTH   28 ☐☐
SKINFOLDS: TRICEPS   30 ☐☐☐ 0·2 or 0·5 mm
            SUBSCAPULAR   33 ☐☐☐
WEIGHT   36 ☐☐☐☐ 0·1 kg

OPTIONAL DATA

SKELETAL AGE ASSESSMENT   40 ☐☐☐☐ (in decimal years)
GENITAL DEVELOPMENT   44 ☐
AXILLARY HAIR DEVELOPMENT   45 ☐
PUBIC HAIR DEVELOPMENT   46 ☐
BREAST DEVELOPMENT   47 ☐
SOMATOTYPE: Endomorphy   48 ☐☐ (to nearest 0·5 unit)
            Mesomorphy   50 ☐☐
            Ectomorphy   52 ☐☐

Measurement Recording Form for Full List, Card 3

IBP MEASUREMENTS—FULL LIST

STUDY NUMBER	1 ☐☐
CARD NUMBER	3 ☐
GEOGRAPHICAL AREA	4 ☐☐
SEX: (1=Male; 2=Female)	6 ☐
EXAMINATION DATE	7 ☐☐☐☐☐
BIRTH DATE	12 ☐☐☐☐☐
AGE	17 ☐☐☐☐
Code for Age:	21 ☐
SUBJECT NUMBER	22 ☐☐☐
IBP NUMBER	25 ☐☐
HEALTH: (Code 1, 2 or 3)	27 ☐
MENARCHE/MENOPAUSE: (Code 1, 2 or 3)	28 ☐
Code: (1=Stature; 2=Supine)	29 ☐
STATURE/SUPINE LENGTH	30 ☐☐☐☐
SUPRASTERNAL HEIGHT	34 ☐☐☐☐
HT. ANTERIOR SUPERIOR ILIAC SPINE	38 ☐☐☐☐
HEIGHT OF TIBIALE	42 ☐☐☐
LOWER LEG LENGTH	45 ☐☐☐
TOTAL ARM LENGTH	48 ☐☐☐
UPPER ARM LENGTH	51 ☐☐☐
FOREARM LENGTH	54 ☐☐☐
BICONDYLAR HUMERUS	57 ☐☐
WRIST BREADTH	59 ☐☐
HAND BREADTH	61 ☐☐☐
BICONDYLAR FEMUR	64 ☐☐☐
ANKLE BREADTH	67 ☐☐☐
FOOT LENGTH	70 ☐☐☐
Code: 1=Sit. Ht.; 2=Crown-rump	73 ☐
SITTING HEIGHT/CROWN RUMP	74 ☐☐☐☐

Codes:

HEALTH:

1=Apparently healthy.
2=Minor chronic or acute illness.
3=Definitely ill.

MENARCHE/MENOPAUSE:

1=No menarche.
2=Menarche occurred (no menopause).
3=Menopause occurred.

Measurement Recording Form for Full List, Card 4

IBP MEASUREMENTS—FULL LIST

STUDY NUMBER	1 ▢▢
CARD NUMBER	3 ▢
SEX: (1=Male; 2=Female)	4 ▢
AGE	5 ▢▢▢▢
SUBJECT NUMBER	9 ▢▢▢
IBP NUMBER	12 ▢▢
THIGH CIRCUMFERENCE	14 ▢▢▢
CALF CIRCUMFERENCE	17 ▢▢▢
BIACROMIAL DIAMETER	20 ▢▢▢
TRANSVERSE CHEST	23 ▢▢▢
ANTERO-POSTERIOR CHEST	26 ▢▢▢
BIILIOCRISTAL DIAMETER	29 ▢▢▢
CHEST CIRCUMFERENCE	32 ▢▢▢
UPPER ARM CIRCUMFERENCE (relaxed)	35 ▢▢▢
UPPER ARM CIRCUMFERENCE (contracted)	38 ▢▢▢
SKINFOLDS: TRICEPS	41 ▢▢▢ 0·2 or 0·5 mm
SUBSCAPULAR	44 ▢▢▢
SUPRAILIAC	47 ▢▢▢
HEAD LENGTH	50 ▢▢▢
HEAD BREADTH	53 ▢▢▢
BIZYGOMATIC DIAMETER	56 ▢▢▢
BIGONIAL DIAMETER	59 ▢▢▢
FACE HEIGHT (Nasion to Gnathion)	62 ▢▢▢
NOSE HEIGHT	65 ▢▢
NOSE BREADTH	67 ▢▢
MOUTH WIDTH	69 ▢▢
LIP THICKNESS	71 ▢▢
HEAD HEIGHT	73 ▢▢▢
WEIGHT	76 ▢▢▢▢ 0·1 kg

Code:

AGE:

1=Birth Date known to within one day.
2=Birth Date known to within one month only.
3=Birth Date known to within three months only.
4=Birth Date known to within one year only.
9=Birth Date may be inaccurate by more than one year.

Measurement Recording Form for Full List, Card 5

IBP MEASUREMENTS—FULL LIST

STUDY NUMBER	1 ▢▢
CARD NUMBER	3 ▢
SEX: (1=Male; 2=Female)	4 ▢
AGE	5 ▢▢▢▢
SUBJECT NUMBER	9 ▢▢▢
IBP NUMBER	12 ▢▢

OPTIONAL DATA

SKELETAL AGE ASSESSMENT	14 ▢▢▢▢	(in decimal years)
GENITAL DEVELOPMENT	18 ▢	
AXILLARY HAIR DEVELOPMENT	19 ▢	
PUBIC HAIR DEVELOPMENT	20 ▢	
BREAST DEVELOPMENT	21 ▢	
SOMATOTYPE: Endomorphy	22 ▢▢	(to nearest 0·5 unit)
Mesomorphy	24 ▢▢	
Ectomorphy	26 ▢▢	

Recording Sheet for Card 6

IBP—PRIMARY DENTITION

STUDY NUMBER	1	☐☐
CARD NUMBER	3	☐
GEOGRAPHICAL AREA	4	☐☐
SEX: (1=Male; 2=Female)	6	☐
EXAMINATION DATE	7	☐☐☐☐☐
BIRTH DATE	12	☐☐☐☐☐
AGE	17	☐☐☐☐
Code for Age	21	☐
SUBJECT NUMBER	22	☐☐☐
IBP NUMBER	25	☐☐

MAXILLA

	Subject's RIGHT			Subject's LEFT		
Central incisor	27	☐		32	☐	
Lateral incisor	28	☐		33	☐	*Tooth ratings:*
Canine	29	☐		34	☐	1 = not emerged.
First molar	30	☐		35	☐	2 = two or more cusps.
Second molar	31	☐		36	☐	3 = more than $\frac{1}{3}$ crown.

4 = fully erupted.

MANDIBLE

5 = exfoliated.

Central incisor	37	☐		42	☐	6 = misplaced/crowded.
Lateral incisor	38	☐		43	☐	7 = agenesis.
Canine	39	☐		44	☐	8 = extracted.
First molar	40	☐		45	☐	
Second molar	41	☐		46	☐	

TOTAL NUMBER ERUPTED: PRIMARY	47	☐☐
SECONDARY	49	☐☐
ESTIMATED DENTAL AGE	51	☐☐☐☐
Code for Dental Age	55	☐
Code for standard used for age estimation	56	☐

Code for Dental Age:

1 = Primary—specific teeth emerged.
2 = Primary—number of teeth emerged.
3 = Primary—specific teeth exfoliated.
4 = Secondary—specific teeth emerged.
5 = Secondary—number of teeth emerged.

Code for Standard used:

1 = "European"—(Tables A1/1–A1/5).
2 = Subsample (specify).
3 = Other (specify).

Recording Sheet for Card 7

IBP—SECONDARY DENTITION

STUDY NUMBER	1	☐☐
CARD NUMBER	3	☐
GEOGRAPHICAL AREA	4	☐☐
SEX: (1=Male; 2=Female)	6	☐
EXAMINATION DATE	7	☐☐☐☐☐
BIRTH DATE	12	☐☐☐☐☐
AGE	17	☐☐☐☐
Code for Age	21	☐
SUBJECT NUMBER	22	☐☐☐
IBP NUMBER	25	☐☐

MAXILLA

	Subject's RIGHT		Subject's LEFT		
Central incisor	27 ☐		35 ☐		
Lateral incisor	28 ☐		36 ☐		
Canine	29 ☐		37 ☐		
First premolar	30 ☐		38 ☐		*Tooth ratings:*
Second premolar	31 ☐		39 ☐		1 = not emerged.
First molar	32 ☐		40 ☐		2 = two or more cusps.
Second molar	33 ☐		41 ☐		3 = more than $\frac{1}{3}$ crown.
Third molar	34 ☐		42 ☐		4 = fully erupted.
					5 = exfoliated.

6 = misplaced/crowded.

MANDIBLE

7 = agenesis.

8 = extracted.

Central incisor	43 ☐	51 ☐	
Lateral incisor	44 ☐	52 ☐	
Canine	45 ☐	53 ☐	
First premolar	46 ☐	54 ☐	
Second premolar	47 ☐	55 ☐	
First molar	48 ☐	56 ☐	
Second molar	49 ☐	57 ☐	
Third molar	50 ☐	58 ☐	

TOTAL NUMBER ERUPTED: PRIMARY	59	☐☐
SECONDARY	61	☐☐
ESTIMATED DENTAL AGE	63	☐☐☐☐
Code for Dental Age (See Card 6 for details.)	67	☐
Code for Standard used (See Card 6 for details.)	68	☐

A2. PUBERTY RATING

I. INTRODUCTION

    (a) General

    (b) Observations to be made

    (c) Sampling

II. TECHNIQUES

III. DATA COLLECTING SHEET

I. INTRODUCTION

(a) General *

Some designation of how far a child has progressed through adolescence is frequently required. A relatively simple and quite practical scheme is as follows: in boys genital development and pubic hair development are rated separately, and in girls breast development and pubic hair development are rated separately, as well as menarche. All ratings are on a scale from 1 to 5 (see Figs. A2/1 and A2/2 under II. TECHNIQUES, below) and the standard for pubic hair can in this way be made the same in both sexes. If a composite sex-character-development rating is required, the pubic hair ratings can be averaged with the genital ratings for boys, and with the breast ratings for girls. Naturally, the ratings can be assigned with more accuracy if a longitudinal study of a child is available, since they are really based on the occurrence of change from a previous state. However, fair accuracy is attainable even when a child is only seen once. Pubic hair ratings are perhaps easier to give than genital and breast development ones under these circumstances. The rating in a longitudinal series refers to the actual time the stage in question is first observed, and is not interpolated backwards half-way to the previous examination, since this would be impossible for cross-sectionally given ratings.

(b) Observations to be made:

(1) Stages of male genital development.
(2) Stages of pubic hair development.
(3) Stages of axillary and facial hair development.
(4) Stages of breast development.
(5) Age at menarche.

* (Modified from J. M. Tanner: '*Growth at Adolescence*', 2nd Edition. Blackwell Scientific Publications, Oxford, 1962.)

(c) **Sampling**

For cross-sectional, longitudinal, and mixed longitudinal surveys, sample sizes as laid down for general growth and physique studies (see **A1**) are appropriate. That is at least 100, but preferably 150, of each sex in the 10–20 age group.

II. TECHNIQUES

The assessment of pubertal stages can of course be done by direct observation. For a permanent record for later study, however, photographs are recommended. For details of the photographic technique, see under **A3**.

(1) **Stages of male genital development.**

The stages of development are to be scored as follows: (see Fig. A2/1 facing page 48).

Stage 1 Pre-adolescent. Testes, scrotum and penis are of the same size and proportions as in early childhood.

Stage 2 Enlargement of scrotum and testes. The skin of the scrotum reddens, and changes in texture. Little or no enlargement of the penis at this stage.

Stage 3 Enlargement of penis, which occurs at first mainly in length. Further growth of testes and scrotum.

Stage 4 Increased size of penis with growth in breadth, and development of glans. Further enlargement of testes and scrotum; increased darkening of scrotal skin.

Stage 5 Genitalia adult in size and shape. No further enlargement takes place after stage 5 is reached.

(2) **Stages of pubic hair development.**

The stages of development are to be scored as follows: (see Fig. A2/2 after p. 48).

Stage 1 Pre-adolescent. The vellus over the pubes is not further developed than that over the abdominal wall, i.e. no pubic hair.

Stage 2 Sparse growth of long, slightly pigmented downy hair, straight or only slightly curled, appearing chiefly at the base of the penis or along the labia.

Stage 3   Considerably darker, coarser and more curled. The hair spreads sparsely over the junction of the pubes. It is at this stage that pubic hair is first seen in the usual type of black and white photograph of the entire body; special arrangements are necessary to photograph stage 2 hair.

Stage 4   Hair now resembles adult in type, but the area covered by it is still considerably smaller than in the adult. No spread to the medial surface of the thighs.

Stage 5   Adult in quantity and type with distribution of the horizontal (or classically 'feminine') pattern. Spread to medial surface of thighs but not up linea alba or elsewhere above the base of the inverse triangle.

In about 80% of Caucasoid men and 10% of women, the pubic hair spreads further, but this takes some time to occur after stage 5 is reached. When it does occur the pubic hair is rated as stage 6, a terminology which retains the uniform rating for male and female over the 5-point scale, and at the same time places this longer-term development, often not completed until the mid-twenties or later, beyond the more concentrated period of adolescence.

(3)   **Stages of axillary and facial hair development.**

Axillary hair may be rated on a 3-point scale: 1 when none is present; 2 for slight growth; and 3 for adult quantity or distribution if shaved.

In boys **facial hair** begins to grow at about the time the axillary hair appears. First there is an increase in length and pigmentation of hairs at the corners of the upper lip: this development then spreads medially to complete the moustache. Hair next appears on the upper part of the cheeks and in the midline just below the lower lip, and finally along the sides and lower border of the chin; the actual distribution observed is best recorded.

The remainder of the body hair appears from about the time of the first axillary hair development up to a considerable period after puberty. The hair on the thigh, calf, abdomen and forearm usually precedes that on the chest and upper arm.

(4) **Stages of breast development.**

The stages of development are to be scored as follows: (see **Fig.** A2/3 after this page).

Stage 1   Pre-adolescent: elevation of papilla only.

Stage 2   Breast bud stage; elevation of breast and papilla as small mound. Enlargement of areolar diameter.

Stage 3   Further enlargement and elevation of breast and areola, with no separation of their contours.

Stage 4   Projection of areola and papilla to form a secondary mound above the level of the breast.

Stage 5   Mature stage; projection of papilla only, due to recession of the areola to the general contour of the breast.

The appearance of the breast bud is as a rule the first sign of puberty in the female, though the appearance of pubic hair may sometimes precede it. The stage 4 development of the areolar mound does not occur in all girls; in probably about a quarter it is absent, and in a further quarter relatively slight. Furthermore, the areolar mound, when it does occur, often persists well into adulthood; it seems to be at least as much a matter of adult physique as a passing stage of adolescent development. Areolar diameter enlargement continues from stage 2 to stage 5 but proceeds faster in the early stages. Accurate breast development ratings on a cross-sectional basis may be very difficult, but in longitudinal work the general increase in breast size enables stages 3, 4 and 5 to be assigned fairly confidently.

(5) **Age at Menarche.**

The trend toward earlier maturing in Europe and North America during the last hundred years is perhaps best shown by the statistics on the age at menarche. From longitudinal studies it is known that age at menarche is distributed in a Gaussian fashion, and as a consequence the statistical technique of probits or logits can be used to estimate the mean age of menarche from cross-sectional data.

It is therefore only necessary to select a proper sample—for instance, of the schools in a certain area, or of all girls belonging to a certain occupational group—and ask each girl whether or not she has experienced her first period. Ideally, all girls aged 9 to 17 should be interrogated, but very little information is lost by restricting the ages to 10·0 to 15·9 years.

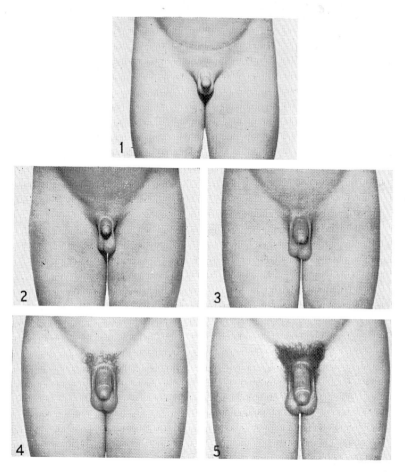

Fig. A2/1   Standards for genitalia maturity rating in boys: stages 1 to 5.
(Reprinted from J. M. Tanner, *Growth at Adolescence*, 2nd. Ed. Plate 5. Oxford:
Blackwells Scientific Publications. 1962.)

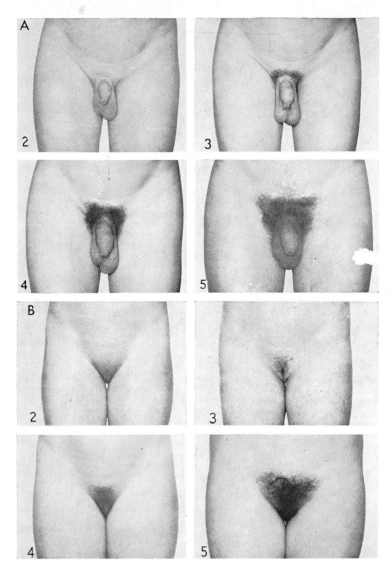

Fig. A2/2 Standards for pubic hair rating in boys (above) and girls (below).
Reprinted from J. M. Tanner, Growth and Endocrinology of the Adolescent, in *Endocrine
and Genetic Diseases of Childhood*: Ed. Lytt Gardner. W. B. Saunders, Philadelphia and
London (in press).

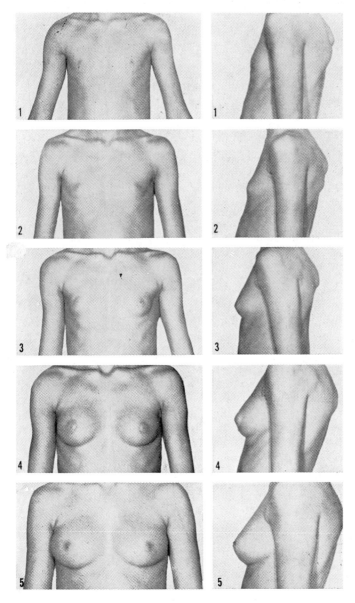

Fig. A2/3   Standards for breast development rating during adolescence: stages 1 to 5. (Reprinted from J. M. Tanner, *Growth at Adolescence*, 2nd. Ed. Plate 7. Oxford: Blackwell Scientific Publications. 1962.)

A plot of per cent menstruating against age (ranging from, say, 10% at 10·0 years to 90% at 15·5 years) gives a sigmoid curve, which repeated experience has shown to be very well fitted by either probits or logits.

An equally valid procedure is that of the longitudinal study where every child is examined repeatedly until menarche has occurred.

A procedure that does **not** usually give a valid estimate of the mean age at menarche in cross-sectional data is that of enquiring of all girls in a school or college what age they were when first they menstruated. There are difficulties of exact recollection on the part of those who had their menarche several years previously, and there is an important bias introduced if there remain any girls who have not yet menstruated. These girls will have high values for menarcheal age and if these values are omitted, the mean age obtained will be spuriously low. Either only girls above 17·0 years must be interrogated, or else the rather complex statistics of the truncated normal distribution must be used to allow for the absent tail.

As many surveys will include subjects of all ages, it will be of value to collect data on the age at menopause. Again, only the occurrence of menopause should be recorded, and not the recollected age of onset.

Menarche/menopause ratings should be recorded on the anthropometric data recording sheet (see **A1**) in col. 28.

III. DATA COLLECTING SHEET

Stages assessed for puberty ratings are to be recorded on the codified forms provided in Section A1.

A3. PHOTOGRAMMETRY: BODY TYPING

I. INTRODUCTION

    (a) General

    (b) Observations to be made

    (c) Sampling

II. TECHNIQUES

    (a) Somatotyping by photogrammetry

    (b) Body Typing by measurement

    (c) Instruments

III. DATA COLLECTING SHEETS

    (a) For somatotyping by photogrammetry

    (b) For body typing by measurement

I. INTRODUCTION

(a) General.

Standardised full-length photographs are useful in population studies for several reasons. Not only do they help to identify the subject, and provide some anthroposcopic information (see **B15**), but when used for somatotyping, they provide important information on body size, shape, and composition. Modifications of the method using direct measurements (and not photography) have been introduced by Parnell, R. W., (**Amer. J. Phys. Anthrop; 12,** 209–239, 1954), and Heath, B.H., and J. E. L. Carter. (**Amer. J. Phys. Anthrop., 27** 57–74, 1967).

(b) Observations to be made:

Somatotype ratings for the 5 body regions from photographs.

Final somatotype rating

(c) Sampling:

Photogrammetry would usually be carried out on adults. A sample size of 150, and not less than 100 (of each sex) should be obtained within the age range of 20–25, or 20–30. For children and adolescents, see the sampling recommendations given under **A1.**

II. TECHNIQUES

(a) Somatotyping by photogrammetry.*

If possible the subject should be photographed in the nude; otherwise very brief shorts may be worn, but these should not obscure the iliac crests nor the

---

* For a description of the technique to be employed for close-up photography of the face and head, see **B15.**

gluteal folds. Full-length front, side and rear view pictures should be taken. The lens-subject distance should be 10 metres, or as near as possible to this distance, to reduce parallax error (see Fig. A3/1, p. 55).

The subject must be posed in a standard way, standing upright with his head in the Frankfort plane, feet slightly apart, arms held a little away from the sides of the body, palms of the hands facing towards the body with the fingers stretched downwards and thumbs adducted. A well-posed set of pictures is shown in Fig. A3/2, facing p. 55.

Ideally, the subject should be posed on a turntable and stand against a specially lighted background grid, but this may not be practicable in the field. For a more detailed description of this technique see Dupertuis, C. W., and Tanner, J. M. " The pose of the subject for photogrammetric anthropometry with special reference to somatotyping ", **Amer. J. Phys. Anthrop., 8,** 27–248, 1950. A metre rule and the subject's serial number should in any case be clearly visible on the photograph.

Suitable pictures may be taken with a Rolleicord-type or 35 mm camera fitted with a long-focus lens to reduce the field, and mounted on a tripod. Also a single-shot cine-film camera may be used, and this too should be fitted with a long-focus lens. This type of camera has the advantage for field work that about 200 shots may be taken on one roll of film.

For a lens-subject distance of 10 metres, used a 13·5 cm lens.

For a lens-subject distance of 7 metres, use a 7·5 cm lens.

A useful portable back-grid assembly incorporating lighting strips, etc., is described by Jones, P. R. M. and Stone, P. G. in **Amer. J. Phys. Anthrop., 22,** 259–264, 1964.

From the somatotype photograph, the somatotype ratings are to be assessed in accordance with the somatotype criteria. An abbreviated list of these criteria is given below; the full list with illustrations of somatotypes is found in Sheldon, W. H. ' The Varieties of Human Physique ', New York, Harper, 1940, and in ' Atlas of Men ', Harper, 1954.

With non-European populations, the investigator may find that a few of the criteria are not easy to apply, do not apply at all, or require modification. This should be noted in the Data Collecting Sheet. (In this context, reference may be made to, for example, Danby, P. M.: **J. Roy. Anthrop. Inst. 83** (2) 194, 1953.

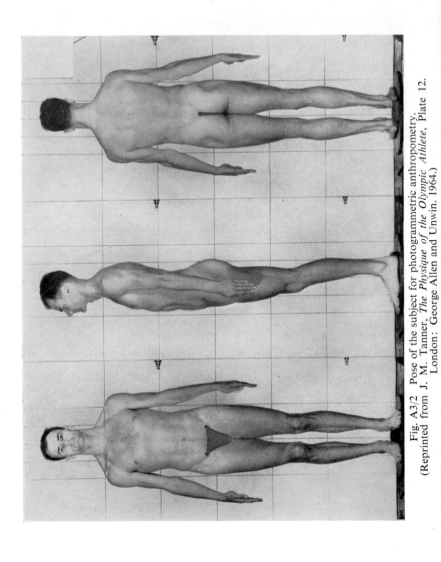

Fig. A3/2 Pose of the subject for photogrammetric anthropometry.
(Reprinted from J. M. Tanner, *The Physique of the Olympic Athlete*, Plate 12.
London: George Allen and Unwin. 1964.)

facing p. 55

PHOTOGRAMMETRIC TECHNIQUE

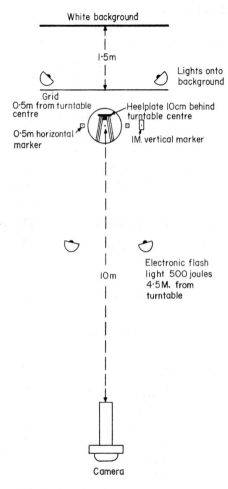

Fig. A3/1   Photogrammetric technique.

Investigators who have no previous experience of Somatotyping should seek an initial period of training in a laboratory where this technique is well-established

Abbreviated list of Somatotype criteria.

REGION I—Head and Neck.

Endo	Meso	Ecto
1. Front view head large and round; little bony relief.	Front view, head and face rugged, square or oblong; face large.	Face tends to small-ness, linearity. No obvious muscle or fat on head.
2. Fat cheeks.	Massive cheek-bones, heavy jaw, sometimes square.	Thin, fragile-boned face.
3. Chin angle blunted in side view.	Sharp chin angle, square chin.	Sharp chin angle, pointed or lightly boned chin.
4. Soft round features.	Heavy features.	Delicate features.
5. Smooth, cylindrical neck, often short.	Heavily muscled neck, pyramiding of trapezius.	Thin long neck, often inclined forwards.
6. Soft, fat-covered clavicular region.	Heavy strong clavicles.	Delicate, sharp clavicles.
7. Large AP=T* for neck.	AP < T for neck.	Small AP=T for neck.

REGION II—Thoracic Trunk.

1. Back smooth, no muscle relief.	Back rugged, high muscle relief.	Back bony, little muscle.
2. Back broad, some-times with reversed taper.	Back broad, sharp taper to waist (taper disappears in high mesomorphs).	Narrow back, taper highly variable.
3. Deep puffy chest in side view.	Deep muscular chest.	Flat shallow chest.
4. Lower depth of chest exceeds upper.	Lower depth of chest approximates to upper.	Lower depth of chest generally less than upper.

*Antero-Posterior = Transverse.

Endo	Meso	Ecto
5. Side view: abdomen predominates.	Thorax predominates over muscle-controlled abdomen.	Thorax either predominates over small compressed abdomen, or small convexity.
6. High wide indistinct rib angle.	Heavy, well-muscled ribs, moderate rib angle.	Skinny ribs, sharp rib angle.
7. Short chest cage.	Spinal curve S-shaped. (Long chest cage compared to abdomen).	No lumbar curve (linear midriff area).

REGION III—Shoulders, Arms, and Hands.

Endo	Meso	Ecto
1. Little bony relief. Shoulders square and high.	Shoulders broad, muscular, and often sloping.	Shoulders narrow, bony, thin, height variable, often flexed forwards.
2. Proximal hamming.	Arm segments evenly proportioned, length variable.	Arms long, especially distal segments.
3. Little muscle relief.	Rugged deltoid, triceps and biceps.	Weak upper arms, stringy muscles.
4. Smooth tapering forearm.	Massive muscular forearm.	Long weak bony forearm.
5. No bony projections.	Bones large, muscles and joints prominent.	Bones light and linear.
6. Wrists fat.	Wrists massive, bony.	Wrists fragile, bony.
7. Short-fingered, fat small-boned hands.	Massive, muscular, square bony hands.	Thin, narrow hands, slender fingers. Joints not usually prominent.

REGION IV—Abdominal Trunk.

Endo	Meso	Ecto
1. Full large abdomen, AP > T.	Compact, well-muscled abdomen, AP > T.	Small, non-muscular abdomen frequently with slumped convexity. Waist small, non-muscular.

Endo	Meso	Ecto
2. Waist high, indistinct.	Low, distinct, well-muscled waist of variable breadth.	Waist small, non-muscular.
3. Broad pelvis, with fat pads showing in lateral outlines.	Heavy bony pelvis.	Narrow and shallow pelvis.
4. Lack of lumbar curve; fat lumbar area.	Pronounced lumbar curve.	Flat lumbar area; no fat.
5. Abdomen prominent, no muscle relief.	Abdomen muscular.	Thin stringy muscle relief on abdomen, if any.
6. Buttocks large, rounded gluteal folds tend to disappear.	Buttocks muscular and laterally dimpled.	Thin, non-muscular buttocks.
7. Abdominal folds, or obvious superficial fat.	Distinct inguinal line and rippling of muscles.	Anterior superior iliac spine visible.

REGION V—Legs and Feet.

Endo	Meso	Ecto
1. Proximal predominance.	Even development of proximal and distal segments.	Long legs relative to abdomen. Distal segments long.
2. Thighs large and soft.	Thighs ruggedly muscled.	Weak muscling of thighs, thin.
3. Approximation of thighs when heels together.	Lateral muscling of thighs prominent.	Space between thighs when heels together
4. Little bony relief.	Large bones and joints.	Lightly boned. Joints small (but knee joints sometimes prominent).
5. Outer calf curve predominates.	Conspicuous inner gastrocnemius.	Little muscling or curvature of calves.
6. Small rounded ankles.	Thick bony ankles; $A < PT$.	Narrow delicate ankles.

Endo	Meso	Ecto
7. Small-boned fat feet, toes usually short.	Large heavy bony feet. Prominent toe joints.	Long thin delicate feet. Toe joints not usually prominent.

(b) Body Typing by measurement.

Various systems are available using body measurements, all of which are described in the " Full List " (see A1).

(c) Instruments.

1. For somatotyping by photogrammetry.

The following cameras are available, and suitable for photogrammetric work, although many cameras with appropriate lenses fitted are suitable.

Similar equipment to the two cameras described below is of course available in many other countries.

Auto Camera Mark 3.

200 exposures $1'' \times 1''$, but can be adapted for any required exposure size. Fully automatic: 12 v. or 24 v. d.c. Focus can be preset. Dallmeyer $6''$ f/4·5 lens, tripod, carrying case, etc.

Approx. price: £260.

Obtainable (in U.K.) from:

D. Shackman and Sons, Chiltern Works, CHESHAM, Bucks., England.

Nikon F Photomic.

With motor drive, tripod, 135 mm. lens, f/3·5.

Approx price: £500.

Obtainable (in U.K.) from:

Wallace Heaton Ltd., 127 New Bond Street, LONDON, W.1., England.

Further details of suitable photographic equipment may be obtained from:

IBP Growth and Physique Centre.

Department of Growth and Development,

Institute of Child Health,

30 Guilford Street.,

LONDON, W.C.1., England.

2. For Body Typing by measurement.

The recommended instruments for taking the measurements described under TECHNIQUES, above, are listed with their manufacturers or distributors in **A1.**

III.   DATA COLLECTING SHEET
Somatotyping by photogrammetry.

Name:*   Place of examination:
Age: Date of examination:
Sex: Subject No.:
Date of birth: Tribe or social group affiliation:
Name of Observer: Occupation:

Height:
Weight:
Surface Area:
Ponderal index $\dfrac{Ht.}{\sqrt[3]{Wt.}}$

REGION	ENDOMORPHY							Rating	MESOMORPHY							Rating	ECTOMORPHY							Rating	Regional Somatotype En:Mes:Ec.
	1	2	3	4	5	6	7		1	2	3	4	5	6	7		1	2	3	4	5	6	7		
I																									
II																									
III																									
IV																									
V																									

Total..............   Total..............   Total..............
Average............   Average............   Average............

FINAL BODY SOMATOTYPE.....................

*Full details of the subject and his population group are to be entered in the **BASIC IDENTIFICATION SHEETS,** as laid down in the Technical Introduction.

Final somatotype ratings may also be recorded at the end of the anthropometric data sheet (see **A1**)—'Basic List' and 'Full List'—under 'Optional Data'.

A4. RADIOGRAPHIC MEASUREMENTS

I. INTRODUCTION

(a) Observations to be made

(b) Sampling

II. TECHNIQUES

(a) Protection

(b) Skeletal age (wrist and hand)

(c) Limb X-rays

(d) Equipment

III. DATA COLLECTING SHEETS

(a) Skeletal maturity recording form

(b) Soft-tissue measurements

(c) Foot and ankle

I. INTRODUCTION

(a) Observations to be made:

(1) Hand and wrist (skeletal age).

In children X-rays of the hand and wrist may be taken if facilities are available. When the exact chronological age is known, the skeletal age assigned to the X-ray will give valuable information about the relative rates of growth and development both between individuals in a given study, and between studies in different countries. When the chronological age is not known, the skeletal age assessment is helpful.

(2) Upper arm, calf, and thigh.

Radiographs may be taken in such a manner that accurate measurements of bone, muscle and fat widths can be taken from them. Fat- and- skin thicknesses measured in this way correlate well with skin-fold measurements taken with calipers.

If the opportunity is available at the time of X-ray examination of the hand and wrist and/or the limbs, consideration may be given to radiographic study of the foot and ankle. Data on age changes analagous to those from X-rays of the wrist and hand can thereby be obtained. In addition there are interesting comparative studies to be made on the development of the epiphyses of the different toes. (See Abbie and Adey **Hum. Biol. 25,** 265, (1954)).

(b) Sampling:

For studies of developmental age, sample sizes comparable to those given in **A1** should be considered. For body composition studies, the recommendations given in **A1** and **A3** should be followed.

II. TECHNIQUES

(a) **Protection:**

Suitable protective clothing should be worn by the subject to prevent ir-radiation of the gonads. Such protection is provided by the ' Armadillo '. This consists of small overlapping plates of lead, constructed in the form of an apron for female subjects, and a jock-strap for male subjects. Full details are given in Tanner, J. M., Whitehouse, R. H., and Powell, J. H., **Lancet, 2,** 779–80,–1958. An alternative gonadal protective garment has recently been developed; enquiries regarding this garment should be addressed to Mr. Peter Jones, Department of Ergonomics, University of Technology, Loughborough, Leics., England.

(b) **Skeletal age (hand and wrist):**

Positioning:

The palmar surface of the hand is placed in contact with the cassette, with the elbow bent at right angles and the upper arm, lower arm and hand in the same horizontal plane. The fingers should be slightly separated and the thumb held in a natural degree of rotation. The anode is centred over the head of the third metacarpal, at an anode-film distance of 75 cm. A correctly posi-tioned hand and wrist radiograph is shown in Fig. A4/1, facing this page.

The assessment of skeletal age should be made either by the Greulich-Pyle method (W. W. Greulich and S. I. Pyle, **Radiographic Atlas of Skeletal Development of the Hand and Wrist,** 2nd Edition, Stanford University Press, California, 1959) or the Tanner-Whitehouse method (J. M. Tanner, R. H. Whitehouse and M. J. R. Healy, **A New System for estimating skeletal maturity from the hand and wrist, with standards derived from a study of 2,600 healthy British children.** Parts I and II. Paris, Centre International de l'Enfance, 1962.) For each child, the skeletal maturity recording forms prepared by Tanner, Whitehouse and Healy (see p. 69) should be filled in. (See Data Collecting Sheets, pp. 69–71.)

(c) **Limb X-rays:**

Upper arm

A metal pin is stuck over the skin - fold line (see **A1**) to act as a marker on the radiographic plate. The elbow should be posed in the lateral position with the two epicondyles appearing superimposed in the film. The central vertical plane of the arm is placed exactly 5 cm. in front of the film, and, if possible,

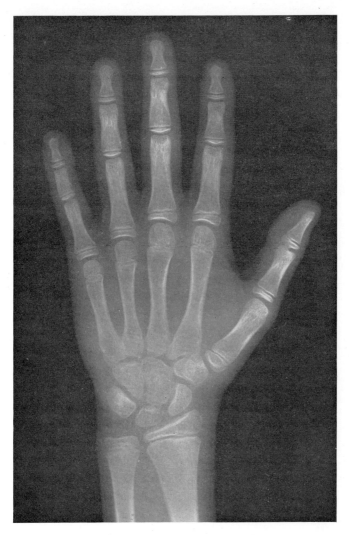

Fig. A4/1 Radiograph of the hand and wrist.

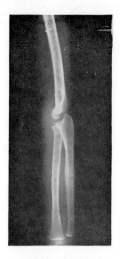

Fig. A4/2 (a)   Soft-tissue radiograph of the upper arm.

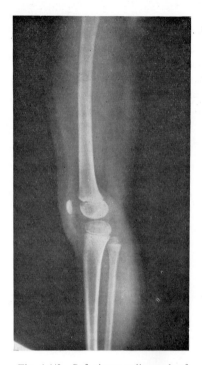

Fig. A4/3   Soft-tissue radiograph of the thigh.

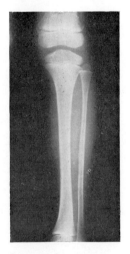

Fig. A4/2 (b)   Soft-tissue radiograph of the calf.

the anode of the X-ray machine should be an exact distance—2·0 or 2·5 metres—from the film (the distance will depend upon the power of the X-ray machine used.) The chosen anode-film distance should be carefully recorded so that corrections can be made. A correctly positioned upper arm radiograph is shown in Fig. A4/2(a), facing this page.

Calf

The left foot should point directly forwards and the weight of the body be evenly distributed on both feet. The central plane of the calf is placed exactly 10 cm. in front of the film. The anode-film distance will again depend upon the X-ray machine used, and should be recorded. A correctly positioned calf radiograph is shown in Fig. A4/2(b), facing this page.

Thigh

The top of the film holder should be placed as high into the pubes as possible, so that the lower part of the buttocks appears on the X-ray. The left leg is placed in the lateral position with the two femoral condyles appearing superimposed on the film. The knee is in a natural degree of extension. The central plane of the thigh is placed exactly 10 cm. in front of the film, and the anode-film distance should be recorded. A correctly positioned thigh radiograph is shown in Fig. A4/3, facing this page.

Soft-tissue measurements

Soft-tissue measurements should be made to the nearest 0·1 mm. using an X-ray caliper or Helios dial caliper with pin-points.

Upper arm: A line is drawn on the X-ray passing down the long axis of the upper arm, as nearly parallel to the two skin borders as possible. A second line is drawn perpendicular to the first at the level of the marker pin. The width of the whole arm and of the anterior and posterior fat areas are measured along this line. Total humerus and humeral medulla are measured at right angles to the long axis of the bone.

Calf: A line is drawn on the X-ray at right angles to the long axis of the tibia at the maximum overall width of the calf. The following widths are measured along this line: medial fat, lateral fat, total tibia, tibial medulla, total fibula, fibular medulla, total calf.

Thigh: A line is drawn on the X-ray at right angles to the long axis of the femur, at a level one-third of the sub-ischial measurement (stature less sitting height) up from the lower border of the femoral condyles. This level approximates the point of maximum width of the thigh in the majority of healthy young adults. The following widths are measured along this line: anterior fat, posterior fat, total femur, femoral medulla, total thigh.

(d) **Equipment:**

All X-Ray Accessories, including Protective Clothing

(in U.K.) Cuthbert Andrews Ltd.,
             5 High Street,
             Bushey Village,
             Hertfordshire.

Portable X-Ray Units

(in U.K.) Mini-Triton Portable X-ray apparatus:

             85 kVp/15 MA.

             90 kVp/20 MA.

             Tubehead: $8'' \times 7\frac{1}{2}'' \times 5''$: 28 lbs.

             Control: $11\frac{1}{2}'' \times 9\frac{1}{2}'' \times 5\frac{1}{2}''$: 29 lbs.

             Stand: 34 lbs.

             Supplied with a variety of stands, and carrying case.

             Approx. price: £350–£550.

             Available from: (in U.K.) Rank Medical Organisation,
                                          Welwyn Garden City,
                                          Hertfordshire, England.

(in U.K.) Practix Portable X-ray apparatus:

             80 kVp/15 MA.

             90 kVp/20 MA.

             Largest dimension: $3'$ $2''$.

             Approx. price: £635.

             Available from: (in U.K.) Philips Ltd.,
                                          45 Nightingale Lane,
                                          LONDON, S.W.12.

(in U.K.)   Portable X-ray unit, type MX-2:

   83 kVp/10MA.

   76 kVp/20 MA.

   Supplied with control support;   stand and carrying case extra.
   Shipping: gross weight 239 lbs.   (108 kg.);   3′ 8″ × 3′ 4″ × 1′ 8″.

   Approx. price: £510.

   Available from: (in U.K.) Watson & Sons Ltd.,

   East Lane,
   Wembley,
   Middlesex, England.

An instrument which has proved particularly suitable for field use is the American-made Buckey Model 20 field portable miniature model.   This instrument weighs 18 lbs. and is described by Garn, S. M., *et al.*, in **Amer. J. Phys. Anthrop., 26,** 101–105, 1967.

   Picker Portable X-ray unit: (cat. 1685A):

   80 kVp/15MA.

   Carrying case: 16″ × 18¼″ × 8½″ 80 lbs.

   Tube-stand: cat. 1344C.

   Tube-stand: carrying case: cat. 10129C.

   (For soft-tissue radiography, this instrument requires an intensifying screen (which necessitates having a portable dark-room).

   Available from: (in U.S.A.) Picker X-ray Corp.,
   Waite Mfg. Division,
   17325 Euclid Avenue.
   Cleveland 12, Ohio, U.S.A.

   Available from: (in U.K.)   Electronic and X-ray Applications
   Ltd.,
   Handmills Estate,
   BASINGSTOKE,
   Hants.,
   England.

PORTABLE GENERATOR

Portable petrol-driven generator Model E-300.

4-stroke, single-cylinder, side-valve, blower air-cooled. Capacity 55·4 cc.
Weight 39¼ lbs.

Tank capacity: 3·52 pints.

Consumption: 0·62 pint/hour.

Output: 220 v. AC/250 watts.

       12 v. DC/5·4 amps.

Price: £73.

Available from (in U.K.):   Honda (U.K.) Ltd.,
                              Power Road,
                              Chiswick,
                              LONDON, W.4.

RADIOGRAPHIC FILM

In general, fast film should be used in order to reduce radiation to a minimum. When darkroom facilities are available, cassettes fitted with standard speed screens are preferable for soft-tissue radiographs, but for hand and wrist films required for maturity assessments, fine-definition screens or non-screen film give a better result.

For field-work it is convenient to use non-screen film.

Exposure factors will depend upon the following variables:—

(a)   Machine—inherent filter thickness
                  added filtration
                  machine power
                  machine type
                  rectification, etc.

(b)   Anode-film distance.

When screens are used, the dose of radiation approximates 10 milli-r for the hand and wrist, and 80 milli-r for arm, calf and thigh. When screens are not used, the dose is approximately 4 times higher. This dose should be compared with the background radiation which is about 100 milli-r per year at sea-level, rising to 300 milli-r per year at 2000 metres. Problems of dosage are discussed in S. M. Garn, R. H. Helmrich, K. M. Flaherty and F. N. Silverman: " Skin dosages in radiation-sparing techniques for the laboratory and field ", **Amer. J. Phys. Anthrop., 26,** 101–106, 1967.

III.   DATA COLLECTING SHEETS
(a) Skeletal Maturity Recording Form

Name:*

Serial number:

Age: Date of birth:

Sex:

Occupation:

Ethnic group or tribal affiliation (or nationality):

Height:

Date of examination·

Place of examination:

Radius:

Ulna:

Metacarpal 1:

    ,,   3:

    ,,   5:

Prox. phalanx 1:

    ,,   ,,   3:

    ,,   ,,   5:

Mid. phalanx 3:

    ,,   ,,   5:

Term. phalanx 1:

    ,,   ,,   3:

    ,,   ,,   5:

Capitate:

Hamate:

Triquetral:

Lunate:

Navicular:

Gt. mult.:

Lr. mult.:

LONG BONE SCORE:

ROUND BONE SCORE:

OVERALL BONE SCORE:

GREULICH-PYLE BONE AGE:

Name of investigator:

*Full details of the subject and his population group are to be entered in the **BASIC IDENTIFICATION SHEETS**, as laid down in the Technical Introduction.

III. DATA COLLECTING SHEET
(b) Soft-tissue measurements

*For full details see Individual
Identity Sheet (01)

Subject's name:*

Place of examination:

IBP/HA Project ref. no.   1 □□□□
Study number   5 □□
Serial number   7 □□□
Sex (M=1 ; F=2)   10 □
Age (years)*   11 □□
Examination date (year + 3
  decimals—see table in
  Technical Introduction)   13 □□□□□
Procedure category   18 □□

CODE FOR "NOT APPLICABLE"=X; CODE FOR "DATA NOT RECORDED"=Y

ARM:
Anterior fat   20 □□□
Posterior fat   23 □□□
Total humerus   26 □□□
Humeral medulla   29 □□□
Total arm width   32 □□□□

CALF:
Medial fat   36 □□□
Lateral fat   39 □□□
Total tibia   42 □□□
Tibial medulla   45 □□□
Total fibula   48 □□□
Fibular medulla   51 □□□
Total calf width   54 □□□□

THIGH:
Anterior fat   58 □□□
Posterior fat   61 □□□
Total femur   64 □□□
Femoral medulla   67 □□□
Total thigh width   70 □□□□

Signature of investigator: ....

III.   DATA COLLECTING SHEETS
(c) Foot and Ankle

Name :*   Date :

Serial number :   Place :

Age :   Ethnic group or nationality :

Sex :   Birth date :

X-ray apparatus used :   Exposure at :   (kV)   (MA)

Film type used :   Exposure time :

Screen used : yes/no   Anode-film distance :

Tibial epiphysis :   appeared — yes/no
(distal)   fused   — yes/no
Fibular epiphysis :   appeared — yes/no
(distal)   fused   — yes/no
Presence of tarsal ossification centres :
Calcaneum :   yes/no
Talus :   yes/no
Cuboid :   yes/no
Cuneiform III :   yes/no
Cuneiform I :   yes/no
Cuneiform II :   yes/no
Navicular scaphoid :   yes/no

Metatarsal epiphyses :   Foot phalangeal epiphyses :

					Proximal phlx.		Middle phlx.	Distal phlx.
I :	appeared —	yes/no	Dig. I :	appeared —	yes/no	—	yes/no
	fused	— yes/no		fused	— yes/no	—	yes/no
II :	appeared —	yes/no	Dig. II :	appeared —	yes/no	yes/no	yes/no
	fused	— yes/no		fused	— yes/no	yes/no	yes/no
III :	appeared —	yes/no	Dig. III :	appeared —	yes/no	yes/no	yes/no
	fused	— yes/no		fused	— yes/no	yes/no	yes/no
IV :	appeared —	yes/no	Dig. IV :	appeared —	yes/no	yes/no	yes/no
	fused	— yes/no		fused	— yes/no	yes/no	yes/no
V :	appeared —	yes/no	Dig. V :	appeared —	yes/no	yes/no	yes/no
	fused	— yes/no		fused	— yes/no	yes/no	yes/no

Notes on suppression of bony elements in feet :

*Full details of the subject and his population group are to be entered in the **BASIC IDENTIFICATION SHEETS,** as laid down in the Technical Introduction.

A5. BODY DENSITY BY UNDERWATER WEIGHING

Field work obviously places limitations on the extent to which assessment of bodily components (muscle, fat, bone and water), can be made. Anthropometric measurements (see **A1**), particularly circumferences, skin-folds, and bicondylar diameters, and radiography of the limbs (see **A4**), if a suitable portable X-ray machine is available, as well as somatotype measurements and photogrammetry (see **A3**), will provide useful quantitative descriptions of body composition.

For such components as specific gravity, lean body mass, and body water compartments, the work will call for specialised laboratory facilities. Assessment of body density using the method of hydrostatic weighing and simultaneous assessment of the volume of air in the lungs by the nitrogen dilution method, is described in outline below.

The lean body weight as estimated from the body density, and determinations of the total body water, have been shown (on male European subjects) to bear a fairly high correlation to estimates made from skeletal (anthropometric and X-ray) measurements. (See Behnke, A. R., **Hum. Biol., 31,** 295–315, 1959). Lean body mass can be " determined from the measurement of skin-fold thicknesses **provided** the regression equations relating skin-fold thicknesses to percentage body fat have been established for the population in question ". Percentage body fat can be calculated from a measurement of body density by underwater weighing (e.g. Behnke, *et al.*), by the measurement of total body water (e.g. Keys and Brozek), or by the measurement of body volume by the displacement of an inert gas in a closed system (e.g. Siri). Using the regression equations for Caucasians to determine percentage body fat in individuals of other ethnic groups is not advisable.

Fairly elaborate installations, as well as respiratory equipment, are required for making these measurements. The procedure is not suitable for field-work unless the subjects can be brought to a well-equipped laboratory.

The available techniques are described in detail in the following references: Rahn H., Fenn, W. O., and Otis, A. B. (1949) **J. Appl. Physiol., 1**: 725. Siri, W. E. (1956) In: Advances in Biological and Medical Physics, Ed. J. H. Laurence and C. A. Tobias. Academic Press, London and New York. Brozek, J., Grande, F., Anderson, J. T., and Keys, A. (1963) **Ann. N.Y. Acad. Sci. 110**: 113.

In outline, the method is as follows: the measurement of density is made by weighing the subject in air, and under water in a large tank with a correction being made for the residual air in the lungs. The subject expels as much air from his lungs as possible before immersion, and, as soon as his weight has been recorded, a measurement is made of the residual volume by the three-breath nitrogen-dilution technique. The oxygen, CO_2, and nitrogen in the bag are measured in a Lloyd-Haldane apparatus. The whole procedure is repeated twice more, each time after an interval of a few minutes. The mean of the three calculated results for density is taken as the final value for the subject.

Before the measurements, each subject is accustomed to the procedures by several trial runs. However, in general, only those who feel reasonably confident in water—usually swimmers—are suitable subjects.

Calculations of the body fat are based on the equation given by Siri (1956):

$$\text{Fat}(\%) = [(4 \cdot 95/\text{density}) - 4 \cdot 5] \times 100$$

Similar results are obtained by the use of other equations, such as that of Brozek, Grande, Anderson, and Keys (1963).

B. GENETIC CONSTITUTION

B1   Blood collection and subdivision
B2   Transport of blood specimens
B3   G6PDD testing in the field
B4   Testing for acetylator phenotypes in the field
B5   Detection of foetal red cells in maternal blood (Kleihauer technique)
B6   Phenylthiocarbamide (PTC) taste-testing in the field
B7   Tests on saliva and urine
B8   Cytogenetics
B9   Colour-confusion charts for testing colour vision
B10 Tests of colour vision by anomaloscope
B11 Skin colour measurement by spectrophotometry
B12 Dermatoglyphics
B13 Morphological measurements in genetic studies
B14 Dentition
B15 Anthroposcopy

B1. BLOOD COLLECTION AND SUBDIVISION

I. INTRODUCTION

II. TECHNIQUES
    (a) Collection of blood samples
    (b) Subdivision of blood samples

III. RECORD OF BLOOD COLLECTIONS

I. INTRODUCTION

The ultimate object in organizing the collection of blood specimens, for red-cell grouping* and for most other purposes, is that it should arrive at the laboratory with the red cells intact and with their blood group antigens unaltered. The cells must therefore be protected from any conditions which might damage them mechanically, chemically or by infection. They must not be exposed to salt-free water or to alcohol (spirit), nor must they be subjected to shaking and frothing.

The great majority of the difficulties and disasters which affect population surveys of blood factors occur in the field rather than in the laboratory. Methods of collection and transport can be divided into two main categories, those to be used with ordinary refrigeration and those to be used with liquid nitrogen.

Ideally, specimens should be taken by venepuncture by a closed method into a sterile container which is refrigerated within a few hours to $+4°C$ and transmitted within three days to the testing laboratory. The main causes of deterioration are:

—Prolonged keeping without refrigeration (either immediately after collection, or owing to long delays in transportation). This is of course especially deleterious in the tropics;

—Lack of sterility—usually due to collection in or transfer to an open container;

* There may be cases where it seems worth-while establishing a field laboratory which would include facilities for blood-group testing. A detailed guide on the provision of these testing facilities, including equipment requirements and techniques, has been drawn up by D. Tills and M. Godber, of the Serological Population Genetics Laboratory, St. Bartholomew's Hospital, LONDON, E.C.1. This manual (Document HA 120, ' Methods of Blood Grouping') is obtainable from the Convenor's Office, 21, Bedford Square, LONDON, W.C.1.

—Freezing solid (transport in unheated part of aircraft; more rarely erroneous use of solid carbon dioxide or storage in deep freeze);

Delays in transport are probably the main source of deterioration.

II. TECHNIQUES

(a) Collection of blood samples:

Specimens for detailed testing for genetic factors should each consist of at least 10 ml. of blood, and preferably 15 ml. As it will usually be necessary for a variety of purposes to obtain more than one sample of blood from each subject, and as most laboratories require samples to reach them unopened, it is desirable to use a method which permits several closed samples to be taken from a single venepuncture. One device which makes this possible is the ' Vacutainer ' (available (in the U.K.) from: Becton-Dickinson (U.K.) Ltd., York House, Empire Way, Wembley, Middlesex).

The ' Vacutainer ' tube is a vacuum-test tube sealed with a rubber stopper. The complete assembly consists of a disposable double-ended needle and a plastic holder. The rubber stopper also serves as a diaphragm. When in use the needle is attached to the holder and the tube is inserted into the holder until the top of its stopper is even with the clearly marked holder guide line. The distal needle is now buried in the rubber stopper without releasing the vacuum.

The proximal needle is now inserted into a vein—preferably of large calibre in the cubital fossa—and the Vacutainer pressure is now released by firmly pressing it completely into the holder. Blood now fills the Vacutainer. If more than one sample is needed then the full Vacutainer can be replaced by an empty one, the proximal needle remaining in situ. This can be repeated as often as needed. The blood remains in a sealed easily portable container.

Although Vacutainers are a little more difficult at first to use than a needle and syringe, after a little practice this difficulty is overcome. The greatest advantage is that they eliminate almost entirely the possibility of bacterial or chemical contamination of the specimens taken. This is particularly important where there is a time delay between the taking of the samples and their analysis.

The Vacutainers are of known volume, i.e. 5 ml., 7 ml., 10 ml., 15 ml., and 20 ml., and can be 'plain' for serum collection, or can be supplied containing various anticoagulants. For most purposes, 10 ml. Vacutainers with 0·1 ml. of 30% EDTA are ideal. Slightly better preservation of red cells over prolonged periods is assured by the use of 1·5 ml. of ACD (acid citrate dextrose solution) per 10 ml. of blood. Where the methods of taking the specimens, or the necessity of opening the containers, introduces a risk of contamination, some workers recommend the use of a combination of anticoagulant and antibiotic.

If serum or plasma has to be separated from a blood specimen in a Vacutainer, it should be drawn directly into a second Vacutainer, a separate needle being inserted as an air inlet. If at all possible, however, the work should be planned so that each central laboratory receives Vacutainers that have never been opened.

If Vacutainers are unobtainable, one of the numerous available devices should be used which permit a single specimen to be taken directly into a sterile tube by means of an attached hypodermic needle. Such a device is the 'Venule' (available (in the U.K.) from Bayer Products Ltd., Oyster Lane, West Byfleet, Surrey).

Each glass tube should have a serial number scratched on it with a diamond; plastic bags, if used, should be identifiable by a pre-printed serial number. This is the nearest that can be devised to a disaster-proof identification system, the need for which has been repeatedly shown when some or even all, the specimens from an expedition has been unidentifiable on arrival at the testing laboratory (e.g. owing to labels getting washed off by melting ice).

(b) Subdivision of blood samples:

It may be necessary to send a number of samples of blood to different laboratories (where the serum or red cells or both may come under test). It is much preferable to use the Vacutainer method to collect the number of samples required from one venepuncture. The subdivision of a single large sample in the field should be avoided if at all possible, because of the considerable risk of contamination. If this is not possible, the following is a suggested scheme whereby 14 ml. of blood (taken in a 15 ml. Vacutainer) can be subdivided and made available for different tests. All the samples are to be maintained at about 4° C. until they or their derivatives reach their ultimate destination.

The sample is to be separated within 24 hours according to the following schedule:

Serum 5 ml.

3 ml. for all virological studies.

2 ml. for: plasma proteins by electrophoresis;
cholesterol and cholesterol esters;
sodium potassium, and urea;
enzyme variants.

Serum 2 ml. (in separate bottles)

1 ml. for: rickettsial antibody studies;
leptospiral antibody studies;

1 ml. for: immunoparasitological studies.

Blood clots 7 ml. in Vacutainers, with about $\frac{3}{4}$ ml. of remaining serum for:
blood groups;
haemoglobin types;

$\frac{1}{2}$ ml. of serum to be removed from clot and used as required.

(Whole blood 2 ml. (with EDTA—separate tube) for:
E.B.C. count;
W.B.C. count;
direct eosinophile count;
P.C.V., E.S.R., Hb. concentration.)

III. RECORD OF BLOOD COLLECTIONS

Under 'Name' below, record also ethnic and tribal origin, or nationality.

HA/IBP Project No. and Study number	Date of Collec-tion	Place collected	Name*	Subject number	No. of collec-tions	Con-tainer no.	Details of speci-men(s)

*Details of the subject and his population group are to be entered in the **BASIC IDENTIFICATION SHEETS,** as laid down in the Technical Introduction.

Name of Investigator: ....

B2. TRANSPORT OF BLOOD SAMPLES

I. INTRODUCTION

II. INSTRUCTIONS

I. INTRODUCTION

(a) Rationale:

The instructions laid down in detail for the transport of blood samples must be followed strictly. Failure to do so will mean that blood may arrive at the testing laboratory with the red cells haemolysed, thereby making blood-group tests impossible. There is also a danger, with certain methods of preservation, that false positive reactions may be obtained. There may also be the risk of bacterial contamination if inadequate methods are used.

(b) Precautions are particularly necessary in relation to the following:

    (1) Packing, cooling, and recharging.

    (2) Labelling.

    (3) Despatch and receipt.

II. INSTRUCTIONS

1. Packing, cooling, and recharging.

(a) Cooling by ordinary ice.

In the field, the specimens are collected in B-D 'Vacutainers', Bayer 'Venules', or plastic bags, containing an anticoagulant, and are placed immediately in a 9″ diameter vacuum flask or other insulated container (see **B1.**) A closed bag of stout polythene containing crushed ice should be enclosed and, if the journey has to be a long one, provision should be made for its renewal (preferably, if possible, by substituting another ready-frozen container). Alternatively, a strong, square, 200 cc polythene water-bottle, which has been filled with water and placed over-night in a refrigerator and allowed to freeze solid, may be used. Only in quite exceptional cases is it justified to collect blood specimens more than one day's travel from a road-head.

If a thermos flask is to be used it is safer for each tube to be separately wrapped in cotton wool. A layer of cotton wool is placed on the bottom of the thermos; the wrapped tubes are packed above this, right side up and in fairly firm contact with one another, with a further layer of cotton wool over them. If a completely sealed plastic or other ice container is available this should be placed on top of the cotton wool. If, however, it is necessary to use broken ice this must similarly be placed on top of the cotton wool. It is most inadvisable to pack ice between the tubes, as they are then liable to jostle one another when the ice melts and to break both one another and the thermos flask.

Containers made of plastic foam material, which are as effective or almost as effective, as thermos flasks, are now becoming available. If at the same time these can be provided with completely sealed ice packs, renewable on the journey, or if reliable refrigeration (between 4° and 10° C) can be secured on the journey, the problem of packing is greatly simplified and all that is needed is to pack the tubes firmly in some soft material so that they cannot break loose or jostle against one another.

The flask is suitably labelled, including a note " **Keep cool: do not freeze** " and handed, without further packing, to the air hostesses of the respective aircraft, to be placed in the cooler compartment of the refrigerator.

Every effort must be made to prevent the addition of " dry ice " (solid carbon dioxide) on the journey by enthusiastic airline officials, or storage in " deep freeze ", as either procedure will freeze the samples solid, so causing the red cells to lyse, and making blood group tests impossible.

Where possible, arrangements should be made with the air transport company for the additition of fresh ice at intervals throughout the journey, and it must be made clear that " dry ice " (solid carbon dioxide) **must never be used** for packages containing red cells as it will freeze them, causing lysis (where sera and salivas alone are being sent, " dry ice " is, however, preferable, as it maintains a lower temperature). It is sometimes possible to pack specimens into ordinary stout cardboard boxes and to arrange for their continuous refrigeration throughout the journey, and for them to be stowed in the domestic type refrigerator on the plane, and placed in the airport domestic refrigerator in between flights if necessary. This method can, however, seldom be used except for accompanied specimens. There is at times a risk that the freight compartment of a plane may reach very low temperatures and specimens become frozen solid, and it is well to inquire about this.

(b) Frozen red cell suspensions (" dry ice ").

There is a growing tendency to send specimens for survey purposes in the form of red cell suspensions frozen solid with a glycerol mixture. They can then very readily be packed in thermos flasks or other insulated containers with " dry ice ". Unless, however, very careful precautions can be and are followed in the taking of blood and the making of suspensions, the re-suspended cells tend to give false positive reactions in the important and numerous anti-human-globulin tests necessary for the detection of many blood group antigens. Thus if it is proposed to use this method it is essential to discuss the method and the required precautions with the staff of the laboratory which will do the tests.

(c) A portable refrigerator.

A convenient portable refrigerator for field use is the MIVIS model 22, manufactured by the Mivis Co., Viale Pallavicino 28, Ravenna, Italy. The unit measures 32·5 cm. × 31 cm. × 59 cm., and weighs 10·8 kg. It can operate from an input of 12 or 24 v. d.c. or via a transformer from an a.c. source of any voltage from 110 to 280 v. The contents can be maintained near freezing point in ambient temperatures up to 40°C. The price is 58,500 Lire.

(d) Use of liquid nitrogen during transport.

Some workers are planning to make use of preservation in liquid nitrogen for the transport of survey specimens. At present a method which is satis-factory in all respects is not available, and consultation should be made with a laboratory experienced in the use of this method. Huntsman, R. G., *et al.*, (**Brit. Med. J., 4,** 458–460, 25th. November, 1967) describe the condition of specimens stored over a 5-year period using this method in the laboratory.

2. Labelling.

The object of labelling blood specimens is that each should be readily and unambiguously identifiable at the time of testing. A laboratory may justi-fiably refuse to test specimens received unlabelled or with illegible labels.

Unless means are available for keeping the specimens at the correct temperature without any danger of direct contact with ice and melt-water, it must be assumed that they may be exposed to prolonged contact and severe friction from ice, water, cotton wool and glass, and identification numbers or other marks must therefore be able to resist all these insults. The only really satisfactory means of marking is with a diamond point or with a completely waterproof paint.

Where possible, duplicate lists of identification numbers should be sent, one enclosed with the specimens but suitably protected from moisture, and one separately by air mail post.

Ready printed stick-on and untearable tie-on labels should be taken with the expedition, as follows:

—labels addressed to the receiving laboratory including its telephone number and instructions to telephone on arrival at the home airport;

—striking red labels, " Blood samples—Urgent—Fragile ";

—labels with instructions on care of specimens: " Blood samples in fragile glass tubes. Cool on ice or in refrigerator at $+4°C$ to $+10°C$. DO NOT FREEZE in ice-box or in unheated part of airplane. Do not allow to re-warm ".

3. Despatch and receipt.

It is usually important that only a single airline should handle specimens, as long and disastrous delays have been found to occur at interchange airports. Therefore a member of the expedition staff should personally hand over specimens to an official of the airline on which the main transport of the specimens is to be undertaken, even if this means that he should travel with the specimens on a local airline. Any person accompanying specimens to the airport should carry clearly written and obviously authoritative instructions as to their care, both for his own reference and to show to officials. Where large numbers of specimens have to pass through a particular airport or other transport centre it is most important to secure the understanding and goodwill of both the transport and the customs officials. Alternatively, one member of the expedition staff could hand the specimens to the local airline and a second member supervise the interchange. Such expensive precautions have repeatedly been found to be necessary and worth-while, for their neglect has at times led to the serious deterioration or loss of most of the specimens collected by an expedition at a consequent great financial loss. The condition of the specimens is of such importance that financial provision for such an officer is, in suitable cases, a fully justifiable charge on expedition expenses. Even when this is done, it is necessary to make detailed preliminary arrangements with a senior official at the transmitting airport, preferably the airport manager. It is also necessary to make special arrangements to ensure in advance the prompt delivery of specimens to the receiving laboratory, except in the case of airlines which are known by experience to have efficient arrangements for delivery.

It is worth taking a great deal of trouble to notify recipients by the fastest available means as soon as specimens are despatched, stating the number of specimens and giving, where relevant, the flight number. It is important, also, to ensure that there is no delay at points of transhipment or in customs clearance.

The testing laboratory should have a cablegram address and one should if possible also be arranged for the expedition in the field. A prearranged code for cables may also be useful.

The laboratory should report back on date of receipt, condition of specimens and, if necessary, instructions for remedying errors in collection or transport. All field records and letters should be written in duplicate books so that one copy is sent to the laboratory and one retained in the field. It is best to make lists of specimens in triplicate, one to be sent with the specimens (but suitably protected from moisture), one separately by airmail and one retained in the field. In any case a note should be enclosed with the specimens stating the names and addresses of sender and recipient, the nature of the specimens, and, where relevant, the tests to be done.

B3. G6PDD TESTING IN THE FIELD

I. INTRODUCTION
   (a) General
   (b) Sampling

II. TECHNIQUES
   (a) Methaemoglobin reduction test
   (b) Brilliant cresyl blue dye test

III. DATA COLLECTING SHEET

I. INTRODUCTION

(a) General:

All screening tests depend upon the fact that when G-6-PD catalyses the oxidation of glucose-6-phosphate, the reduced co-enzyme $NADPH_2$ is simultaneously formed, and can be made to reduce a variety of substances, including glutathione, methaemoglobin, dichloroindephenol (DCIP), brilliant cresyl blue, methylene blue, and M.T.T. Tetrazolium.

Although the two screening methods given below are satisfactory for application in the field, the samples should if at all possible be sent to a laboratory which is able to carry out assay and electrophoretic procedures.

The results obtained by these two methods are both affected by anaemia, necessitating adjustment of the packed-cell volume. The method chosen must of necessity depend upon the facilities available: for the brilliant cresyl blue method, NADP is required, and this substance is not stable unless refrigerated. Both methods described require temperature regulation at 37°C.

(b) Sampling:

No screening method so far developed is capable of reliably detecting all female heterozygotes, and therefore for survey purposes, only males should be tested. The size of the sample should be at least 100. For genetic studies, however, it would be generally necessary to test both sexes, the sample size and composition depending upon the nature of the study. For such studies, it would be necessary to carry out a more sensitive test only applicable in the laboratory.

II. TECHNIQUES

(a) **Methaemoglobin reduction test (M.R.T.):***
    Collection of Blood Samples

Collect blood into acid citrate dextrose solution (ACD) (4 ml. blood to 1 ml. ACD). Samples so collected should be tested the same day and kept in the refrigerator if possible until tested. If inosine (2·4 g. per 100 ml. ACD) is added, samples may be stored at 2°–4°C for seven days. The ratio of blood to ACD is critical, if too little blood is added the enzyme will be damaged, so giving an abnormal result.

Reagents

1. **ACD Solution.** Standard blood transfusion anti-coagulant.

2. **Haemoglobin diluting fluid.** 0·04% ammonia.

3. **0·18M Sodium Nitrite.** 1·25 g. sodium nitrite in 100 ml. distilled water. Stable one month at 4°C.

4. **0·0004 M. Methylene Blue Solution.** Certified Eastman Organic Chemicals Cat. No. 573. Supplied by Kodak Ltd., Kirkby, Lancs., England, or K. and K. Laboratories, Inc., 121 Express Street, Engineers Hill, Plainview, New York 11803, U.S.A.
149·5 mg. in 100 ml. distilled water. Dilute 1 in 10 with normal saline for use. Discard concentrated solution. Stable one month at 4°C.

Equipment

It is advisable to pre-weigh all the reagents before the field-work begins.
    (i) 5 ml. bottles containing 1 ml. ACD solution.

    Preparation of ACD

    2 g. disodium citrate
    3 g. dextrose
    120 ml. deionized water
    Filter through sintered glass filter, distribute in 1 ml. amounts and autoclave at 5 lb. for 30 minutes.

* Motulsky, A. G., and J. M. Campbell-Kraut (1961). Proceedings Conference on Genetic Polymorphisms and Geographical Variations in Disease. New York, Grune and Stratton. pp. 159–180.

 (ii) 0·04% ammonia.
(iii) Sodium nitrite ' AR '.
(iv) Methylene blue Cat. No. 573. Eastman Kodak.
 (v) 0·1 ml., 2 ml. and 10 ml. graduated pipettes.
(vi) 1 × 10 cm. test tubes. Plastic disposable tubes are also suitable.
(vii) 37°C water-bath with suitable racks and thermometer.
(viii) Pasteur pipettes.
(ix) Deionized water.
 (x) Saline.
(xi) Bottles graduated in 100 ml. These will be used for the preparation
     and storage of the reagents.
(xii) Deionized water.

Method

Place 2 ml. blood in a clean 1 × 10 cm. test tube.

Add 0·1 ml. of sodium nitrite and 0·1 ml. of methylene blue and mix
by inversion.

Incubate in a water bath at 37°C for 180 minutes.

At 60 and 120 minutes, mix and aerate by blowing one breath through
sample with a fine pipette.

At 180 minutes the test is complete and ready to read.

Reading

Colour differences are usually apparent in the actual sample but are seen
better if 0·1 ml. of the sample is added to 10 ml. of ammoniated water and
mixed. If standards are required to aid comparison they may be prepared
as follows:

To 10 ml. ammoniated water add 0·1 ml. normal blood (100% haemoglobin).

To 10 ml. ammoniated water add 0·1 ml. blood and 0·1 ml. sodium nitrite
(100% methaemoglobin).

Results

Differentiation of individuals having full expression of the enzyme defect,
i.e. hemizygous males (and homozygous females) from normal subjects can
readily be made by visual inspection of the diluted tests. The identification of
heterozygous female carriers is difficult. It is recommended that for survey
purposes male subjects only are tested see (b) Sampling, above.

Normal—red like 100% haemoglobin standard.

Male hemizygote (and female homozygote)—brown like 100% methaemo-globin standard.

(Female heterozygote carrier—colour varies from that of 100% haemo-globin standard through range of red-browns to that of 100% methaemo-globin standard.)

(b) Brilliant cresyl blue dye test:*
Collection of blood samples
See under (a) above.

Reagents

1. **Buffer solution.** Dissolve 44·75 g. Tris-(hydroxy methyl)-amino-methane in about 400 ml. of distilled water, adjust the pH to 8·5 with hydrochloric acid (approximately 9 ml. conc. HCl) and dilute to 500 ml.

2. **Buffer dye solution.** Dissolve 16 mg. brilliant cresyl blue in 50 ml. buffer solution. Prepare freshly as required, or store at 4°C.

3. **NADP (TPN) solution.** Dissolve 5 mg. of NADP in distilled water; dilute to 10 ml. Prepare freshly as required, or store in small quantities in deep freeze (−20°C).

4. **Sodium glucose-6-phosphate (G-6-P) solution.** Dissolve 89·5 mg. sodium glucose-6-phosphate in distilled water and dilute to 10 ml. Prepare fresh or store small amounts in deep freeze (−20°C).

5. **Combined reagent solution.**
   4·5 ml. buffer-dye solution
   +1·0 ml. NADP solution
   +1·0 ml. G-6-P solution
   Prepare as required.

6. **Mineral oil.** (liquid paraffin).

Equipment

(It is advisable to pre-weigh all the reagents before the field-work begins.)
   (i) " TRIS " (Tris (hydroxy-methyl)-amino methane).
   (ii) Brilliant cresyl blue (Sigma or Gurr).
   (iii) Nicotinamide adenine dinucleotide phosphate.
   (iv) Sodium glucose-6-phosphate.

* Additional information on methods for G6PDD testing, with further references, may be found in the Report of the WHO Scientific Group, T.R.S. 366 (1967) ' Standardisation of Procedures for the study of glucose-6-phosphate dehydrogenase deficiency '.

(v) Mineral oil (liquid paraffin).
(vi) 5 ml., 1 ml. and 0·02 ml. pipettes.
(vii) 50 × 9 mm. test tubes.
(viii) 37°C water bath and suitable racks.
(ix) Stop watch or clock.
(x) Distilled water.
(xi) Universal containers for mixing reagent.
(xii) Most anticoagulants suitable.

Method

To each row of test tubes (50 mm × 9 mm) add 1·0 ml. distilled water. To one add 0·02 ml. normal whole blood and to the others 0·02 ml. of the whole bloods under test.

Mix without inverting, until the blood is haemolysed. Add to each tube 0·65 ml. of the combined reagent solution, mix by inversion and add a layer of mineral oil to each.

Incubate in a water bath at 37°C and examine the tubes at 40 minutes and then at 5-minute intervals for a change of colour. The colour changes first to a streaky blue and pink and finally to clear pink with a layer of blue immediately under the oil. Note the time at which this point is reached and compare with the time taken by the normal blood.

Reading

Decolourisation time: Normals—   40–55 minutes.
                              Male (hemizygotes)—   90 minutes–24 hours.
Heterozygote females partly overlap with normals.

III. DATA COLLECTING SHEET

Date of examination:

Place of examination:

Test used: M.R.T./Cresyl blue

Name of investigator:

Name*	Serial no.	Age	Sex	Ethnic group or nationality	Relationship to other subjects studied	Result of test

*Full details of the subject and his population group are to be entered in the **BASIC IDENTIFICATION SHEETS** as laid down in the Technical Introduction.

B4. TESTING FOR ACETYLATOR PHENOTYPES IN THE FIELD

I. INTRODUCTION

    (a) General

    (b) Observations to be made

    (c) Sampling

II. TECHNIQUES

    (a) Method

    (b) Calculation

    (c) Dosage schedule

III. DATA COLLECTING SHEET

I. INTRODUCTION

(a) General:

Certain individuals convert sulphamethazine (synonym: sulphadimidine) and related substances (including the anti-tuberculous drug Isoniazid) much more rapidly than others into an acetyl derivative which is excreted in the urine. Fast acetylation is controlled by a gene with dominant manifestation, but a partial quantitative separation can be made between homozygotes and heterozygotes. The acetylation process is controlled by a specific enzyme, N-acetyl transferase, which has been partially purified from human liver. The distribution of fast and slow acetylation alleles varies between populations.

The distribution of these alleles is of general interest in population genetics, but it would in addition be of some medical importance in populations where mass treatment of tuberculosis was to include Isoniazid therapy.

(b) Observations to be made:

The essential observations are the concentrations of free (i.e. unconjugated) sulphamethazine and of total sulphamethazine in an 8-hour urine sample.

(c) Sampling:

' Desirable ' and ' Realistic ' minimal sample characteristics are the same as those for other genetic studies.

II. TECHNIQUES

(a) Method:
(i) Testing the subjects.

1. Subjects should have fasted for 12 hours prior to the beginning of the test. Water is allowed to quench thirst during this period.

2. Fasting subjects must be observed to swallow a dose of 40 mg sulfamethazine (which is the same drug as sulphadimidine) per kg of metabolically active mass (viz. weight to the power of 0·7). The dose is worked out from the dosage schedule below. The substance is supplied in the form of tablets which should first be crushed with a spoon, and swallowed with a drink of water.

3. The subjects remain fasting for two hours following drug ingestion and are then allowed a light meal of tea and toast. Subjects then remain fasting until 6 hours following drug ingestion. Drinking of water during the test is allowed but not encouraged.

4. The bladder is emptied 5 hours following drug ingestion and this urine thrown away. All urine passed during the next hour is collected. The bladder is emptied at 6 hours following drug ingestion and this urine is added to the collection.

A clean glass vessel such as a jam-jar, or beaker, preferably of 1 litre (or 2 lb.) size, is labelled with the subject's name: subjects are made to understand that all urine is to be passed into this vessel. The conditions of privacy required will depend upon the customs of the population being tested. It will not usually be possible to test women unless special provision, including assistance of a woman attendant and suitable funnels, e.g. of polythene, can be arranged. The total volume of urine is measured, the sample stirred to ensure uniformity, and a 20 ml. sample removed to a suitable container. This may be a test-tube if tests are to be done on the spot, but otherwise should be a stout tube or vial with a firm closure. If a colorimeter and a supply of electric current are available in the field, the test can be done there without difficulty. Otherwise it may be necessary to send samples by air or otherwise to a central laboratory. (See also **B2**). The specimens should be kept as cool as possible during transport: there is no objection to their being frozen solid.

(ii)   Testing the urine

Reagents   1.   Trichloroacetic acid (TCA) 25% (w/v) soln.
             2.   Sodium nitrite ($NaNO_2$) 0·1% soln.
             3.   Ammonium sulphamate (AS) 0·5% soln.

4.   0·1 % N (l-naphthyl) ethylenediamine dihydrochloride (NED)
REAGENTS 2, 3 and 4 HAVE TO BE FRESHLY MADE
IMMEDIATELY BEFORE USE.

5.   Hydrochloric acid 4N (HCl).

6.   Standard soln. of sulphamethazine (=sulphadimidine)
5 mg. % (= 500 µg per ml.)

Free (i.e. unconjugated) sulphamethazine

Standards are made by diluting reagent (6) above 1 in 25 to give 20 µg/$\frac{1}{2}$ ml.
This working standard is then further diluted to give 1, 2, 3, 4, and 5 µg. in
10 ml. Beer's law can thereby be checked, and when this has been done, the
20 µg/ml. standard need only be included in the determination procedure.

A water blank is included in each determination procedure.

The urine specimen is diluted 1 in 100 by volume. To 2·0 ml. of the
diluted urine are added 0·2 ml. water and 0·5 ml. 25% TCA. Mix and stand
3 minutes. Add 0·2 ml. NaNO$_2$—mix and stand 3 minutes. Add 0·2 ml.
AS—mix and stand 3 minutes. Add 1·0 ml. NED—mix and stand 10 minutes.
Read optical density at 540mµ.

The standards and the water blank are processed in the same way as the
diluted urines.

Total (i.e. conjugated + unconjugated) sulphamethazine

The procedure with standards is as given above under ' Free sulphamethazine '.

Urine specimens are diluted 1 in 500. To 2·0 ml. of the diluted urine add
0·2 ml. 4 N HCl. Heat in a boiling water-bath for 1 hour, then cool. Adjust
volume to 2·2 ml. with water if necessary. Evaporation can be reduced by
placing large marbles in the mouths of the test tubes. Add 0·5 ml, 25%
TCA—mix and stand 3 minutes. Then continue exactly as under ' Free
sulphamethazine ', above. The standards and the water blank are processed
in the same way as the diluted urines.

(b)   Calculation:

1.   Calculate concentration of ' free ' = F from standard curve produced
at time of determination procedure. Remember to correct for urine
dilution 1 in 100.

  2. Calculate concentration of ' total ' = T in a similar manner. Remember urine dilution now 1 in 500.

  3. Urinary sulphamethazine in acetylated form = $\dfrac{T - F}{T}$ %

(c) **Dosage schedule:**

    40 mg. sulfamethazine per kg. metabolically active mass.

Body Weight		Dose (mg)	Number of scored 500 mg tablets
lbs.	kilos.		
below 112	below 51	500	1
112–182	51–83	750	$1\frac{1}{2}$
above 182	above 83	1000	2

III.   DATA COLLECTING SHEET

Name:*

Age:

Sex:

Serial number:

Ethnic and tribal origin (or nationality) :

Birth-place:

Place of examination :   Altitude of domicile : (m.)

Date of examination :

Name of investigator :

Weight of subject (kg.) :

Total volume of urine collected in 8 hrs. (ml.) :

Conditions under which specimen stored and transported to laboratory (length of time, etc.) :

If test completed in field, record result:

*Full details of the subject and his population group are to be entered in the **BASIC IDENTIFICATION SHEETS** as laid down in the Technical Introduction.

B5. DETECTION OF FOETAL RED CELLS IN MATERNAL BLOOD (KLEIHAUER TECHNIQUE)

I. INTRODUCTION
   (a) General
   (b) Observations to be made
   (c) Sampling

II. TECHNIQUE
   (a) Field procedure
   (b) Laboratory analysis

III. DATA COLLECTING SHEET

I. INTRODUCTION

(a) General:

The object of this test is to discover the frequency and the amount of trans-placental bleeding in parturient and puerperal women in different populations, and to compare this with the frequency of maternal immunisation to the Rh factor and other blood-group antigens.

This is done by testing (in the laboratory) for the presence of foetal cells in the maternal blood taken within at most 7 (and preferably 4) days of parturition. At the same time, the maternal and paternal ABO and Rhesus blood-groups must be ascertained.

Full details of this technique are given in Kleihauer, E., Hildegard Braun and K. Betke; **Klin. Wschr. 35,** 637, 1957.

(b) Observations to be made:

Mother's ABO and Rh blood-groups
Father's ABO and Rh blood-groups
Presence/absence of foetal red cells in maternal blood
Pregnancy history
Interval between parturition and blood collection

(c) Sampling:

To obtain a reliable estimate of the frequency of transplacental bleeding (by estimation of foetal red cells in the maternal circulation) in the population, and to relate this to the paternal and maternal blood-groups, it is necessary to obtain as many specimens as possible. In most surveys, however, it is unlikely that the number of subjects available for this test will be large, and it may therefore be necessary to combine the data from related populations to gain an overall estimate of the frequency of transplacental bleeding.

II. TECHNIQUES

(a) **Field procedure:**

Blood for this test should be taken by venepuncture into sequestrine (or other anti-coagulant)*. 2 ml. of blood can be taken specially for this purpose (in sequestrine bottles) and sent to the laboratory where the test will be performed. (In this case a separate collection of blood for ABO and Rhesus grouping will have to be made—see **B1**). Alternatively, a portion of the large quantity of sequestrinated blood, taken for blood-grouping purposes, can be used.

No attempt should be made, for the purpose of this test, to prepare smears on microscope slides in the field. Blood should, if possible, be taken within 4 days of parturition, but may be taken up to the 7th day. The interval should in any case be clearly recorded.

(b) **Laboratory analysis:**

1. Make a dilution of the sequestrinated blood to 1 in 3 with saline. Mix well. Make a smear on a microscope slide and dry by waving in air at room temperature.
2. Fix in 80% alcohol for 5 minutes.
3. Elute in sodium phosphate citric buffer pH 3·3 (see below) at 37° for 5 minutes. Wash. Dry.

(**Note:** The pH of the buffer is critical; excellent results are obtained at pH 3·3 but complete elution of haemoglobin A has been found not to occur consistently at pH 3·4.)

4. Stain in Ehrlich's haematoxylin for 3 minutes. Wash. Dry.
5. Counterstain in 2·5% watery eosin for 2 minutes. Wash. Dry. Read under microscope for presence of foetal cells, which are deeply stained. If general eosin staining is too pink, dip in 50% alcohol.

BUFFER

Anhydrous sodium phosphate (Na_2HPO_4)
Citric acid

Na_2HPO_4 0·75528 g. ⎫
Citric acid 1·54250 g. ⎬ per 100 ml. of distilled water.

$Na_2 HPO_4$ 1·8882 g. ⎫
Citric acid 3·85625 g. ⎬ per 250 ml. of distilled water.

Controls:—Negative control—Adult blood.

　　Positive control–Cord blood diluted 1 in 1000 with adult blood of same group.

* e.g. EDTA with Vacutainers, see **B1.**

III.   DATA COLLECTING SHEET

Name:*
Serial number:
Age:
Place of examination:
Date of examination:
Days since parturition:
Pregnancy history:

Ethnic group or tribal origin (or nationality):
Name of investigator:

Results of test

Foetal cells present/absent
Maternal ABO Group:
Maternal Rh Group:
Paternal ABO Group:
Paternal Rh Group:
Other comments:

*Full details of the subject and his population group are to be entered in the **BASIC IDENTIFICATION SHEETS** as laid down in the Technical Introduction.

B6. PHENYLTHIOCARBAMIDE (P.T.C.) TASTE TESTING IN THE FIELD

I. INTRODUCTION
   (a) General
   (b) Observations to be made
   (c) Sampling

II. TECHNIQUE

III. DATA COLLECTING SHEET

I. INTRODUCTION

(a) General:

This is a test of the ability to distinguish by tasting between water and solutions of varying concentration of phenylthiocarbamide (phenylthiourea, P.T.C.).

(b) Observations to be made:

The essential observation to be made in this test is the lowest concentration of PTC in a dilution series at which the subject declares a bitter sensation (i.e. the 'taste threshold').

(c) Sampling:

To obtain a reliable distribution of taste thresholds for PTC, at least 100 individuals of each sex within the age range of 20–40 should be tested.

II. TECHNIQUE

Preparation of solutions:

To obtain repeatable results it is necessary to devote about 5 minutes to testing one individual and to proceed in the following manner. A series of solutions of PTC is prepared from a standard solution No. 1, containing 1·3 grams of the substance dissolved in one litre of hot water. Some workers use boiled tap water while others use distilled water. This solution is stirred and filtered and should be kept in a dark bottle with a glass stopper. By diluting one half litre of No. 1 solution with another half litre of water, again boiled tap water or distilled water, solution No. 2 is obtained and so on until No. 13. Care must be taken that the liquids are completely mixed before dividing them into two. Another method for obtaining these solutions is to top up the following amounts of solution No. 1.

Dilution Chart for P.T.C.

Standard = (1) = 1·3 grams in 1000 ml.

For (2) take 250 ml. of (1) and make up to 500 ml.

(3)	125	,,	,,
(4)	62·5	,,	,,
(5)	31·25	,,	,,
(6)	15·625	,,	,,
(7)	7·813	,,	,,
(8)	3·906	,,	,,
(9)	1·953	,,	,,
(10)	0·976	,,	,,
(11)	0·488	,,	,,
(12)	0·244	,,	,,
(13)	0·122	,,	,,

In addition to this series of 13 bottles, 4 bottles of the boiled or distilled water should be prepared simultaneously. All the solutions and the water must have the same temperature, roughly room temperature, at the time of the test, as people are able to distinguish between temperature differences of less than one degree centigrade. The series of solutions thus prepared is sufficient to test about 100 people and can be kept for several months. It is of course possible to " regenerate " the weaker concentrations by making them up afresh from the stronger ones.

Sorting Test

The testing of the " threshold ", (which incidentally does not correspond to the 50 : 50 threshold of sense physiologists), proceeds in two stages. Every individual is offered a small amount (about 5 ml.) of solution No. 9 to savour or to swallow. He is then asked to describe the taste, of which the answers will vary from " strongly bitter " to " just water ". If the answer is " bitter ", it is assumed that the individual is a " taster ": and the investigator then proceeds to test him with solution No. 10, using the 8-tumbler technique (see below). If the sample is declared tasteless, the subject is again offered 5 ml. of solution No. 7, 5, etc., until a level is reached at which he declares some bitter sensation. Most subjects experience this sensation at the back of the tongue after a delay of almost a second.

Eight Tumbler Test

Having formed a preliminary opinion of an individual's taste threshold, the 8 tumbler test is applied. For this 8 small containers are required, such as beakers, egg cups or paper cups which can stand on a table, and of which 4 are marked at the bottom in a way not visible to the tested individual. While he looks away the investigator pours 5 ml. of the estimated threshold solution into each of the 4 marked tumblers and equal amounts of distilled water into the others and randomizes their positions. The tested individual is then asked to sort all the tasting tumblers from the non-tasting tumblers and he is also told that there are 4 of each. If perfect separation is achieved one assumes that the offered concentration is perceived as being different from water, and the weaker solution, that is the one with the next higher number, is applied by repeating the 8 tumbler test; and so on until the performance breaks down. If the individual separates 3 pairs of tumblers correctly but one pair incorrectly, he is given another chance to correct the result, and if successful, his performance is accepted.

If conversely the tested individual cannot separate the tumblers, he is given the 8 tumbler test at a higher concentration, that is with a solution bearing a lower number, until he succeeds. Some individuals cannot make a distinction even with the strongest solution, No. 1. Their threshold is recorded under " smaller than one " (< 1). Otherwise the individual is given the highest solution number at which he can distinguish the solution from water as defined above.

The described procedure is much easier to perform than would at first appear and a few hours' practice are sufficient to master the technique to an extent that gross misjudgement during the preliminary test becomes rare. Suggestions to use a simpler technique have been frequently made but retesting has shown that the reliability of such procedures is so low that such attempts should be discouraged.

The results are usually presented in the form of a histogram, and the frequency of the homozygous (tt) non-tasters ascertained from the antimode. It is impossible to distinguish between individual homozygous and heterozygous tasters.

For further details, see: Harris, H., and H. Kalmur, **Ann. Eugen.** (London), **15,** 24–31, 1949.

Materials Necessary

Phenylthiourea can be obtained from any large drug firm and should be kept cool, dry and in a dark bottle.

Sets of 8 tumblers are required, half of which are marked.

Sets of 16 one litre bottles, dark and with glass stoppers, one-litre and two-litre measuring cylinders and pipettes of 50, 10 and 1 ml. are required.

Several flasks for boiling, a bunsen burner or electric plate, funnels, and filter paper are required.

III. DATA COLLECTING SHEET

Sample: Male/Female Ethnic and tribal origin (or nationality):

Place:

Date:

Concentration of standard solution (1):
(recommended: 1·30 g/litre)

Name*	Subject no.	Age	Threshold solution no. (for tasters). If non-taster, record 'none'

Arbitrary position of antimode in sample:

Name of Investigator: ....

*Full details of the subject and his population group are to be entered in the **BASIC IDENTIFICATION SHEETS**, as laid down in the Technical Introduction.

B7. TESTS ON SALIVA AND URINE

I. INTRODUCTION

II. TECHNIQUES
(a) Collection and storage of saliva
(b) Procedure for testing

III. DATA COLLECTING SHEET

I. INTRODUCTION

The following tests should be carried out on samples of saliva collected in the field:—

All series

Secretor status ABH.
Secretor status Le^a and Le^b

Selected series:

Titration of A, B, H.
Titration of Le^a and Le^b.

Known Group A or B individuals who are non-secretors, as well as Group O individuals, must be available to provide saliva for purposes of standardising the test.

It is preferable to obtain blood from the individuals in the populations studied for ABO sampling, in addition to the present test. (See **B1, B2**).

Urine samples may be tested in the laboratory for a number of amino-acids which are of genetic interest. Of these, beta-amino-iso-butyric acid is of particular interest because the available data show a striking variation in frequency in different populations.

II. TECHNIQUES

(a) Collection and storage of saliva:
(i) Collection of specimens:

If there is oral sepsis or if food has been taken recently, the mouth should be rinsed with water before 2–4 ml. of saliva is spat into a clean test-tube. If there is a cough it may be necessary to point out that sputum (" phlegm ") should not be spat into the tube but only saliva from the mouth. Experiments have not shown any effect of lipstick in the test but it may be wise to ask for it to be removed before saliva is collected if this can be done without risk of offence. It is preferable to avoid stimulation of saliva flow, e.g. by means of chewing a rubber band, though in dehydrated patients this may be necessary.

According to Race and Sanger (Blood Groups in Man, 3rd Ed., 1958, p. 63) " a very small cotton wool swab held in Spencer-Wells forceps can conveniently be used to absorb saliva from a baby's mouth. The wet swab is then squeezed by the forceps, and drops expressed into a small tube. If the swab is too large the squeezing simply forces the saliva into another part of the swab. With patience, neat saliva can often be collected; if this is not achieved the wet swab is squeezed in 0·5 cc of saline ".

As soon as possible after collection of the specimen, and certainly within one hour, it should be placed in a boiling water bath for 15 minutes. It should then be centrifuged hard for 10 minutes. **In the field,** testing must be done immediately on the supernatant fluid. Even though the specimens themselves should not boil, the froth on some specimens may expand considerably and in some cases overflow. If even a small amount of froth from one tube should overflow into another tube it may completely falsify the results of tests. This is thought to have been the cause of some anomalous results in the past. A careful watch should be kept and any tendency to overflow forestalled.

(ii) Storage of specimens:

For storage, the supernatant fluid must be transferred to a small tube and kept at $-20°C$. The test may be carried out on this fluid soon after centrifuging, but some highly viscous specimens are made easier to work with by preliminary freezing. At this temperature, there is no degradation of the A, B, and H group specific substances, and specimens of saliva may be stored at this temperature for a year or more before testing. Repeated thawing for an hour or two for re-testing does not have any significant effect on the inhibition titre. If stored at $-4°C$, testing of specimens should not be delayed for more than a month, and at $4°C$ there is rapid degradation and the tests should be made within 24 hours. There appears to be some doubt about the stability of the Lewis (Le^a and Le^b) substances and it should not be assumed that they will necessarily remain unchanged even at $-20°C$.

(b) Procedure for testing:

Reagents

Physiological saline.

Standardised anti-A and anti-B sera.

A standardised anti-H, the cheapest and most reliable being a saline extract of the seeds of **Ulex europaeus.**

3–5% suspensions in saline of washed red cells of groups A, B and O.

To make Ulex extract

Finely grind (a pepper mill is suitable) 10 gm. of the seeds and put in a strong bottle. Add 100 ml. of physiological saline and shake vigorously. Freeze and thaw several times and then centrifuge hard. A clear amber-coloured supernatant fluid should be obtained. If a mechanical mixer is used an emulsion will be obtained which can only be cleared with great difficulty.

Standardisation of anti-sera and Ulex extract

If the anti-sera used are too strong they may not be inhibited by a weak secretor and if they are too dilute non-specific inhibition will complicate the interpretation of results. It seems best to use them at the highest dilution which will give good agglutination of the appropriate red cells after being mixed with an equal volume of neat saliva from non-secretors. This dilution may be found by making up dilutions of the anti-serum from 1/2 to 1/8. A volume of each of these dilutions is mixed with a volume of saliva known not to contain its group specific substance and which has been heated as already described—i.e. if standardising an anti-A use saliva from group O individuals, or if standardising an anti-H use saliva from group A or B individuals who do not secrete A or B. (Saliva may contain a trace of anti-A or anti-B antibody corresponding to that in the blood, but it will be destroyed by the heating.) It is advisable to use the saliva of several known non-secretors of the blood group substance as some saliva specimens have more non-specific inhibitory effects than others. After the saliva/anti-serum mixture has been at room temperature for $\frac{1}{2}$–1 hour, add a volume of the appropriate red-cells (group A for anti-A serum and group O for anti-H). After a further two hours at room temperature examine for agglutination.

The strength at which to use the anti-serum is the weakest which gives good agglutination in the presence of all the neat salivas.

Agglutination-inhibition tests

Three series of double dilutions (starting at 1 in 2) in physiological saline of the saliva under test are made in precipitin tubes 50 × 7 mm. An equal volume of standardised anti-A is added to each tube of the first series of saliva dilutions, standardised anti-B to the second series and standardised anti-H to the third series. The mixtures are left at room temperature for $\frac{1}{2}$–1 hour and then a volume of the appropriate red cells (group A to the first, group B to the second and group O to the third series) is added to each tube. After a further two hours at room temperature the red cells are examined for agglutination.

A known secretor and a known non-secretor saliva should be tested with each batch of unknowns.

Interpretation of results

With anti-sera standardised as above, complete inhibition by even the first (1 in 2) dilution only, signifies secretion. Except in group AB individuals the tubes containing anti-A or anti-B serve as a control against non-specific inhibition. In practice the saliva of group O secretors will always inhibit the **Ulex** extract in the first two tubes. (On rare occasions groups A and B individuals secrete very little A or B substance but plenty of H substance— the so-called " aberrant " secretors.)

Where there is agglutination in the first tube, the individual can be scored as a non-secretor.

Number of saliva dilutions

1.   When the titre of the various blood group substances is required, serial dilutions up to 1 in 2048 (11 tubes) should be tested against anti-A, anti-B and anti-H. In this case measured volumes should be delivered by a marked pipette and the presence of agglutination detected microscopically.

2.   When the blood group of the individual is not known with certainty, and all that is required is to score as secretor or non-secretor, only three dilutions (1 in 2, 1 in 4, 1 in 8) of saliva need be tested against anti-A, anti-B and anti-H standardised as above. Even when the blood group is known it is best to test the saliva for its ability to inhibit all three anti-sera, as non-specific inhibition is thus detected.

3.   When very large numbers of specimens have to be tested much bench time can be saved and there is only slight loss of accuracy by:

(a)   using wider bore tubes (50 × 9 mm) and a drop technique instead of measured volumes delivered from a marked pipette, and examining for agglutination microscopically, and

(b)   first testing all the saliva specimens in 1 in 2 and 1 in 4 dilutions for ability to inhibit a **Ulex** extract standardised as above. All these, of whatever blood group, which inhibit the **Ulex** completely in both tubes can be scored as secretors. Then 1 in 2 and 1 in 4 dilutions of those salivas which do not inhibit the **Ulex** completely should be tested with anti-A and anti-B and only those which fail to inhibit all three anti-sera are scored as non-secretors. Though the saliva of nearly all secretors inhibits **Ulex** extract, a few secretors of groups B and AB do so only slightly and would be wrongly scored as non-secretors if the tests with anti-A and anti-B were omitted.

Collection and storage of urine

Unless the urine is very dilute, a 5 ml. specimen will suffice for most purposes. It is advisable to put a crystal of thymol in the container as preservative. The urine should be kept cool and transported in the same way as blood samples (see **B2**).

III.   DATA COLLECTING SHEET

Place:

Date:

Name* and ethnic and tribal origin (or nationality)	Subject No.	Age	Sex	Birth-place	Secretor Status	ABO blood group	Relation-ship to other subjects in the sample

Name of Investigator: . . . .

*Full details of the subject and his population group are to be entered in the **BASIC IDENTIFICATION SHEETS.** as laid down in the Technical Introduction.

B8. CYTOGENETICS

I. INTRODUCTION
  (a) General
  (b) Observations to be made
  (c) Sampling

II. TECHNIQUES
  (a) Collection of blood samples
  (b) Collection of skin biopsies
  (c) Transport
  (d) Sex chromatin methods
  (e) Karyotype analysis

III. DATA COLLECTING SHEET

I. INTRODUCTION

(a) General:

Data on the frequency of sex chromatin anomalies and chromosome abnormalities in different populations would be of considerable value. The techniques are simple and can be readily adapted to field conditions.

It would be desirable to carry out the examination of buccal smears in a variety of populations and this simple technique is detailed. Lymphocyte culture is also simple and can be carried out on a population basis using a very small quantity of blood. Skin biopsies can be taken readily in the field; this technique has however certain disadvantages in terms of culture procedures. It should therefore only be employed where the blood culture technique is contra-indicated (see p.134).

(b) Observations to be made:

(i) Buccal smears. Smears of the oral mucosa are easily obtained from cooperating adults as well as from young children. They can be screened rapidly in the field if a microscope and simple laboratory facilities are available, and provide a quick means of identifying certain types of sex chromosome anomalies within an hour or so of collection.

(ii) Blood smears. These are also useful and are perhaps more easily prepared by the average technician not familiar with chromosome technique. They do however require greater experience in interpretation and take considerably longer to analyse.

(iii) Hair roots. A simple method for studying sex chromatin in the external root shaft of single hairs has recently been described. (**Cytogenetics, 6,** 342, 1967).

The buccal smear is therefore the method of choice, and by using this technique large populations can be sampled.

(iv)   Chromosome analysis. Technical refinements of the blood culture technique have made chromosome analysis of large population samples a relatively simple matter. Heparinised whole blood can be kept at 4°C or at room temperature in temperate zones for a week or perhaps longer before culture. In the tropics, cooling, but not freezing, would be essential if the blood is to be transported over long distances. If relatively simple laboratory facilities are available the blood could be cultured and the slides made in the field. If not, the heparinised blood or cultures should be sent to the collaborating cytogenetics centre as soon as possible.

Skin biopsies have the advantage that longer periods of transport are possible if the skin is collected into sterile culture medium and kept cool. Far fewer samples can however be handled, and the culture procedures take much longer.

For chromosome analysis, lymphocyte culture is the method of choice provided the remoteness of the collecting area does not prevent its culture within seven days.

Sib and kinship data should be collected wherever possible, also parental ages at time of subject's birth, and any physical abnormalities observed in the subject.

(c) Sampling:

For population studies, as large a number as is practicable should be studied from any given population, whether by sex chromatin or chromosome analysis. The choice of sample size must naturally be determined in relation to the frequency of the various types of abnormality in the general population with which the study seeks to deal. The actual numbers studied will of course depend on the staff and facilities available. Frequently, even a small number of individuals will give some information. If, for instance, variation in the size of the Y chromosome between different populations is being studied, a realistic answer could be obtained from as few as 10 to 20 males per population. On the other hand, microtechniques for the culture of peripheral blood should now enable a large number of individuals to be studied with relatively little difficulty.

Sampling should be random, and should take into account age distribution, population structure, and sex ratio. Samples should be collected to include subjects from each age-group. In order to give some guidance, some frequencies of commoner chromosomal abnormalities and anomalies found in the general population are given below; these refer to the newborn populations, particularly in relation to the sex chromosome abnormalities. Additional data can be obtained from the following publications: Court Brown, W. M., Human Population Cytogenetics, North Holland Publishing Co., 1967; Court Brown, W. M., *et al.*, Chromosome Studies on Adults, **Eugen. Lab. Mem. 42,** Cambridge University Press, 1966.

Sex chromosome abnormalities:

47, XXY	1·9 per 1000
47, XXX	0·9 per 1000
45, X	0·4 per 1000
47, XYY	
48, XXXY, etc.	Less than 0·05 per 1000

Autosomal abnormalities:

47, XX or XY, G+   1·6 per 1000

47, XX or XY, D+
47, XX or XY, E+ } Each 0·1–0·2 per 1000

Reciprocal translocations and other structural rearrangements:

        5–10 per 1000

Autosomal variants:

46, XX or XY, Dp+
       16q+ } 54·5 per 1000
       Gp+
46, XYq+ or Yq−   28·0 per 1000

These frequencies refer largely to European and North American populations and there is some evidence that in some African, and particularly North African populations, the Y chromosome is considerably larger than in European populations. In certain special groups such as penal colonies and other enclosed groups, mental defective institutions etc. the frequency of sex chromosome anomalies is much higher. Sex chromatin studies will usually locate all the abnormal sex chromosome complements with the exception of the XYY, which of course is chromatin negative. Mongolism and other autosomal trisomics will be detected by clinical means, and the autosomal variants will require populations of 100 or less screened to see if the frequencies are significantly different. These, together with the structural rearrangements are perhaps the most interesting on a population basis, but also require more cytogenetic skill to detect.

II. TECHNIQUES

(a) Collection of blood samples (see also B1)

Blood can either be collected as whole blood into a sterile tube containing heparin, (or Vacutainer), or it can be inoculated directly into prepared sterile culture medium. If the first method is being used, 5 ml. of venous blood should be inoculated into a sterile tube containing 0·1 ml. of a 5,000 i.u./ml heparin solution and mixed gently. If the blood is being collected into prepared culture medium, 0·2–0·5 ml. of blood should be inoculated into the prepared tube. The blood or the prepared cultures should be stored in a cool place until either cultures are set up, in the case of whole blood, or until the prepared cultures can be incubated. If incubation and further culture procedures are being carried out in a cytogenetics laboratory at some distance from the collecting area they should be transported to this laboratory in cooled containers and should reach the laboratory within one week of collection. (See B2.)

(b) Collection of skin biopsies

(1) Clean the flexor surface of the forearm with Phisohex or soap, and dry with a sterile swab.

(2) Spray a small area with ethyl chloride spray.

(3) Raise a small cone (approx. 3 mm) of skin with sterile forceps and cut it off at the base with a scalpel. The cut should be deep enough to bleed a little, but not deep enough to require a stitch.

(4) Place at once in sterile medium. A synthetic medium obtainable from the cytogenetics centre should be employed. Otherwise glucose saline $+$ 100 i.u./ml penicillin and 100 μg/ml of streptomycin may be used. The collecting medium should be kept cool (4°C—not frozen) and must be stored out of direct sunlight.

(c) Transport

In tropical countries blood and skin biopsies should be kept cool and out of direct sunlight and should be transported to the laboratory for culture as soon as possible. Blood should reach the laboratory within seven days; skin remains viable within fourteen days. It is therefore likely that the collection of skin biopsies should be the method of choice in the more remote areas. It should however be noted that far fewer samples can be handled in the laboratory if a skin culture technique is being used.

(d) **Sex chromatin methods**

(i) **Oral mucosa smears.** Take at least **two** smears per subject. If the smears look too thin, additional ones are desirable. Make the smears on slides which have been cleaned in absolute alcohol. Write the name of the subject, in pencil, on the ground glass surface at the edge of the slide.

Taking the smears:

Scrape the oral mucosa **firmly** with:

Either—a clean metal spatula if the subject is a young child,

or   —a clean slide if the subject is old enough and cooperative. Holding the taking slide at an angle of about 30°, draw it along the other slide for about one inch. Do not try to spread the material too far, or press too hard, as this will lead to distortion of the cells.

Fixation

Smears are fixed immediately in 95% alcohol, before the cells have had time to dry on the slides. They may be returned in a plastic container of alcohol.

(ii) **Blood smears.** Use capillary blood. After cleaning with 75% alcohol, pierce the skin with the ' Haemolet '. Absorb the first 1-2 drops of blood on a cotton wool swab as they will be diluted with tissue fluid. Collect a small drop of blood on the slide near the ground glass surface. Place the slide on a firm flat surface, and using a second clean slide as a ' spreader ', make a blood film using the standard procedure: keeping firm contact with the flat slide push the spreader along in this direction to deposit a blood film, as shown in Fig. B8/1.

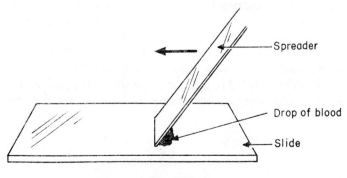

Fig. B8/1

Shake vigorously in the air until dry. Label the slide clearly with the subject's serial number and the date of collection.

In order to prevent loss of cells from oral mucosa smears during transport, the smears should be stained if possible before being sent to a cytogenetics centre.

Staining oral smears:

(a) Leave smears in 95% alcohol fixative for at least five minutes.
(b) Transfer to lacto-aceto-orcein stain.
(c) Transfer through two changes of 45% acetic acid.
(d) Transfer through three changes of Cellosolve.
(e) Transfer to Euparal Essence.
(f) Mount in Euparal.

All these reagents will be available from a cytogenetics centre. The stain may be used repeatedly, but must be filtered at weekly intervals to remove the precipitate.

(e) Karyotype Analysis

The morphological characterisation of the karyotype will be carried out in a centre equipped for the work and specified in accordance with agreed criteria. (See: Chicago conference: Standardisation in Human Cytogenetics. Birth defects: Original Article Series, II: 2, 1966. The National Foundation, New York.)

Notes

It is advisable before undertaking collection of material for sex chromatin or chromosome analysis in the field, to make contact with a recognised cytogenetics laboratory for advice. In this way it should be possible for the laboratory to advise on media and to provide the necessary tubes and made up culture medium. If it is proposed to carry out culture in the field, and if a cytogeneticist is not included in the team, then some brief period of training by a recognised laboratory of one member of the team would be essential.

III. DATA COLLECTING SHEET

Name* and ethnic and tribal origin (or nationality)	Serial no.	Age	Sex	Date	Place	Buccal Smear Result	Karyotype Characterisation	Chromosomal abnormalities

Name of Investigator: . . . .

Sib and kinship data :

Parental ages at subject's birth :

Phenotype :

*Full details of the subject and his population group are to be entered in the **BASIC IDENTIFICATION SHEETS,** as laid down in the Technical Introduction.

B9. COLOUR-CONFUSION CHARTS FOR TESTING COLOUR VISION

I. INTRODUCTION
    (a) General
    (b) Observations to be made
    (c) Sampling

II. TECHNIQUE
(**Note:** Full procedural instructions are given in the standard charts)

III. DATA COLLECTING SHEET

I. INTRODUCTION

(a) General:

There is wide agreement that the Ishihara and similar pseudo-isochromatic tests can be used for overall screening of a population to detect major red-green defectives, but not satisfactorily for the differentiation of degrees and types of defects.

Of these isochromatic or confusion charts, the German Stilling are not much used outside the continent of Europe, while the Ishihara charts printed in various editions by Kanehara, Tokyo-Osaka-Kyoto and by H. K. Lewis, Gower Street, London, W.C.1., as well as the HRR Polychromatic Charts of the American Optical Company, are most commonly used elsewhere. The Ishihara charts are more numerous and therefore it takes longer to test a person with their aid. On the other hand, by their very redundancy they give the tester more confidence in his judgement of the colour discriminating efficiency of the subject. Also the Ishihara charts provide more scope for testing illiterate subjects and children, by providing non-numerical charts.

The borderline between deuteranomaly, the most prevalent sex-linked colour vision defect, and normal trichromatism is somewhat blurred and the diagnosis of a small number of individuals will remain uncertain even after the use of an anomaloscope, especially under field conditions. Therefore estimates of the frequency of colour blind males in a population will vary somewhat according to the stringency of the investigator's criteria and will always be slightly arbitrary.

(b) Observations to be made:

1. Screen males of a population by means of confusion charts and pick out those showing a standardised minimum of deficiency.

2. Form an opinion concerning:
    (a) the severity of the defect (anomalous trichromasy or dichromasy).
    (b) the type of deficiency, i.e. whether protan or deutan defect.
    This decision can be made either by means of the Ishihara charts, or by the use of an anomaloscope. (See **B10**.)
3. Individuals should be subdivided into: normal, protanopes, protanomalous, deuteranopes, deuteranomalous; and the remainder classified " unspecified ".

(c) **Sampling:**

Care must be taken to exclude from the sample subjects affected with acquired forms of defective colour vision, or defects which are concomitant with diseases of the eye. In most anthropological investigations it is only possible to ascertain with reasonable confidence the frequency of the common sex-linked recessive defects among males above the age of 5 or 6 years. A minimum of 300 males should be examined. Ideally the sample should include 600 males. In population samples it is not usually considered profitable to test females for colour vision. In a very large survey, however, it would be of great interest to have data on the colour-vision deficiencies of females in a population. Names, ages, and kinship relations must be recorded.

II. TECHNIQUE

When using confusion charts care must be taken to perform the tests either under a standard illuminant of a given colour temperature (for instance $6,500°K$), which exists commercially or can be provided by means of filters; or, as will usually be sufficient, in normal diffuse daylight in the middle of the day (that is not during conditions of dusk or dawn). No direct sunlight or incandescent light of an unspecified kind must be used. The lights must not be strongly reflected over the surface of the charts which should be held at about arm's length. Refraction errors should be corrected during the tests but no tinted glasses may be permitted.

The subject tested should be comfortably seated and either turn the pages of the charts himself or be presented with them by the investigator. It is important that nobody else to be tested later is present and that no prompting occurs. It is equally necessary to record all the answers to every chart even if several interpretations are given in succession, as this sometimes provides a great deal of valuable additional information.

Some care must be taken to evaluate the subjects' answers in respect of their literacy and the different conventions they may have concerning the shapes of the numerals. Suspected defectives should be retested: those who perform normally the second time may then be eliminated.

Differential diagnosis.

Individuals who fail the screening by a confusion chart test, even if only marginally, are subsequently tested for more detailed classification and a few are then found to be normal. Further procedure depends on the availability of an anomaloscope, the use of which is described in **B10**. Without such an instrument, and using the chart readings alone, it is possible to distinguish only between some of the protan and deutan defects, and to make a guess concerning their severity. The differences between the more severely affected dichromats (protanopes and deuteranopes) and the more slightly defective anomalous trichromats (protanomalous and deuteranomalous people) is in any case not absolute . About 80–90 % of colour defectives can be classified by the use of tables Nos. 22, 23, 24 and 25 in the 9th H. K. Lewis edition of the Ishihara Tables. Versions of these occur with various slight variations in the other editions also and bear the numbers 26, 42, 35 and 96 respectively. To the normal eye the numerals on the left appear vermilion while those on the right are rather more purplish. Some very severely colour blind people are unable to read any figures on these 4 charts but most protanopes read only the numerals on the right (6, 2, 5 and 6) while most deuteranopes only read those on the left. Protanomalous individuals again may not be able to read one or the other of the numerals on the left and deuteranomalous people are unable to read some of the right hand numerals. A minority of people (up to 15 %) cannot be classified by means of charts alone and should, if no anomaloscope is available, be separately listed.

III. DATA COLLECTING SHEET

This form is designed for use when an all-male sample is being tested using the Ishihara plates.

Place of examination :

Date of examination :

Name of investigator :

CODE FOR RESULT OF TEST

Normal=1 ; protanomalous=2 ; protanope=3 ; deuteranomalous =4 ; deuteranope=5 ; colour-blind (not specified)=6 ; total colour blindness=7.

Name*	Serial no.	Ethnic group or nation- ality	Age	Occu- pation	Relation- ship to other subjects in study	Subject tested with all (=1) plates or 6 (=2)	RESULT (use code)

*Full details of the subject and his population group are to be entered in the **BASIC IDENTIFICATION SHEETS** as laid down in the Technical Introduction.

B10. TEST OF COLOUR VISION BY ANOMALOSCOPE

I. INTRODUCTION
   (a) General
   (b) Observations to be made
   (c) Sampling

II. TECHNIQUE
   (a) Methods
   (b) The Pickford-Nicolson Anomaloscope

III. DATA COLLECTING SHEET

I. INTRODUCTION

(a) General:

An anomaloscope is a device for matching additive mixtures of red and green light with a standard yellow light, the brightness of which can be altered. Other colour matches can also be used, as explained below. The instrument carries a scale indicating the relative amounts of green and red light which a particular observer chooses in order to match the yellow field. People having normal colour vision, i.e. over 90% of males and almost all females (more than 99%) will effect matches which are mutually acceptable or vary little from each other, when measured on successive occasions. On the other hand, people having defective colour vision will markedly deviate from the normal match, or accept widely different matches, provided the brightness of the yellow stimulus is adjusted to be equal to that of the red-green mixture for them.

Anomaloscopes were originally designed to distinguish between normal and anomalous trichromats. Protanomalous observers tend to produce mixtures which are distinctly too red for the normal investigator while deuteranomalous observers tend to produce too green matches. The degree of deviation from the norm is to some extent a measure of the severity of the anomaly. The other measures are the size of the matching range and the degree of darkening at the red end of the spectrum.

Use can also be made of anomaloscopes for distinguishing between the two types of dichromats, the protanopes and the deuteranopes, since protanopes have marked shortening or darkening of the red.

For the purposes of field investigations, a simple form of anomaloscope is required. Unfortunately, such an instrument is not easily available commercially. Many investigators use models of their own:—the portable anomaloscope introduced by Pickford is described under II (b) below. A comparison of several different anomaloscopes has been published by Willis and Farnsworth.*

(b)   Observations to be made:

For every subject, the age, mother's birthplace, and kinship relation to other subjects in the sample must be noted.

It is impossible to classify decisively every individual in a field investigation according to type of colour vision deficiency, and it is necessary to keep a column in one's record sheet for a minority of undiagnosed types.

(c)   Sampling:

In colour vision testing, records made by many workers have often failed to include frequencies of defective colour vision and of types of defect among women. Since red-green blindness in all its forms is a sex-linked defect, it is most important to know the frequencies among women in the same groups as the groups of men tested, although this testing often seems unrewarding, since very few women defectives are found. When a colour-defective woman is found, it is important to test as many of her relatives as possible, and make up a pedigree showing the types and degrees of defects found among them.

The number of subjects to be tested in two groups to establish an observed difference in frequency of a defect are given by Kalmus (" Diagnosis and Genetics of Defective Colour Vision ". London, 1965.) In a population survey several hundred men and a larger number of women would be required to demonstrate percentage differences between populations.

II.   TECHNIQUES

(a)   Methods.

It is not satisfactory for the subject to make several anomaloscope settings at random, the mean of which is taken. The technique required is as follows:—

    (1)   The tester, not the subject, must adjust the controls, although the subject may be allowed to make adjustments afterwards to check observations and to satisfy himself.

---

* Willis, M. P., and D. Farnsworth. Comparative evaluation of anomaloscopes. Med. Res. Lab. U.S. Naval Submarine Base, New London, Connecticut, **9**, No. 7, Report 190, 1952.

(2) The test must be started at a point in the red-green (or other) mixture which the subject sees as different in colour from the yellow (or other) standard when the latter has been carefully adjusted to give equal brightness with the mixture for this subject. This point may be at the red or green (or other) side of the scale. For dichromats no such point exists.

(3) Steps in colour-mixture change must now be taken towards the other end of the scale, and the brightness of the standard must be adjusted after each step to be again equal to that of the mixture before a claim of colour difference or equality is accepted.

(4) The steps continue throughout the matching range until its limit in the other direction is passed. This should be done in each direction several times, the sizes of the steps being chosen appropriately, and careful records of all the results should be made. Some subjects are consistent, others variable, but it is useful to record consistency or inconsistency and to know the subject's best and worst performance. The deviation from the normal setting is taken from the mid-point of the matching range.

All protanopes (P) and deuteranopes (D) are by definition dichromats, and can match the red or green lights, or the red-green mixture, with the yellow standard throughout the scale, provided a brightness match is first obtained for the subject in question at every step. The protanope requires great darkening of the yellow towards the red end, while the deuteranope requires little or no change in brightness throughout the red-green scale.

Simple protanomalous subjects (PA) make a match widely deviated to the red side, with a small or fairly small matching range, and usually requiring very considerable darkening of the yellow standard. The darkening at the extreme red end should be noted, in addition, even though there is not a colour match at this point.

Extreme protanomalous subjects (EPA) make matches over a wide range including or almost including the normal mid-matching point, requiring marked darkening of the yellow standard towards the red end of the scale, and with the mid-matching point usually deviated towards the red. Again, the darkening at the extreme red end should be noted, even if there is not a colour match at this point.

Simple deuteranomalous subjects (DA) make a match, with a small or fairly small matching range, widely deviated to the green side, with little change in brightness from the normal throughout the scale.

Extreme deuteranomalous subjects (EDA) make matches over a wide range including or almost including the normal mid-matching point, with little change in brightness from the normal throughout the scale and with the mid-matching point usually deviated to the green.

If the major defectives so far mentioned are excluded, the remainder of a population may show minor variations which are of considerable interest and can be measured with anomaloscopes. These are given in terms of deviations of mid-matching points and magnitudes of matching ranges in the red-green or other tests. Those subjects with about two or more times the normal sigma of deviation may be called deviants, while those with about two or more times the normal modal matching range may be called colour weak. Colour weakness and deviation may go together, of course, and may occur together in two or more tests.

It would be valuable if measurements on the blue-green and yellow-blue tests could be made whenever possible, because there are interesting variations on these tests among different groups of people, especially in relation to pigmentation and age. In addition, it is important that the frequencies of major blue-yellow colour vision defects should be established.

Total colour blindness should be recorded whenever possible, and may be determined by the use of the anomaloscope. On the Nagel anomaloscope, Model II, the whole spectrum may be shown, step by step, by shutting off all but one of the slits and turning the telescope micrometer screw. For the achromat no colour change will be reported. In the Pickford-Nicolson anomaloscope (see below) the five colour filters (red, yellow, green, blue-green and blue) may be taken in pairs, one on each side, and, with appropriate brightness adjustments, the achromat will make matches between them; red with yellow, yellow with green, green with blue-green, blue-green with blue, and blue with red, or any other pairs.

Comparative experimental studies have been made by several workers of the Ishihara and similar pseudo-isochromatic tests (see **B9**) and there has been wide agreement that these kinds of test can be used for over-all screening to detect major red-green defectives, but not satisfactorily for the differentiation of degrees and types of defect.

b)   **The Pickford-Nicolson anomaloscope:**

The instrument is a simple colorimeter, based on the use of integrating boxes. The outside dimensions of the apparatus are about $10 \times 10\frac{1}{2} \times 5$ inches, and it is light enough to be carried about in a small suitcase. Since a 12-volt lamp is used it would be easy to rearrange the apparatus for use with a motor-car battery, by cutting out the transformer, when it would be independent of the mains electricity supply.

It has the advantages of lightness and portability, large size of the test spot when required, great flexibility in the sense that any filters can be used in it provided that they are of the right dimensions, namely, about 2 mm. thickness and 1 inch square, and both additive and subtractive combinations may be made on either side, while the luminance of either side of the test spot may be controlled independently of its hue, and saturation is also under independent control. There is another very important advantage, namely, that the person being tested is able to look at the test spot at a convenient viewing distance, just as he would inspect a coloured object or objects to be judged, while the tester is able to see the colour matches being considered by the subject, without either tester or testee having to look with one eye into an eyepiece. Lastly, there is the important possibility of a yellow-blue test, and a blue-green test.

A full description is supplied with the instrument, which is manufactured by Messrs. Rayner and Keeler Limited, 100 New Bond Street, LONDON, W.1., England. A detailed description will also be found in ' The Pickford-Nicolson Anomaloscope ': Pickford R. W., and R. Lakowski, **Brit, J. Physiol. Optics, 17,** 131–150, 1960.

III.   DATA COLLECTING SHEET

Subject's name :*
Serial number :
Age :   Sex :
Ethnic and tribal origin (or nationality) :
Occupation :
Birth-place :   Mother's birth-place :
Date of examination :
Place of examination :
Name of investigator :
Result with Ishihara chart (see **B9**) : (give exact record of readings)
Relationship to other subjects in this study sample :
Eye colour (Martin-Saller scale—see **B15**) :
Has hair colour (see **B15**) been measured ? : yes/no
Has skin colour (see **B11**) been measured ? : yes/no
I.Q. :
Name of I.Q. test used :

Name of anomaloscope used :
Anomaloscope dial readings:—

	Range	Mid-matching point
Test 1 (red–green)		
Test 2 (green–blue)		
Test 3 (blue–yellow)		

RESULT : Normal/protanomalous/protanope/deuteranomalous/deuteranope/
tritanomalous/tritanope/colour blind undiagnosed/totally colour blind.

*Full details of the subject and his population group are to be entered in the **BASIC IDENTIFICATION SHEETS** as laid down in the Technical Introduction.

B11. SKIN COLOUR MEASUREMENT BY SPECTROPHOTOMETRY

I. INTRODUCTION
   (a) General
   (b) Observations to be made
   (c) Sampling

II. TECHNIQUES
   (a) The EEL instrument
   (b) The Photovolt instrument
   (c) Intercalibration of EEL and Photovolt instruments

III. DATA COLLECTING SHEET

I. INTRODUCTION

(a) General:

Skin colour has long been a character of anthropological importance, since it shows marked geographical variation. Progress in its study has been delayed by the lack of suitable objective methods of measurement, but recently reflectance spectrophotometers have been used, and appear to fulfil most of the necessary requirements. The reflectance of the skin over the range of the visible spectrum is specified as a percentage of the reflectance of a pure white standard. The colour is defined by the shape and magnitude of this spectral curve. The use of these instruments has permitted not only more accurate descriptions of pigmentary variation, but also analyses into genetic determination, tanning, and selective significance.

(b) Observations to be made:

Routine measurements are most commonly made on the medial aspect of the upper arm, where the effect of tanning may be considered to be minimal. This is recommended as a standard site in all surveys. Measurements may also be taken on the flexor surface of the forearm, at the junction of the middle and proximal thirds, or on the forehead. Where measurements are taken on the arm sites, it is recommended that these be taken always on the left side of the body, in conformity with other standardised anthropological measurements. The actual site chosen for examination will naturally depend upon the purpose of the survey, for example, tanning capacity can be ascertained by comparing reflectance value from the forearm or forehead with those from the medial aspect of the upper arm or other areas which are normally protected from the sunlight by clothing.

The measurement of **ultra-violet light radiation** is an important ancillary observation. For Technique, see **H.**

(c) **Sampling:**

A sample of at least 100 individuals of each sex, and preferably of a narrow age range should be studied. There has been shown to be marked and consistent sex difference in all populations studied, and according to Huizinga, there is also evidence for increased darkening of the skin with age, this ageing effect being greater on the forearm than on the upper arm.

II. TECHNIQUES

(a) **The EEL instrument:**

The portable reflectance spectrophotometer suitable for field use was introduced in 1951. (Weiner, J. S., **Man, 51,** No. 253, 1951). The EEL Model 99 Reflectance Spectrophotometer (the battery/mains version must be specified), which costs about £100 complete, may be operated with a 6-volt accumulator, and has been used successfully on numerous expeditions. This instrument is quite robust, but nevertheless requires careful packing; special care must be taken of the applicator head, which contains the photocell. The photocell itself (for which spares should be taken), should be protected whenever possible in regions of high humidity by packing with silica gel. Special care should also be taken to ensure that the galvanometer unit is clamped whenever it is moved.

The EEL is manufactured by Evans Electroselenium Ltd., Halstead, Essex.

This instrument is usually used for skin colour measurements with a series of nine Ilford filters, set into a single rotatable disc in the applicator head. These are numbered 601 to 609, and are narrow-waveband filters which transmit the following dominant wavelengths: 425 mμ (601); 465 mμ (602); 485 mμ (603); 515 mμ (604); 545 mμ (605); 575 mμ (606); 595 mμ (607); 655 mμ (608); and 685 mμ (609). In some skin-colour studies measurements have been made using all these filters, and this is the preferred procedure, but in others just three (601, 605 and 609), and in a few only the 609 filters have been used. It has been shown that the most genetically and anthropologically meaningful measurements of skin colour can be obtained using the longer wavelengths. Other filters can also be obtained for this instrument.

The measurement is normally taken on the medial surface of the left upper arm. Some identity of site can be ensured by placing the rear edge of the applicator head against the medial epicondyle of the humerus. The procedure is as follows:—

(1) Gently wipe the area to be measured with cotton-wool soaked in soapy water. Care must be taken not to cause reddening of the skin by application of excess pressure. It is advisable to wait at least 20 minutes after cleaning the skin surface before the subject is examined.

(2) With sensitivity control set to zero, adjust galvanometer reading to zero on the measurement scale.

(3) Check magnesium carbonate block is clean, if necessary scrape the surface gently to remove dirt, but ensure that the surface remains perfectly flat.

(4) Place applicator head on magnesium carbonate block with filter 601 (or whichever filter is required) in place, and turn up sensitivity control to 100% reflectance on the galvanometer measuring scale.

(5) Apply applicator head to skin surface and record the reading on the percentage reflectance (lower) scale.

(6) Replace applicator head on magnesium carbonate block, and again check the galvanometer reading is 100%.

(7) Repeat operations (4) to (6) above, using each filter of the range in turn, and standardising each filter separately against the magnesium carbonate block standard.

(8) Comparability of the instrument from one occasion to another can be checked and corrected for by calibration on a grey paper standard. A supply of this paper must be kept quite clean and dry.

(b) **The Photovolt instrument:**

The principle of this instrument, which has also been used in field surveys, is the same as that of the EEL, but it differs slightly in its detailed operation.

The Photovolt Reflectance Spectrophotometer (manufactured by Photovolt Corporation, 1115 Broadway, New York 10010, U.S.A.), is supplied with three filters, those often used in skin colour work being the Corning Glass Filters CS 5–60/5543, CS 4–64/4010, and CS 2–59/2404, with dominant wavelengths of 420 mμ, 525 mμ, and 670 mμ respectively. Other filters can also be obtained for this instrument, and have frequently been used in surveys; a mirror galvanometer (i.e. similar to that of the EEL instrument) can also be supplied.

For a standard, the Photovolt instrument is supplied with a robust white tile, which has itself been calibrated by the manufacturers with a ' pure white ' standard. Thus, in using this instrument, standardisation is made on the white tile at some specified percentage reflectance which varies according to which filter is being used, but which corresponds to 100% reflectance against the original standard.

The procedure is in other respects the same as that described above for the EEL instrument.

(c)   **Intercalibration of EEL and Photovolt instruments:**

A figure illustrating the two instruments is given, Fig. B11/1, facing this page.

There are problems in making a conversion scale from one type of instrument to the other, but such a scale has been devised using a least-squares method of fitting. A summary of the estimated quadratic equations is presented in the following table. (Table B11/1.)

Instrument EEL	Photovolt	a	b	S.E.	c	S.E.
425 mμ	420 mμ	3·93	0·91	0·185	0·0042	0·0044
515 mμ	525 mμ	4·08	1·11	0·186	0·00017	0·0039
545 mμ	525 mμ	5·24	1·12	0·172	−0·00030	0·0036
655 mμ	670 mμ	1·60	1·03	0·197	0·00012	0·0023
685 mμ	670 mμ	2·63	1·33	0·168	−0·0049	0·0020
Photovolt	EEL					
420 mμ	425 mμ	−0·55	0·80	0·174	0·0015	0·0034
525 mμ	515 mμ	0·13	0·65	0·167	0·0032	0·0028
525 mμ	545 mμ	−0·02	0·56	0·202	0·0070	0·0035
670 mμ	655 mμ	6·57	0·61	0·154	0·0035	0·0017
670 mμ	685 mμ	2·95	0·50	0·230	0·0058	0·0024

Table B11/1.

Linear functions have also been calculated for subgroups of Negroes, Indians and Europeans. These can be found in Garrard, Harrison & Owen, **Amer. J. Phys. Anthrop. 27,** p. 389, 1967.

In any comparative assessment of the two instruments, the following points must be borne in mind. The EEL instrument is cheaper and more studies have been made using this instrument than the Photovolt. Furthermore, the EEL is provided with a convenient filter system (the filters set in a rotateable disc in the applicator head), and virtually every worker who has

Fig. B11/1   E.E.L. (left) and Photovolt (right) instruments for the measurement of skin-colour by reflectance spectrophotometry.

used this instrument has used the same set of filters, thus making work on different populations more readily comparable. The EEL, however, is the less robust of the two instruments, and the mirror galvanometer unit, especially, must be handled with care if it is to give trouble-free service over an extended period under field conditions.

Besides being somewhat stronger, the Photovolt instrument is slightly more accurate, and produces more repeatable results. However different workers have used filters with different transmission maxima, in different combinations, and it is felt that this disadvantage to the use of this instrument is sufficient to make the recommendation that for the convenience of comparability of results, the EEL instrument should be used for field surveys wherever possible.

(The following warning must be heeded with regard to the EEL instrument:—

" The galvanometer suspension will be irretrievably damaged if:

(i) the instrument is switched on before the suspension is released. Therefore, before use, **first** release the clamp, **then** switch on.

(ii) the galvanometer, after use, is left unclamped and the instrument moved. Therefore, after use and after switching off, and **before moving the instrument,** make sure that the galvanometer is clamped again.")

III.   DATA COLLECTING SHEET

Name:*   Instrument used:
Study no.:   Birth-place:
Age: Mother's birth-place:
Sex: Father's birth-place:
Date: How long in present location:
Place: Relationship to other subjects
Ethnic and tribal origin   in sample:
  (or nationality):

Readings:
(a) EEL

Filters	601	602	603	604	605	606	607	608	609
Skin site: Medial aspect of upper arm									
Flexor surface of forearm									
Forehead									

(b) Photovolt
If the Photovolt instrument is used, it is essential, for the purposes of intercalibration with the EEL, for the filters specified here to be used.

Filters	CS5—60/5543	CS4—64/4010	CS2—59/2404
Skin site: Medial aspect of upper arm			
Flexor surface of forearm			
Forehead			

Name of investigator: ....

*Full details of the subject and his population group are to be entered in the **BASIC IDENTIFICATION SHEETS,** as laid down in the Technical Introduction.

B12. DERMATOGLYPHICS

I. INTRODUCTION
   (a) General
   (b) Observations to be made

II. TECHNIQUES
   (a) Collection of finger- and palm-prints in the field
   (b) Use of liquid plastic for skin prints

III. DATA COLLECTING SHEET

I. INTRODUCTION

(a) General:

The value of dermatoglyphics as markers in population studies has been realised for many years. From the time of their formation in the foetus until after death, the dermopapillary ridges remain unaltered: it must be borne in mind, however, that in certain circumstances some of the ridges on the fingers may be worn down so as to be invisible (e.g. in stenographers), and the same case may obtain in groups who habitually travel around barefoot, with regard to the plantar and toe patterns.

(b) Observations to be made:

The usual method of recording the variation in populations is to compare the percentage of the three main pattern types (arches, loops, and whorls), and to give the index of pattern intensity (total number of digital triradii on both hands).

A number of abnormalities of the patterns on the fingers and palms are associated with chromosomal abnormalities, and wherever possible in population studies, these should be recorded.

II. TECHNIQUES

(a) Collection of finger- and palm-prints in the field

Since this procedure may be foreign to some populations, it may be difficult to explain to the subjects what they are expected to do, or ask them to copy a demonstration, so that prints must be obtained with the subject completely passive. The hands of the subject moreover are likely to be filthy and ingrained with dirt. Fear may engender sweating of the subject's hands which will prevent satisfactory prints being obtained. The following procedures have proved satisfactory under field conditions.

(i)   ADULTS AND OLDER CHILDREN.

Materials:

Bucket, soap and water, and towel.
Surgical spirit and cotton wool.
Table.
Sensitizing fluid, applicator or pad, and sensitive paper, obtainable from:

> Faurot Inc.,
> 299, Broadway,
> New York 10007,
> USA.

or:

> Reed Research Laboratories,
> 33, Carlyle Square,
> LONDON, S.W.3.,
> England.

Pencil for marking prints.
Roller (a domestic pastry rolling-pin is ideal, but a beer bottle serves almost as well.)

Procedure:

The subject's hands are washed with soap and water, to remove as much as possible of the grease and dirt, and dried. The palms and fingers of the right hand are then swabbed with alcohol and this is allowed to dry; prints are then obtained from this hand by the following procedure, and when this is completed, the left hand is similarly swabbed and prints taken.

The palm and fingers of the subject's hand are covered with a thin film of sensitizing fluid, using the special applicator provided by Faurot, or the pad provided by Reed, care being taken to ensure that the film covers the sides, as well as the tips, of the fingers and the depression in the centre of the palm. This film must not be applied before the alcohol is dry, and must not be applied too thickly. The subject stands in front of the table, the investigator at the side of it. A sheet of the sensitive paper is placed on the table in front of the subject's right arm, with the edge furthest from him resting on the top of the roller. The tip of the subject's middle finger is placed on the paper on top of the roller. The subject's hand is then pushed gently forward maintaining contact with the paper, the roller being rolled away from the subject as the paper passes over it. As the tips of the remaining digits come into contact with the paper, they are pressed firmly onto it, and, as the palm passes over the roller, firm pressure is exerted to ensure that the mid-palmar depression makes contact with the paper. The rolling motion continues until the heel of the hand has passed over the roller. The subject's fingers are kept straight as they pass over the roller, so that the actual point of firm contact of the subject and the paper is only on the top of the roller, and the paper drops away from the subject's hand as it passes this point. The print is inspected, and if there is any blurring of the ridges, any blots obscuring detail (occasioned by too much sensitizing fluid, or by sweating), or any portions of the palm which have not registered an impression on the print, the hand is again cleaned and the procedure repeated. The print is labelled with the subject's name, serial number, sex, and the hand—**left or right.**

Digital prints are next taken, and are spaced around the edges of the sheet on which the palm print has been taken. The sensitizing fluid is applied to each finger in turn. The sheet of paper is placed with the edge along which the impressions are to be obtained along the edge of the table nearest the subject. The side of the digit is placed firmly on the paper, and the digit is rolled so that the ball of the fingertip and then the other side of the digit tip comes into contact with the paper. The print is marked with the number of the digit and is carefully inspected for any blurring of the ridges, or any absence of triradius, particularly on the lateral aspects of the tip. If there is any obscuring of detail, the print is repeated. It is also repeated if there is any scar tissue which may interfere with the analysis of the print. The procedure is repeated for each digit in turn. Digits on the right hand are printed on the same sheet of paper as the right palm, and left hand digits with the left hand palm.

The above procedure is suitable for adults, and has been satisfactorily applied to small children down to the age of about six years.

(ii) INFANTS.

The smaller the child the more difficult it is to obtain satisfactory prints, and the following method (derived from Cotterman) can be applied even on very young babies:

Materials:

Transparent adhesive tape in rolls of $\frac{1}{2}''$, $1''$, and $2''$ widths.
Indian Ink.
Artist's brush with a $\frac{1}{2}''$ wide tip.
Lantern slide glasses $3\frac{1}{4}'' \times 4\frac{1}{4}''$.

Procedure:

The hand is cleaned as outlined above for the adult. The ink is painted on to the entire palm and allowed to dry, taking care that the surface is evenly blackened. Drying requires about 60 seconds. The strips of adhesive tape are then applied to the inked skin, rolling these on from one side of the hand to the other, taking care to make sure of contact over the whole surface. In applying the strips to the palms, these are applied as a series of transverse overlapping bands. The first strip is applied over the distal end of the palm, paying particular attention to the important inter-digital areas and proximal finger segments. Each strip overlaps the preceding one by about $\frac{1}{4}''$, until the whole palm is covered. A gentle massaging action is applied with the finger and a pencil is drawn over the tape along the flexion creases. Since the tape is transparent, it can easily be seen whether good contact is being made. The entire sheet covering the palm is removed in one piece, and is applied to the glass lantern-slide plates, and the impressions are then ready for direct study. The balls of the fingers can be wrapped individually using tapes of 1″ width, but it is just as easy to print the entire finger including the proximal and middle phalanges, which themselves provide useful information, and for this strips are applied lengthwise to the finger. The remaining Indian ink can be removed from the subject with soap and water.

(b) Use of liquid plastic for skin prints:

The following are the instructions for making up liquid plastic for taking prints.

To 5 gms. polyvinyl formal powder add 100 cc. ethylene choride and 1 cc. butyl phthalate.

Leave for several days to dissolve, stirring occasionally.

Let evaporation continue until the liquid is reduced in volume to about 75 cc.

III.   DATA COLLECTING SHEET

Name :*   Ethnic and tribal origin
Subject no. :   (or nationality) :
Age :
Sex :
Place :
Date :

Fingerprints

Score as follows :   Arch   1
                       Loop   2
                       Whorl or composite   3

(finger)	I	II	III	IV	V
Left hand					
Right hand					
Cummin's Index					

Palm-prints

Score as follows :   No pattern   1
                       Pattern   2

	I/II	II/III	III/IV	IV/V	H
Left hand					
Right hand					

Abnormalities :

Name of Investigator: . . . .

*Full details of the subject and his population group are to be entered in the **BASIC
IDENTIFICATION SHEETS,** as laid down in the Technical Introduction.

B17 Dermatoglyphics

III. – DATA COLLECTING SHEET

Name:
Subject no.
Age:
Sex:
Place of birth:
Observer:

Fingerprints

	I	II	III	IV	V
(fingers)					
Left hand					
Right hand					

Palm prints

	I/II			IV/V	II
Left hand					
Right hand					

Name of Investigator:

B13. MORPHOLOGICAL MEASUREMENTS IN GENETIC STUDIES

I. INTRODUCTION
(a) General
(b) Observations to be made
(c) Sampling

II. TECHNIQUES

III. DATA COLLECTING SHEET

I. INTRODUCTION

(a) **General:**

In many studies of the genetic constitution of a number of populations, an assessment of the ' biological distance ' between them will be attempted. The most rigorous of such analyses of affinity will no doubt be based on characters of defined genetic determination (e.g. blood groups and serum proteins (see **B1**), skin-colour (see **B11**), etc. It is however of considerable importance to ascertain ' biological distance ' also in terms of morphological heterogeneity (see for example Sanghvi, L. D., in ' The Biology of Human Adaptability ', Ed. Baker and Weiner, Oxford, 1966), and this can be done not only by the use of measurements, but also by anthroposcopic observations (see **B15**), (see Howells, W. W., **Current Anthropology, 7,** 531, 1966). There are also situations in which it may be possible to separate the operation of genetic and non-genetic factors influencing body shape and size (see Hiernaux, J., in ' The Biology of Human Adaptability '). It is therefore of importance that the value of morphological measurements taken in relation to genetic studies should not be overlooked or underestimated.

(b) **Observations to be made:**

The following measurements should be taken:
(Extract from Revision of W.H.O. Report No. 297: 'Research in Population Genetics of Primitive Groups'.)

    (i)   Weight
    (ii)   Linear measurements:

1. **Cranial.**   Maximum length.
                          Maximum breadth.
                          Bizygomatic diameter.

1. **Cranial.—**   Total face height.
   (*cont.*)   Nose height.
                    Nose breadth.
                    Minimum frontal diameter.

   (Optional: Bigonial diameter.
                    Ear length.
                    Ear breadth.
                    Upper face height.)

2. **Post-cranial.**   Stature.
                        Sitting height.
                        Biacromial diameter.
                        Transverse chest.
                        Antero-posterior chest.
                        Bi-ilio-cristal diameter.
                        Upper arm length.
                        Forearm length.
                        Buttocks-knee length.
                        Tibial height.

   (Optional: Bicondylar humerus.
                        Wrist breadth.
                        Bicondylar femur.
                        Ankle breadth.
                        Wrist antero-posterior diameter.)

   (iii) Circumferential measurements:
                        Upper arm (relaxed).
                        Chest.
                        Calf.
                        Head.
                        Abdomen (umbilical level).

   (Optional: Forearm.
                        Wrist.
                        Ankle.)

(iv) Measurements of skin-folds:
>Triceps.
>Subscapular.

(Optional: Supra-iliac.
>Mid-axillary.)

(Other ' Full List ' measurements (see **A1**) which are not included in the above list are the following: suprasternal height, height of anterior superior iliac spine, total arm length, hand breadth, foot length, mouth width, lip thickness, and head height.)

(c) **Sampling:**

The size and composition of the samples will be dictated by the requirements of the genetic study. This may take the form, for example, of comparative studies of several population groups, or be related to family studies, studies of consanguinity, etc.

II. TECHNIQUES

Detailed techniques for taking the measurements listed above under ' Observations to be made ' are to be found under **A1**.

III. DATA COLLECTING SHEET

*For full details, see Individual
Identity Sheet (01).

Subject's name:*

Place of examination:

IBP/HA Project ref. no.	1 ☐☐☐☐
Study number	5 ☐☐
Serial number	7 ☐☐☐
Sex (M=1 ; F=2)	10 ☐
Age (years)*	11 ☐☐
Examination date (year + 3 decimals—see Table in Technical Introduction)	13 ☐☐☐☐☐
Procedure category	18 ☐☐

CODE FOR "NOT APPLICABLE"=X; CODE FOR "DATA NOT RECORDED"=Y

Card no.	20 ☐

Recommended measurements

Stature (mm.)	21 ☐☐☐☐
Upper arm length	25 ☐☐☐
Forearm length	28 ☐☐☐
Buttocks-knee length	31 ☐☐☐
Tibial height	34 ☐☐☐
**Bicondylar humerus	37 ☐☐
**Wrist breadth	39 ☐☐
**Wrist a–p diameter	41 ☐☐
**Bicondylar femur	43 ☐☐☐
**Ankle breadth	46 ☐☐☐
Sitting height	49 ☐☐☐☐
Biacromial diameter	53 ☐☐☐
Transverse chest	56 ☐☐☐
Antero-posterior chest	59 ☐☐☐
Bi-iliac diameter	62 ☐☐☐
Upper arm circumference (relaxed)	65 ☐☐☐
**Forearm circumference	68 ☐☐☐
**Wrist circumference	71 ☐☐☐
Chest circumference	74 ☐☐☐☐

**Optional measurements

Signature of investigator: ....
(*Continued on Card 2*)

III. DATA COLLECTING SHEET (continued)

Study number   1 ☐☐
Serial number   3 ☐☐☐
Procedure category   6 ☐☐

CODE FOR "NOT APPLICABLE"=X; CODE FOR "DATA NOT RECORDED"=Y

Card no.   8 ☐
Abdomen circumference
   (umbilical level)   9 ☐☐☐☐
Calf circumference   13 ☐☐☐
Ankle circumference   16 ☐☐☐
**Head circumference   19 ☐☐☐
Head length   22 ☐☐☐
Head breadth   25 ☐☐☐
Bizygomatic diameter   28 ☐☐☐
**Bigonial diameter   31 ☐☐☐
Minimum frontal diameter   34 ☐☐☐
Total (morphological) face height   37 ☐☐☐
**Upper face height   40 ☐☐☐
Nasal height   43 ☐☐
Nasal breadth   45 ☐☐
**Ear length   47 ☐☐
**Ear breadth   49 ☐☐
Triceps skin-fold   51 ☐☐☐
Subscapular skin-fold   54 ☐☐☐
**Suprailiac skin-fold   57 ☐☐☐
**Mid-axillary skin-fold   60 ☐☐☐
Weight (kg.)   63 ☐☐☐☐

Signature of Investigator: . . . .

**Optional measurements

iii. DATA COLLECTING SHEET (continued).

CODE FOR 'NOT APPLICABLE' OR 'DATA NOT RECORDED'

B.14 DENTITION

I. INTRODUCTION
(a) General
(b) Observations to be made
(c) Sampling

II. TECHNIQUES
(a) Dental examination
(b) Dental impressions and casts
(c) Saliva and buccal smears

III. DATA COLLECTING SHEET

I. INTRODUCTION

(a) General:

Dental examination is important for the following four reasons:

1. For the estimation of age, particularly where chronological age or skeletal age cannot be obtained. The use of dental information for age-grouping is detailed in the Technical Introduction under 'Individual and Group Specification', and also in Section **A1** (4). A data collecting sheet for coding the information appropriate for the assessment of dental age is also given in **A1.**

2. For the study of numerical and morphological variations of the dentition, and the identification of various dental anomalies.

3. For the assessment of dental attrition.

4. For the study of oral health in relation to the general health and nutrition of the individual.

The interested reader is referred to document HA 62: "Field Problems and Objectives in Dental Anthropology," (obtainable from: The Convener, HA Section, 21, Bedford Square, London W.C.1., England), to the paper by D. R. Brothwell: "Some problems and objectives related to the study of dental variation in human populations", **J. Dent. Res., 46**, 938–941, 1967, and to "Standardisation of Reporting of Dental Diseases and Conditions", **W. H. O. Tech. Rep. Ser., 242,** 1962.

The procedures outlined below are intended as a guide for observers without formal dental training, who wish to undertake a scanning survey of the dental features of a population group. Such a survey, however, should not be attempted unless the observer has been given a thorough course of training by dentally-qualified teachers, and has had considerable practical experience in the methods. More intensive and detailed dentition studies should only be carried out by those specially trained in the subject.

The Dental Health Unit of the World Health Organisation is producing a series of manuals entitled: "International Dental Epidemiological Methods Series". It is anticipated that the following manuals in this series should have reached the stage of final production at approximately the same time as the present volume goes to press:— (1) Introduction and General Methodology; (2) International Classification of Diseases—Application to Dentistry and Stomatology; and (3) Basic Dental Health Survey. Workers wishing to undertake extensive investigations including the collection of data on pathological dental and gingival conditions are referred to these documents for guidance.

(b)   **Observations to be made:**

The following should be recorded on the data collecting sheets (see III, below) from direct oral and dental examination:

1.   Number of primary and secondary teeth; eruption status of teeth present and whether misplaced or crowded; teeth missing and whether exfoliated, extracted or agenesis.

2.   Numerical variations: hypodontia, hyperdontia.

3.   Morphological variations: shovel-shaped incisors, anomalous maxillary lateral incisors, Carabelli's cusp, etc.

4.   Mutilations: tooth evulsion, tooth filing, etc.

5.   Attrition: occlusal attrition, attrition index.

6.   Oral health: oral hygiene, dental caries, enamel hypoplasia, periodontal disease, occlusion status.

Wherever possible dental casts should be obtained to supplement the direct observations. Instructions are given under TECHNIQUES below.

(c)   **Sampling:**

If dental information is required for age determination, the sample size will be determined by the purposes of the investigation or survey. (See **A1** for sample size required in growth studies.) Where the dentition is a prime object of the study, samples adequately representative of the whole population will have to be obtained. This can be done on a family or other residential basis.

Dental studies linked with genetic analysis will call for the collection of blood (see **B1** and **B2**), and observations of other features of the genetic constitution, as well as relevant socio-demographic data (see **G1**).

II.   TECHNIQUES

(a)   Dental examination:

1.   Number of primary and secondary teeth:

A direct inspection is made to record the presence or absence of each tooth in the primary and secondary dentitions, and other observations in terms of the following code:

1 – tooth not yet emerged;

2 – one or more cusps visible, but not more than one-third of the whole crown visible;

3 – more than one-third of whole crown visible, but tooth not fully erupted;

4 – tooth fully erupted (attainment of occlusal level);

5 – tooth exfoliated;

6 – tooth misplaced or crowded;

7 – tooth failed to develop (agenesis);

8 – tooth extracted.

Data on tooth emergence may be used to give an estimate of "dental age" as explained in **A1** (4).

2.   Numerical variations:

Record **hyperdontia** (increase in the number of teeth) and note the region of each occurrence. Describe the supernumerary tooth or teeth, and obtain intra-oral photographs if possible. Obtain impressions for casts of the dental arches (see (b) below).

Record **hypodontia** (decrease in the number of teeth) and note the region of each occurrence. Detail the relevant dental history, and if possible obtain intra-oral radiographs to confirm the diagnosis.

It should be noted that facial X-rays are the only certain method of detecting agenesis and most supernumeraries, and of considering internal dental features such as taurodonty (said to be significant in Mongoloid groups), etc. (See (3) below). Details of portable X-ray equipment suitable for field use are given in **A4**.

3. Morphological variations:

Record the occurrence of **shovel-shaped incisors, diminutive** or **peg-shaped maxillary lateral incisors, Carabelli's cusp,** and other dental morphological variations of note. Describe these briefly, together with a sketch if this will help the description.

4. Mutilations:

Record the occurrence of mutilations such as tooth evulsion or tooth filing. Briefly describe the mutilations, note the tooth or teeth involved, and make a sketch.

5. Attrition:*

For each tooth present record the degree of occlusal attrition in the following categories:

1 – enamel worn down without cusp obliteration or dentine exposure;

2 – cusps worn down to the extent of dentine exposure;

3 – appreciable wear of tooth crowns with obliteration of occlusal surface features;

4 – excessive wear resulting in marked reduction in the crown portion of the tooth towards the neck region.

Derive an attrition index (for primary and secondary teeth separately) by dividing the total scores by the number of teeth assessed.

6. Oral health:

The procedures outlined in manuals (1) and (3) of the International Denta Epidemiological Methods Series issued by the World Health Organisation (see above), should be followed.

(b) Dental impressions and casts:

Dental casts provide a durable record of dental morphology, the arrangement

---

* A more extended system of classifying attrition, which should be used for special dental studies, is given by Miles in "Dental Anthropology", (D. R. Brothwell, Ed.), Symposium Volume V, Society for the Study of Human Biology; Pergamon Press, 1963.

of teeth in the dental arches, occlusal and interproximal attrition, and occlusion status. A particular advantage is that detailed metric and non-metric observations can be made from casts under laboratory conditions, which could not be made in the field. However, impression-taking and pouring dental casts are exacting procedures that should not be undertaken without considerable training and experience on actual subjects. Observers without a formal dental training should seek advice from the appropriate department of a dental school. A course of training should be arranged, and advice sought on the special equipment and materials required.

(i)   Method:

Accurate impressions recording fine details can best be obtained with the use of alginate hydrocolloid impression material. Many countries produce their own brand of this material; it is available in England from the S.S. White Dental Mfg. Co. (G.B.) Ltd., 126, Great Portland St., London, W.1. Alginate impressions, however, cannot be transported, as they rapidly dry and shrink. This can be prevented by immersing them in water, but to minimise distortion, casts should be poured immediately (i.e. within no more than an hour or two of taking the impressions), using weighed quantities of good quality dental stone mixed with rain-water to the recommended water/powder ratio.

Thermoplastic impression material* is an unsatisfactory alternative, and should only be used when there is no possibility of using alginate material. Fine details are not recorded, the material distorts on removal from the mouth, and the resultant cast is grossly inaccurate.

(It is important that a fairly tasteless sterilising agent should be used after dental trays have been used.)

(ii) Identification and transport:

Care should be taken to identify the casts with the serial numbers of the subjects. To avoid fracture of the casts during transport, they should be protected by enveloping with cotton wool or foam rubber pads secured with rubber bands, and be carefully crated, labelled "Fragile".

* One such material, 'Paribar', is mouldable in hot water at 60-65°C. Quick impressions can be made of the incisor region, or of the more posterior occlusal region by the subject bitting directly onto the material, which is left in the mouth for 1½ minutes, then placed in cold water for 5 seconds. There may be melting problems with this type of material in the tropics. 'Paribar' is manufactured by Amalgamated Dental Co., 26, Broadwick St., London, W.1, England. A similar material available in the U.S.A. is called 'Kalginate'.

(c)   **Saliva and buccal smears:**

For bacterial examination, smears and saliva samples can be collected and cultured in the field. For the detailed techniques for making these collections, it will be necessary to consult an oral pathologist.

III.   DATA COLLECTING SHEETS

The dentition survey data sheet presented below is used to record miminal personal details of the subject, the types of observation recorded and material collected, and the data from observations (1) to (5) as specified above. Additional data collecting sheets in the format recommended by the W.H.O. will be required for the oral health survey.

Notes

Code in the boxes for an observation recorded or material collected as: no = 0; yes = 1.

Number of primary and secondary teeth: The array of boxes has a space for each of the 20 primary teeth (designated a to e in each quadrant) and the 32 permanent teeth (1 to 8 in each quadrant). Note that Right and Left refer to the subject's right and left sides. Code the observations as specified in 'Techniques,' above. Enter the number of primary and secondary teeth present, as indicated, and also the total. Compute and enter the "dental age".

Attrition: Code the observations as specified in 'Techniques', above. For the primary and secondary teeth enter the total scores. Compute and enter the attrition indices.

III. DATA COLLECTING SHEET

*For full details, see   IBP/HA Project ref. no.   1 ☐☐☐☐

Individual Identity Sheet (01)   Study number   5 ☐☐

Name of subject: Serial number   7 ☐☐☐

Sex (M = 1 ; F = 2)   10 ☐

Age (years)*   11 ☐☐

Place of examination: Examination date(year + 3

decimals—see table in

Technical Introduction)   13 ☐☐☐☐☐

Birth date (code as above)   18 ☐☐☐☐☐

Procedure category   23 ☐☐

CODE FOR "NOT APPLICABLE" = X; CODE FOR "DATA NOT RECORDED" = Y

For 'no', code O; for 'yes', code 1

(1) Number of primary and secondary teeth:

MAXILLA   Casts   25 ☐

Saliva   26 ☐

Buccal smear   27 ☐

Intra-oral

photograph   28 ☐

Radiograph   29 ☐

MANDIBLE

Number of teeth present:

Primary   30 ☐☐

Secondary   32 ☐☐

Total   34 ☐☐

"Dental age "36 ☐☐☐☐

(2) Numerical variations—details:

Hyperdontia   41 ☐

Hypodontia   42 ☐

DATA COLLECTING SHEET (contd.)

(3) Morphological variations—details :

Shovel-shaped incisors	43	☐
Lateral incisor anomalies	44	☐
Carabelli's cusp	45	☐
Other	46	☐

(4) Mutilations—details :

Mutilations	47	☐

(5) Attrition :

MAXILLA

Attrition— primary teeth		
Total scores	48	☐☐
Index	50	☐☐☐

MANDIBLE

Attrition— secondary teeth		
Total scores	53	☐☐
ndex	55	☐☐☐

Signature of Investigator:

B15. ANTHROPOSCOPY

I. INTRODUCTION
    (a) General
    (b) Observations to be made
    (c) Sampling

II. TECHNIQUES
    (a) Inspection (Direct anthroposcopy)
    (b) Close-up photography (Indirect anthroposcopy)

III. DATA COLLECTING SHEETS
    (a) For anthroposcopic rating by inspection
    (b) For anthroposcopic rating by close-up photography

I. INTRODUCTION

(a) General:

There are many 'traditional' features which physical anthropologists have recorded in many populations over the last 100 years. The usefulness of some of these as judged by their value in providing valid information of 'morphological' or 'biological' differences in population studies has been indicated in papers by Howells, W. W., (**Current Anthropology, 7,** 531, 1966), Sanghvi, L. D., (**Am. J. Phys. Anthrop. 11,** 385–404, 1953) and in "The Biology of Human Adaptability", (Ed. Baker and Weiner, Oxford, 1966), and Karvé and Malhotra, (**Current Anthropology** (in press) 1968) Improvements in the scoring of such traits have been made by the introduction of standardised close-up photography, and standardised codes. For much recent field-work, the Harvard field-sheet has to a very large extent been followed. Those characters marked with an asterisk in the list which follows are those which have been adopted by the WHO Population Genetics Group.*

(b) Observations to be made:

The observations recommended are as follows: (those marked (P) may also be rated from the appropriate photographs).

(1) Hair	*(i)	Amount (regional) and texture.	(P)
	*(ii)	Form (head).	—
	*(iii)	Colour (head).	—
	*(iv)	Distribution (head).	(P)
	(v)	Hypertrichosis.	—
	(vi)	Haircut	(P)

* 2nd Revision of WHO Technical Report Series No. 279; "Research on Population Genetics of Primitive Groups ".

(2)	*	Eye form.	(P)
(3)		Eye colour.	—
(4)	*	Eyebrow thickness.	(P)
(5)	*	Brow-ridge and forehead.	(P)
(6)	*	Chin prominence.	(P)
(7)	*	Lips.	(P)
(8)	*	Nose.	(P)
(9)	*	Ear form (size, lobe, attachment, helix).	(P)
(10)		Prognathism.	(P)
(11)		Cheek and jaws.	(P)
(12)		Additional (i) Genitalia.	(P)
		(ii) Breast.	(P)
		(iii) Buttocks.	(P)
		(iv) Hand-clasping and arm-folding.	

These should be rated by the same observer on standardised scales or codes, (see II. TECHNIQUES, below). Most of these can also be rated from standardised close-up photographs.

(c)   **Sampling:**

A minimum of 50 (preferably 100) adults of each sex between the ages of 20 and 40.

II.   TECHNIQUES

General Note:

Anthroposcopy of the face, head, and trunk is best carried out by photography, since many more features can be studied and scored at leisure. The technique for anthroposcopic rating by direct inspection is outlined below. (The codes for the different characters are equally suitable for both direct anthroposcopy by inspection in the field, and indirect anthroposcopy by close-up photography and subsequent examination.)

---

* 2nd Revision of WHO Technical Report Series No. 279. "Research on Population Genetics of Primitive Groups".

(a) INSPECTION (DIRECT ANTHROPOSCOPY).

(1) HAIR

(i) Amount (regional) and texture:

The bodily hair in regions A–M (see Fig. B15/1 below, and under III. DATA COLLECTING SHEETS) is to be scored in terms of three factors, namely: quality, density, and the proportion of the area of the region covered by hair.

Quality refers to the thickness of the hair; this is rated on a scale 1, 2, 3, by palpation.

Density is rated on a 5-point scale (Absent–0; small–1; +–2; ++–3; +++–4) for each specified region, A–M. *

A measure of the *total quantity* of hair for a particular region may be obtained by multiplying the numeral for thickness (i.e. quality) by the numeral for

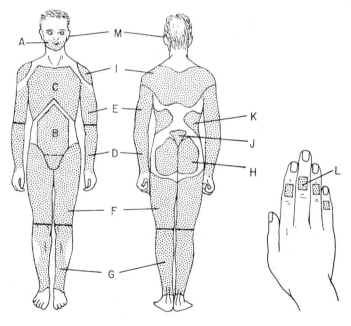

Fig. B15/1   Body hair regions A—M. (See above.)

* The Harvard rating for head hair density (hairs/sq. cm. is 1–10:–1; 10–100:–2; 100–200:–3; 200 or more:–4.)

density, and again by the fraction (in fifths) of the area of the particular region covered by hair. The sum of the regional scores may then be taken as a measure of the total body hair. (See Fig. B15/1 p.193, and III. DATA COLLECTING SHEETS).

(ii)   Form of head hair:

Head hair is to be described in terms of the following categories:

(a)   Straight.
(b)   Slight wave.
(c)   Long wave.
(d)   Wide wave.
(e)   Narrow wave.
(f)   Curly.
(g)   Crinkly.
(h)   Loose woolly (=matted).
(i)   Tight woolly (=frizzled).
(j)   Tufted. (Intermediate between i and k).
(k)   Peppercorn.
(l)   Spiral.

In assigning a descriptive category to the hair, Fig. B15/2 (p.195) may be used.

(iii)   Hair colour (head):

The best method of measuring hair colour objectively, if sufficient hair samples are obtainable, preferably from the crown of the head, is reflectance spectrophotometry. Using this technique, percentage reflectance values may be used as an objective means of denoting brightness and hue. The hair should be 'thinned-out', and, if possible, some 2–3 inches long. It is then both long enough to be fairly easily handled in preparation for measurement and, in the event of hair colour variation on different parts of the head, the thinning might be expected to represent many of the shades which do occur. Care should be exercised in noting any artificially bleached hair and any significant greying. The age of the hair donor (noted on the Data Collecting Sheet) is important, because of changes in hair colour which are known to occur with ageing.

Hair samples from each subject must be kept separate, and thoroughly washed in warm soapy water, then rinsed in clear water. After drying, each

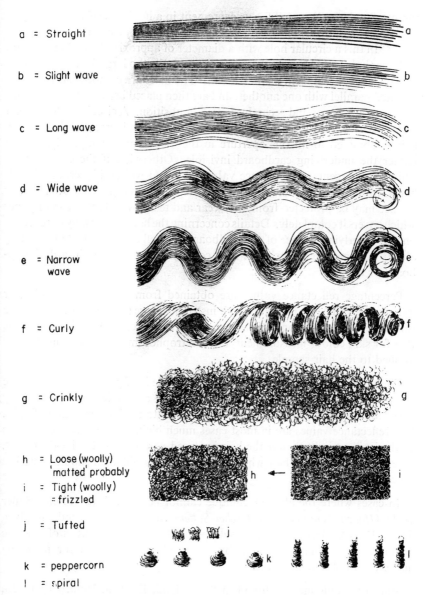

a = Straight

b = Slight wave

c = Long wave

d = Wide wave

e = Narrow wave

f = Curly

g = Crinkly

h = Loose (woolly) 'matted' probably

i = Tight (woolly) = frizzled

j = Tufted

k = peppercorn

l = spiral

Fig. B15/2   Forms of head hair.   (See p.194.)

sample should be mounted for measurement in a holder measuring $2\frac{1}{2}''$ by $3''$ This consists of a piece of cardboard above which is placed a piece of black paper. In this a circular hole with a diameter of approximately 20 mm. is cut. (A larger hole would be useful, but it is then usually too large for the amount of hair one can obtain from an individual.) The hairs are combed until they are oriented parallel with one another, and are then placed between the cardboard and the black paper and securely stapled in position. A circular patch of hair remains visible through the hole in the black paper. It is essential that enough hair is obtained to fill this aperture in the black paper completely, and to render the underlying cardboard invisible. Otherwise, if the cardboard is white, the percentage reflectance values obtained will be higher, and if it is black, lower, than the values obtained from the hair surface itself. The hair surface may be protected from dirt, wear and tear, by a stapled flap of paper which covers it completely. Details concerning the hair sample may be recorded on the underlying surface of the cardboard, as well as on the Data Collecting Sheet. The mounted specimens may conveniently be stored in a dark cupboard or drawer.

Percentage reflectance values are obtained from these mounted circular hair surfaces. The EEL or Photovolt instruments are suitable for this, and are fully described in Section **B11.** The procedure to be carried out is the same as that for skin colour measurement, the spectrophotometer head being directly applied to the hair sample.

The orientation of the hairs in any one sample is of great importance since the percentage reflectance values obtained from a sample vary considerably according to the orientation of the hair relative to the incident beam of light. The reflectance values are in most cases much higher if the hair is transverse to the incident light than if the hair is placed parallel with the incident light. The orientation of the hair when the readings are obtained should therefore be carefully noted.

In cases where the above technique cannot be applied, the Fischer-Saller scale (*Haarfarbentafel nach Fischer-Saller*), for which the code is given in the Data Collecting Sheet, should be used. Larger quantities of hair are required for colour assessment by spectrophotometry than for matching using the Fischer-Saller scale.

Further details may be found in Sunderland, E., **Ann. Hum. Genet., 20,** 312, 1956, and Barnicot, N. A., **Ann. Hum. Genet. 21,** 31, 1956.

(iv)   Hair distribution (head):

Head hair distribution should be scored on a four-point scale as given in the Field Data Sheet.

(v)   Hypertrichosis:

Both ears of the subject are examined as follows: a white card is placed behind the ear and an inspection made by means of a magnifying glass providing a magnification of about $1\frac{1}{2}$ times. Presence or absence of the trait is recorded according to the categories set out in the Data Collecting Sheet. All men with one or more hairs on at least one pinna are designated as affected. (See Stern, C., *et al.*, **Am. J. Hum. Genet., 16,** 455–471, 1964).

(vi)   Haircut:

The observer should also record whether the hair has recently been cut, according to the following categories:

Close-cropped/Medium/Long.

(In some African peoples, for example, the head hair will appear either peppercorn, tufted, or matted (see categories under (iii) Form of Head Hair, above), depending on how long it has been allowed to grow.)

(2)   EYE FORM

The characters to be scored here are the following:

(i)   Epicanthic folds: internal, median (palpebral, or intermediate), and external, each on a 4-point scale 0–1–2–3. The diagrams in Fig. B15/3, (p.198) illustrate the following:

(a)   No fold. (Internal 0; Median 0; External 0.)
(b)   Internal 3; Median 0; External 0.
(c)   Internal 0; Median 0; External 3.
(d)   Internal 0; Median 3; External 0.
(e)   Complete Mongoloid. (Internal 3; Median 3; External 3.)

(ii)   Eye opening height: this should be rated on a 3-point scale.

(iii)   Eye obliquity: this may be rated according to the following code: Absent/Small/Moderate/Marked.

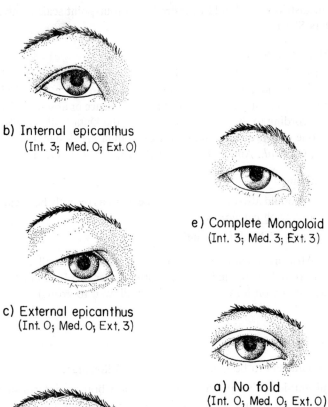

b) Internal epicanthus
(Int. 3; Med. O; Ext. O)

c) External epicanthus
(Int. O; Med. O; Ext. 3)

e) Complete Mongoloid
(Int. 3; Med. 3; Ext. 3)

a) No fold
(Int. O; Med. O; Ext. O)

d) Median fold
(Int. O; Med. 3; Ext. O)

Fig. B15/3   Variations in internal, median, and external epicanthic folds.

(iv) Other eye features which may be rated are included in the Field Data Sheet.

(3) EYE COLOUR

It is preferable to use the Martin-Saller standard set of coloured eyes. A new set of these has recently been published, consisting of eight eyes. This may be obtained from:

> Professor K. Saller,
> 8 MUNICH 15,
> St. Paulsplatz 9/1,
> Germany.

The descriptive categories are to be noted as in the code given in the Data Collecting Sheet below. (In the U.K., standard sets of 12 or 16 eyes may also be obtained from: Rose Millauro, 81, Hodford Rd., Golders Green, LONDON, N.W.11.) Subjects should be examined for iris colour close to a window or open door, with indirect sunlight as the light source.

(4) EYEBROW THICKNESS

Rating for eyebrow thickness should be done according to the categories set out in the Data Collecting Sheet, below; most of these follow the Harvard system.

Eyebrow concurrency may be scored on a 4-point scale as set out in the Data Collecting Sheet.

(5) BROW-RIDGE PROMINENCE AND FOREHEAD SLOPE

Rating for brow-ridge prominence should be done according to the categories set out in the Data Collecting Sheet, where ratings for forehead height and slope are also given.

(6) CHIN PROMINENCE

Rating for chin prominence should be done according to the categories set out in the Data Collecting Sheet, i.e. profile on a 4-point scale; the type (median/bilateral) is also recorded. Ratings for outline and depth are also given in the Data Collecting Sheet.

(7) **LIPS**

Rating for thickness of lip integument, membranous lip size (upper and lower), lip eversion, and seam, should be carried out in accordance with the categories set out in the Data Collecting Sheet.

(8) **NOSE**

Rating for nasion depression, nasal root and bridge height, nasal root and bridge breadth, nasal profile, tip thickness, septum inclination, nostril visibility, nostril shape, direction of nostril axes, and flare and thickness of nasal wings, should be carried out according to the categories set out in the Data Collecting Sheet.

(9) **EAR FORM**

The following characteristics should be scored:

    General shape: See Data Collecting Sheet.
    Ear helix: Flat—1; Slight roll—2; Moderate roll—3; Marked roll—4.
    Antihelix prominence: 0–1–2–3.
    Darwin's point: 0–1–2–3.
    Darwin's tubercle: 0–1–2–3.
    Ear lobe attachment: Absent lobe—0; Soldered 1; Attached—2; Free—3.
    Ear lobe size: Absent—0; Slight—1; Moderate—2; Marked—3.
    Ear protrusion: 1–2–3.
    Ear slant: Slant forward—0; Slant back—1; Slant far back—2.

(10) **PROGNATHISM**

Rating for prognathism should be done according to the categories set out in the Field Data Sheet below, i.e. Midfacial: 0–1–2–3; Alveolar: 4–5–6–7–8.

(11) **CHEEK AND JAWS**

The shape and prominence of the malars, and the gonial angles, should be rated according to the categories set out in the Data Collecting Sheet.

(12) **ADDITIONAL**

    (i)   Genitalia may be rated for size and shape in the male;

(ii) In the female, breasts may be rated for shape and relative size, and nipples for protrusion;

(iii) Buttocks may be rated for shape;

(iv) The manner of clasping the hands allows two possibilities: either the right thumb may be uppermost (type R) or the left (type L). There are the same two possibilities in the case of folding the arms, where types R and L are also recognised. For further details, see Freire-Maia, Quelce-Salgado, and Freire-Maia, **Hum. Biol., 30**: 281, 1958, and Freire-Maia and Almeida, **Hum. Biol., 38**: 175, 1966.

(b) CLOSE-UP PHOTOGRAPHY (INDIRECT ANTHROPOSCOPY)

It is recommended that a camera with a 5 cm. lens be used, set at a subject-lens distance of 1 metre for the full-face view, and for the side view. A built-in exposure meter should be used to determine the correct exposure. The smallest aperture possible (f/22 or f/26) should be used so as to obtain the maximum depth of field. The subject's serial number should appear in large legible numerals on the photograph. One black-and-white and one colour photograph should if possible be taken on the same occasion.

Full body, head, and smaller regional photographs are all of value for anthroposcopic scoring in the laboratory (see Fig. B15/4 p.202). Much, however, depends upon accuracy of scaling and clarity of detail. Thus, for instance, poor focussing may obscure hair detail easily in darkly-pigmented individuals; similarly, heavy shade may prevent an accurate assessment of eye-fold variation or ear shape.

Much anthroposcopic recording is still open to considerable subjective error, and it is thus of real importance to record photographically as much visible bodily variation as possible (even the pigmented sacral spot could be recorded by colour photographs). By doing so, the data may remain on laboratory file, and can be re-worked at a later date if new modes of analysis are devised.

The photographs can be used for subsequent examination of the following features, for which coded and graded reference diagrams and instructions have been given above under " (a) Inspection (Direct Anthroposcopy) ", and under (a) below in the Data Collecting Sheet.

For details of features which can be scored by indirect anthroposcopy, see Table B15/1.

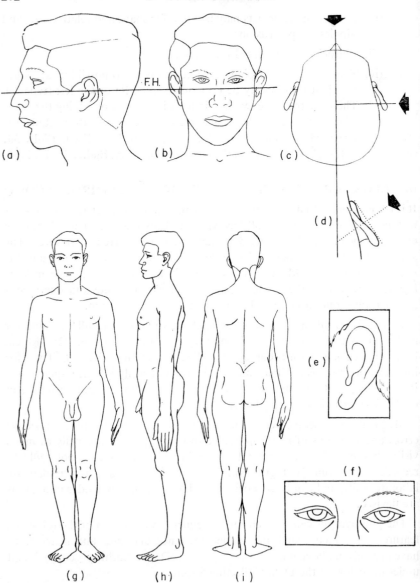

Fig. B15/4 Photographic views required for anthroposcopic scoring in the laboratory.

TABLE B15/1

Features	Views needed (see Fig. B15/4)	Observations to be rated
Body hair	G, H, I	Regions B—K (proportion and pattern only)*
Head hair	A, B	Distribution Baldness Haircut
Facial hair	A and B	Beard and moustache Eyebrows
Eye form	A, F	Folds Opening height Obliquity
Brows and forehead	B	Size Height Slope
Nasal form	A, B	All trait variations
Lips	A, B	All trait variations
Facial shape and prominence	A, B	Chin Prognathism Cheek and Jaws
Ear form	A, B, D, E	All trait variations
Penis	G, H	All trait variations
Breasts	G, H	All trait variations
Buttocks and lumbar curvature	G, H	All trait variations

*Proportion of hair can be simply judged visually, or may be determined with slightly more precision by planimetric comparison of body and hair "contours" in the photographs. Hair patterns may also be considered, as defined by Setty, L. R., (**Amer. J. Phys. Anthrop. 19**: 285 1961).

Measurements from photographs

If the photographs have been taken accurately and incorporate a suitable grid or other calibration, it would be possible to analyse features in terms of their proportions, relative angles, indices, etc. This must be left to the individual investigator, as little comparative material is available. There is also the possibility that some originally non-metrical scoring methods might eventually yield to metrical analysis. For a discussion of this, with special reference to the face, and for examples of photogrammetric techniques, see Brothwell, D. R., and Harvey, R. G., **Eugen. Rev., 57**: 167–181, 1965.

III. DATA COLLECTING SHEET

Name:*   Sex: Ethnic and tribal origin
Subject no.:   Date: (or nationality):
Age: Place:
Relationship to other   Observer:
  subjects in sample:

1. HAIR
(*i*) Amount (regional) and texture: **(RING APPROPRIATE CODE NUMBER)**

Region (see Fig. B15/1)	Quality	Density	Proportion covered	Total quantity
A. Beard and moustache	1 2 3	1 2 3 4 5	1 2 3 4 5	☐☐
B. Hypogastric	1 2 3	1 2 3 4 5	1 2 3 4 5	☐☐
C. Thoracic	1 2 3	1 2 3 4 5	1 2 3 4 5	☐☐
D. Forearm	1 2 3	1 2 3 4 5	1 2 3 4 5	☐☐
E. Upper arm	1 2 3	1 2 3 4 5	1 2 3 4 5	☐☐
F. Upper leg	1 2 3	1 2 3 4 5	1 2 3 4 5	☐☐
G. Lower leg	1 2 3	1 2 3 4 5	1 2 3 4 5	☐☐
H. Gluteal	1 2 3	1 2 3 4 5	1 2 3 4 5	☐☐
I. Upper back	1 2 3	1 2 3 4 5	1 2 3 4 5	☐☐
J. Lumbo-sacral	1 2 3	1 2 3 4 5	1 2 3 4 5	☐☐
K. Lower back	1 2 3	1 2 3 4 5	1 2 3 4 5	☐☐
L. Mid-phalangeal (mid-digital) 1st digit	1 2 3	1 2 3 4 5	1 2 3 4 5	☐☐
2nd digit	1 2 3	1 2 3 4 5	1 2 3 4 5	☐☐
3rd digit	1 2 3	1 2 3 4 5	1 2 4 4 5	☐☐
4th digit	1 2 3	1 2 3 4 5	1 2 4 4 5	☐☐
M. Ear hair (hypertrichosis)	1 2 3	1 2 3 4 5	1 2 4 4 5	☐☐

TOTAL BODY HAIR = sum of the 16 regional scores   ☐☐☐

(*ii*) Form of head hair: a b c d e f g h i j k l
(see Fig. B15/2)

(*iii*) Hair colour:
(see also **B11**)

(a) Spectrophotometer readings:

EEL filter	vertical	horizontal	mean
601			
602			
603			
604			
605			
606			
607			
608			
609			

(b) Fischer scale:

Black	(1)
Brownish black	(2)
Dark brown	(3)
Light brown	(4)
Fair	(5)
Red	(6)
Light medium	(7)
Greying	(8)

| 1 || 2 || 3 || 4 || 5 || 6 || 7 || 8 |

(*iv*) Hair distribution:

(a) Head hair:

Temporal advance	(1)
Temporal retreat	(2)
Frontal-temporal retreat	(3)
Cap-like	(4)

| 1 || 2 || 3 || 4 |

(b) Baldness:

Crown −	(1)
Crown +	(2)
Crown ++	(3)

| 1 || 2 || 3 |

(c) Beard:

Total	(1)
Chin and jowls	(2)
Chin and sideburns	(3)
Chin tip only	(4)
Circumoral	(5)

| 1 || 2 || 3 || 4 || 5 |

(*v*) Hypertrichosis:

Not affected	(1)
Scanty	(2)
Medium	(3)
Marked	(4)
Bushy	(5)

| 1 || 2 || 3 || 4 || 5 |

(*vi*) Haircut:

Close-cropped	(1)
Medium	(2)
Long	(3)

| 1 || 2 || 3 |

III. DATA COLLECTING SHEET (continued)

Name :*

Subject no. :

Observer :

2. EYE FORM

(i) Internal epicanthic fold :   [0][1][2][3]

Median epicanthic fold :   [0][1][2][3]   TOTAL CODE : [ ][ ][ ]

External epicanthic fold :   [0][1][2][3]

(ii) Opening height :
    Large   (1)
    Medium   (2)   [1][2][3]
    Small   (3)

(iii) Eye obliquity :
    Absent   (1)
    Small   (2)
    Moderate   (3)   [1][2][3][4]
    Marked   (4)

(iv) Other eye features :

(a) Superficial pigment—Absent   (1)
              Partial   (2)
              Complete (3)

           [1][2][3]

(b) Limit of pupillary zone—Line   (1)
                          Ridge   (2)
                          Absent   (3)

                        [1][2][3]

(c) Pterygium—Present   (1)
             Absent   (2)

         [1][2]

(d) Arcus senilis—Present (1) (Give colour accord-
                              ing   to   Martin-
                              Saller numbers, see
                              3 below)

                     Absent   (2)

(e) Conjunctival pigment :

    [1][2][3][4][5]

                                 [1][2]

                Colour :   [ ]

3. EYE COLOUR

Martin-Saller scale :

Dark blue	(1)
Medium blue	(2)
Light blue	(3)
Blue-grey	(4)
Grey	(5)
Grey-green	(6)
Green	(7)
Yellow	(8)
Orange	(9)
Light brown	(10)
Red-brown	(11)
Dark brown	(12)
Black	(13)
Purple	(14)
Unmatched	(15)

(i) Major iris colour :

[1][2][3][4][5][6][7][8][9][10][11][12][13][14][15]

(ii) Pupillary zone colour :

[1][2][3][4][5][6][7][8][9][10][11][12][13][14][15]

(iii) Ciliary zone colour :

[1][2][3][4][5][6][7][8][9][10][11][12][13][14][15]

*Details of the subject and his population group are to be entered in the **BASIC IDENTI-FICATION SHEETS,** as laid down in the Technical Introduction.

III. DATA COLLECTING SHEET (continued)

Name:*   Age:

Subject no.:   Sex:

Observer: Date:

---

4. EYEBROWS

(i) Thickness:

Thick   (1)
Medium   (2)
Thin   (3)
Very sparse   (4)

| 1 | 2 | 3 | 4 |

(ii) Concurrency:

— (1)

± (2)
+ (3)
++ (4)

| 1 | 2 | 3 | 4 |

5. BROW-RIDGE AND FOREHEAD

(i) Brow-ridge size:

| 0 | 1 | 2 | 3 | 4 |

(ii) Forehead height:

| 1 | 2 | 3 |

(iii) Forehead slope:

| 1 | 2 | 3 |

6. CHIN PROMINENCE

(i) Profile:

Retreat   (1)
Straight   (2)
Prominent   (3)
Very prominent   (4)

| 1 | 2 | 3 | 4 |

(ii) Type:

Median   (1)
Bilateral   (2)

| 1 | 2 |

(iii) Outline:

Pointed   (1)
Rounded   (2)
Square   (3)

| 1 | 2 | 3 |

(iv) Depth:

Small   (1)
Medium   (2)
Deep   (3)

| 1 | 2 | 3 |

7. LIPS

(i) Thickness of lip integument: | 1 | 2 | 3 |

(ii) Membranous lip size (upper): | 1 | 2 | 3 | 4 | 5 |

(iii) Membranous lip size (lower): | 1 | 2 | 3 | 4 |

(iv) Lip eversion: | 1 | 2 | 3 | 4 |

(v) Seam: | 0 | 1 | 2 | 3 |

III. DATA COLLECTING SHEET (continued)

Name:*

Subject no.:

Observer:

8. NOSE

(i) Nasion depression:
    —   (1)
    ±   (2)
    +   (3)
    ++   (4)
    +++ (5)

| 1 | 2 | 3 | 4 | 5 |

(ii) Nasal root height:
    Very flat (1)
    Low   (2)
    Medium   (3)
    Elevated (4)

| 1 | 2 | 3 | 4 |

(iii) Bridge height:
    Very flat (1)
    Low   (2)
    Medium   (3)
    Elevated (4)

| 1 | 2 | 3 | 4 |

(iv) Nasal root breadth:
    Narrow   (1)
    Medium   (2)
    Broad   (3)
    Very broad (4)

| 1 | 2 | 3 | 4 |

(v) Bridge breadth:
    Narrow   (1)
    Medium   (2)
    Broad   (3)
    Very broad (4)

| 1 | 2 | 3 | 4 |

(vi) Nasal profile:
    Concave   (1)
    Concavo-convex (2)
    Straight   (3)
    Convex   (4)
    Undulating   (5)

| 1 | 2 | 3 | 4 | 5 |

(vii) Tip of nose:
    Upturned (1)
    Pointed   (2)
    Rounded (3)
    Blunt   (4)
    Snub   (5)

| 1 | 2 | 4 | 4 | 5 |

(viii) Septum inclination:
    Markedly up   (1)   Markedly down (5)
    Slightly up   (2)   Concave   (6)
    Level   (3)   Straight   (7)
    Slightly down (4)   Convex   (8)

| 1 | 2 | 3 | 4 | 5 | 6 | 7 | 8 |

(ix) Nostril visibility:
    Frontal— none   (1)
               slight   (2)
               marked (3)

| 1 | 2 | 3 |

    Lateral— yes   (1)
              no   (2)

| 1 | 2 |

(x) Nostril shape:
    Thin   (1)
    Oval   (2)
    Round   (3)
    Triangular (4)

| 1 | 2 | 3 | 4 |

(xi) Direction of nostril axes:
    Parallel (A–P)   (1)
    Oblique   (2)
    Transverse   (3)
    Reverse oblique (4)

| 1 | 2 | 3 | 4 |

(xii) Flare of nasal wings:
    No flare   (1)
    Slight flare   (2)
    Moderate flare (3)
    Marked flare   (4)

| 1 | 2 | 3 | 4 |

III. DATA COLLECTING SHEET—continued

Name: *

Subject no.:

Observer:

---

8. NOSE (continued)

(xiii) Thickness of nasal wings:

Thin (compressed)	(1)
Slightly thick	(2)
Moderately thick	(3)
Very thick	(4)

[1][2][3][4]

9. EAR FORM

(i) General shape:

Long pyriform	(1)
Long oval	(2)
Medium pyriform	(3)
Medium oval	(4)
Medium round	(5)
Squat oval	(6)
Squat round	(7)
Squat square	(8)

[1][2][3][4][5][6][7][8]

(ii) Ear helix:

Slight	(1)
Moderate	(2)
Marked	(3)
Very marked	(4)

[1][2][3][4]

(iii) Anti-helix prominence:

Slight	(1)
Moderate	(2)
Marked	(3)
Very marked	(4)

[1][2][3][4]

(iv) Darwin's point:

Slight	(1)
Moderate	(2)
Marked	(3)
Very marked	(4)

[1][2][3][4]

(v) Darwin's tubercle:

Slight	(1)
Moderate	(2)
Marked	(3)
Very marked	(4)

[1][2][3][4]

(vi) Ear lobe attachment:

Soldered	(1)
Attached	(2)
Free	(3)

[1][2][3]

(vii) Lobe size:

Small	(1)
Medium	(2)
Large	(3)
Very large	(4)

[1][2][3][4]

(viii) Ear protrusion:

Slight	(1)
Moderate	(2)
Pronounced	(3)

[1][2][3]

(ix) Ear slant:

Forward	(1)
Back	(2)
Far back	(3)

[1][2][3]

III. DATA COLLECTING SHEET—continued

Name:*
Subject no.:
Observer:

---

10. PROGNATHISM

(i) Midfacial:

Slight	(1)
Moderate	(2)
Marked	(3)
Very marked	(4)

| 1 | 2 | 3 | 4 |

(ii) Alveolar:

Very slight	(1)
Slight	(2)
Moderate	(3)
Marked	(4)
Very marked	(5)

| 1 | 2 | 3 | 4 | 5 |

11. CHEEK AND JAWS

(i) Shape of malars:

Angled	(1)
Round	(2)

| 1 | 2 |

(ii) Prominence of malars:

Slight	(1)
Moderate	(2)
Marked	(3)

| 1 | 2 | 3 |

(iii) Gonial angles:

Slight	(1)
Moderate	(2)
Marked	(3)

| 1 | 2 | 3 |

12. ADDITIONAL—(1) Genitalia

(i) Scrotum:

(a) Small (1) / Medium (2) / Large (3)

| 1 | 2 | 3 |

(b) High (1) / Medium (2) / Low (3)

| 1 | 2 | 3 |

(c) Tight (1) / Medium (2) / Loose (3)

| 1 | 2 | 3 |

(ii) Penis:

(a) Size—Short (1) / Medium (2) / Long (3)

| 1 | 2 | 3 |

(b) Direction—Pendulous (1) / Oblique (2) / Horizontal (3)

| 1 | 2 | 3 |

(iii) Female external genitalia:

No tablier	(1)
Slight tablier	(2)
Marked tablier	(3)

| 1 | 2 | 3 |

III. DATA COLLECTING SHEET—continued

Name :*

Subject no.:

Observer:

---

(2) Breasts

(i) Shape:
    Conical   (1)
    Pendulous (2)

    1 2

(ii) Relative size:
    Equal   (1)
    Right larger (2)
    Left larger (3)

    1 2 3

(iii) Shape of areolae:
    Flat   (1)
    Raised   (2)
    Prominent (3)

    1 2 3

(iv) Nipples:
    Flat   (1)
    Medium   (2)
    Projecting (3)

    1 2 3

(3) Buttocks

(i) Size and shape:
    Flat   (1)
    Rounded   (2)
    Slight steatopygia (3)
    Moderate steatopygia (4)
    Marked steatopygia (5)

    1 2 3 4 5

(ii) Lumbar hollow :
    None   (1)
    Slight convexity (2)
    Marked convexity (3)

    1 2 3

---

*Full details of the subject and his population group are to be entered in the **BASIC IDENTIFICATION SHEETS,** as laid down in the Technical Introduction.

III.   FIELD DATA SHEET

(b) For anthroposcopic rating by photography:

This Sheet to be filled in in the field

Place of examination :   *Name of Investigator:* . . . .

Date of examination :

Type of camera used :

Details of lenses* used, etc. :
  (*Including filters)

Details of lens-subject distances, etc. :

Place a tick in the columns below for the photographic views taken on each subject. (Refer to Fig. B15/4, above).

Name*	Serial No.	Age	Sex	Photographic Views Taken									Ethnic and tribal origin (or nationality)
				(a)	(b)	(c)	(d)	(e)	(f)	(g)	(h)	(i)	

*Full details of the subject and his population group are to be entered in the **BASIC IDENTIFICATION SHEETS,** as laid down in the Technical Introduction.

The anthroposcopic observations will be read off in the laboratory, and recorded in the Transcription Sheets, which follow.

15. ANTHROPOSCOPY

TRANSCRIPTION SHEET FOR ANTHROPOSCOPIC RATING BY PHOTO-GRAPHY (FULL-LENGTH AND CLOSE-UP), TO BE COMPLETED IN THE LABORATORY.

Name:*   Sex:

Serial no.:   Date of examination:

Age: Name of laboratory:

Place where photographed: Name of examiner:

Date when photographed: State which views (A—I) available:

BODY HAIR   Proportion   **(RING APPROPRIATE CODE NUMBER)**
                  covered (in
                  fifths)

B. Hypogastric   1 2 3 4 5
C. Thoracic   1 2 3 4 5
D. Forearm   1 2 3 4 5
E. Upper arm   1 2 3 4 5
F. Upper leg   1 2 3 4 5
G. Lower leg   1 2 3 4 5
H. Gluteal   1 2 3 4 5
I. Upper back   1 2 3 4 5
J. Lumbo-sacral   1 2 3 4 5
K. Lower back   1 2 3 4 5

HEAD HAIR (including Facial Hair)

(a) Head hair distribution: (b) Baldness: (c) Haircut:

    Temporal advance   (1)   Crown −   (1)   Close-cropped (1)
    Temporal retreat   (2)   Crown +   (2)   Medium   (2)
    Frontal-temporal   Crown ++   (3)   Long   (3)
      retreat   (3)
    Cap-like   (4) | 1 | 2 | 3 | | 1 | 2 | 3 |

    | 1 | 2 | 3 | 4 |

(d) Beard and moustache: (e) Eyebrows:

    Total   (1)   (i) Thickness: (ii) Concurrency:
    Chin and jowls   (2)   Thick   (1)   −   (1)
    Chin and sideburns (3)   Medium   (2)   ±   (2)
    Chin tip only   (4)   Thin   (3)   +   (3)
    Circumoral   (5)   Very sparse (4)   ++   (4)

    | 1 | 2 | 3 | 4 | 5 | | 1 | 2 | 3 | 4 | | 1 | 2 | 3 | 4 |

TRANSCRIPTION SHEET FOR ANTHROPOSCOPIC RATING BY PHOTO-GRAPHY (continued)

EYE FORM

(i) Internal epicanthic fold : [0][1][2][3]
Median epicanthic fold : [0][1][2][3]   TOTAL CODE : [ ][ ][ ]
External epicanthic fold : [0][1][2][3]

(ii) Opening height :
Large   (1)
Medium   (2)
Small   (3)

[1][2][3]

(iii) Eye obliquity :
Absent   (1)
Small   (2)
Moderate   (3)
Marked   (4)

[1][2][3][4]

BROW-RIDGE AND FOREHEAD

(i) Brow-ridge size :

[0][1][2][3][4]

(ii) Forehead height :

[1][2][3]

(iii) Forehead slope :

[1][2][3]

NOSE

(i) Nasion depression :
—   (1)
±   (2)
+   (3)
++   (4)
+++   (5)

[1][2][3][4][5]

(ii) Nasal root height :
Very flat   (1)
Low   (2)
Medium   (3)
Elevated   (4)

[1][2][3][4]

(iii) Bridge height :
Very flat   (1)
Low   (2)
Medium   (3)
Elevated   (4)

[1][2][3][4]

(iv) Nasal root breadth :
Narrow   (1)
Medium   (2)
Broad   (3)
Very broad   (4)

[1][2][3][4]

(v) Bridge breadth :
Narrow   (1)
Medium   (2)
Broad   (3)
Very broad   (4)

[1][2][3][4]

(vi) Nasal profile :
Concave   (1)
Concavo-convex   (2)
Straight   (3)
Convex   (4)
Undulating   (5)

[1][2][3][4][5]

(vii) Tip of nose :
Upturned   (1)
Pointed   (2)
Rounded   (3)
Blunt   (4)
Snub   (5)

[1][2][4][4][5]

(viii) Septum inclination :
Markedly up   (1)   Markedly down   (5)
Slightly up   (2)   Concave   (6)
Level   (3)   Straight   (7)
Slightly down (4)   Convex   (8)

[1][2][3][4][5][6][7][8]

TRANSCRIPTION SHEET FOR ANTHROPOSCOPIC RATING BY PHOTO-GRAPHY (continued)

NOSE (continued)

(ix) Nostril visibility:

Frontal—none	(1)	
slight	(2)	1 2 3
marked	(3)	

Lateral—yes	(1)	
no	(2)	1 2

(x) Nostril shape:

Thin	(1)
Oval	(2)
Round	(3)
Triangular	(4)

1 2 3 4

(xi) Direction of nostril axes:

Parallel (A–P)	(1)
Oblique	(2)
Transverse	(3)
Reverse oblique	(4)

1 2 3 4

(xii) Flare of nasal wings:

No flare	(1)
Slight flare	(2)
Moderate flare	(3)
Marked flare	(4)

1 2 3 4

(xiii) Thickness of nasal wings:

Thin (compressed)	(1)	
Slightly thick	(2)	
Moderately thick	(3)	1 2 3 4
Very thick	(4)	

LIPS

(i) Thickness of lip integument: 1 2 3

(ii) Membranous lip size (upper): 1 2 3 4 5

(iii) Membranous lip size (lower): 1 2 3 4

(iv) Lip eversion: 1 2 3 4

(v) Seam: 0 1 2 3

FACIAL SHAPE AND PROMINENCE

(a) Chin:

(i) Profile:

Retreat	(1)
Straight	(2)
Prominent	(3)
Very prominent	(4)

1 2 3 4

(ii) Type:

Median	(1)
Bilateral	(2)

1 2

TRANSCRIPTION SHEET FOR ANTHROPOSCOPIC RATING BY PHOTO-GRAPHY (continued)

FACIAL SHAPE AND PROMINENCE (continued)

(iii) Outline:

Pointed (1)
Rounded (2)
Square (3)

`1` `2` `3`

(iv) Depth:

Small (1)
Medium (2)
Deep (3)

`1` `2` `3`

(b) Prognathism:

(i) Midfacial:

Slight (1)
Moderate (2)
Marked (3)
Very marked (4)

`1` `2` `3` `4`

(ii) Alveolar:

Very slight (1)
Slight (2)
Moderate (3)
Marked (4)
Very marked (5)

`1` `2` `3` `4` `5`

(c) Cheek and Jaws:

(i) Shape of malars:

Angled (1)
Round (2)

`1` `2`

(ii) Prominence of malars:

Slight (1)
Moderate (2)
Marked (3)

`1` `2` `3`

(iii) Gonial angles:

Slight (1)
Moderate (2)
Marked (3)

`1` `2` `3`

EAR FORM

(i) General shape:

Long pyriform (1)
Long oval (2)
Medium pyriform (3)
Medium oval (4)
Medium round (5)
Squat oval (6)
Squat round (7)
Squat square (8)

`1` `2` `3` `4` `5` `6` `7` `8`

(ii) Ear helix:

Slight (1)
Moderate (2)
Marked (3)
Very marked (4)

`1` `2` `3` `4`

(iii) Anti-helix prominence:

Slight (1)
Moderate (2)
Marked (3)
Very marked (4)

`1` `2` `3` `4`

TRANSCRIPTION SHEET FOR ANTHROPOSCOPIC RATING BY PHOTO-GRAPHY (continued)

EAR FORM (continued)

(iv) Darwin's point:

Slight	(1)
Moderate	(2)
Marked	(3)
Very marked	(4)

1	2	3	4

(v) Darwin's tubercle:

Slight	(1)
Moderate	(2)
Marked	(3)
Very marked	(4)

1	2	3	4

(vi) Ear lobe attachment:

Soldered	(1)
Attached	(2)
Free	(3)

1	2	3

(vii) Lobe size:

Small	(1)
Medium	(2)
Large	(3)
Very large	(4)

1	2	3	4

(viii) Ear protrusion:

Slight	(1)
Moderate	(2)
Pronounced	(3)

1	2	3

(ix) Ear slant:

Forward	(1)
Back	(2)
Far back	(3)

1	2	3

PENIS

(a) Size—Short (1)
      Medium (2)
      Long (3)

1	2	3

(b) Direction—Pendulous (1)
      Oblique (2)
      Horizontal (3)

1	2	3

BREASTS

(i) Shape:

Conical	(1)
Pendulous	(2)

1	2

(ii) Relative size:

Equal	(1)
Right larger	(2)
Left larger	(3)

1	2	3

(iii) Shape of areolae:

Flat	(1)
Raised	(2)
Prominent	(3)

1	2	3

BUTTOCKS AND LUMBAR CURVATURE

(i) Size and shape:

Flat	(1)
Rounded	(2)
Slight steatopygia	(3)
Moderate steatopygia	(4)
Marked steatopygia	(5)

1	2	3	4	5

(ii) Lumbar hollow:

None	(1)
Slight convexity	(2)
Marked convexity	(3)

1	2	3

C. WORK CAPACITY AND PULMONARY FUNCTION

C1. Indirect measurement of maximum aerobic power

C2. Direct measurement of maximum aerobic power

C3. Anaerobic power

C4. Forced expiratory volume and vital capacity

C5. Morphological measurements in work capacity and pulmonary studies

C6. Assessment of habitual physical activity

C7. Tests with dynamometers

C8. Simple performance tests

C1. INDIRECT MEASUREMENT OF MAXIMUM AEROBIC POWER

I. INTRODUCTION

    (a)   General

    (b)   Observations to be made

    (c)   Sampling

II. TECHNIQUES

    (a)   Supervision of the subjects

    (b)   Bicycle ergometer test

    (c)   Step-climbing test

    (d)   Measurements and calculations

III. DATA COLLECTING SHEET   (for indirect and direct (C2) tests)

I. INTRODUCTION

(a) General:

The assessment of an individual's maximum aerobic power ($VO_{2\,max}$) by extrapolation from the measurement of cardiac frequency (f_h) and oxygen consumption (VO_2) at one or more submaximal work rates is based upon certain premises. These are:

(i)   That f_h and VO_2 measured on an individual have a linear relationship with each other, up to and including maximal levels of work.

(ii)   That the variability of the $f_{h\,max}$ of individuals in a population, for a particular age-group, around the population mean is sufficiently small for the population mean to be used in the test procedure without the introduction of a significant error.

These premises have been tested extensively and it has been shown that using the method of two, three, or four submaximal work rates, estimates of the maximum oxygen intakes of individuals can be made with an error variance of 15%. This estimate of error variance takes into account variances due to day-to-day variability, differences between observers, and differences between individuals, in the various measurements. This variation can be reduced to about 9% on the second or third successive test on the same subject by the same observer.

From the results of the IBP Working Party (Toronto, 1967) it appears that the sub-maximal test may be of progressive form, and that, if desired, it may serve as a " warm-up " for the maximal tests (see **C2**) thus permitting a direct estimate of the aerobic power. The choice of exercise procedure would seem to lie between a step and a bicycle ergometer test. The main advantages of the bicycle ergometer over the step-test are a slightly lesser degree of ' habituation '—the change of f_h at a fixed VO_2—and a more consistent level of mechanical efficiency.

A nine inch step is familiar to most subjects, but some anxiety may arise from tripping at rapid rates of ascent. The apparatus is cheap and portable, and requires no maintenance, calibration, or electricity supply. The mechanical efficiency of effort is a little more variable than on the bicycle ergometer, but if the technique is carried out carefully, the work performed can be estimated quite accurately. The main disadvantage of the step test is a continuous movement of the arms and head; this creates difficulties when making some physiological measurements.

It is difficult to propose a single test that is suited to all needs. In the field situation, there is much to commend a simple stepping procedure, but given the right type of bicycle ergometer (the von Döbeln bicycle ergometer), even such groups as Bushmen have been found to be quite capable of undergoing an ergometer test. For field studies under difficult conditions, however, it would be permissible to use a step-test. Since it is feasible with either the step method or the bicycle ergometer to proceed from the submaximal to the maximal determination (see **C2**), once a choice has been made it will be necessary to continue with the same method for both determinations.

(b) **Observations to be made:**

    (1) Sub-maximal exercise test (bicycle or step):

        (i)   Cardiac frequency (preferably by ECG)

        (ii)   Expired air volume, O_2 and CO_2 content

        (iii) Respiratory rate

        (iv)   Blood pressure (see **F3**)

    (2) Ancillary observations:

        (i)   General medical examination (see **F1**)

        (ii)   Medical cardiovascular history using WHO questionnaire (see **F3**)

        (iii) Occupational history and assessment of habitual activity (see **C6**)

        (iv)   " Basic " lung function tests: FEV and VC (see **C4**)

(v)   Anthropometry (see **A1** and **C5**) and tests of muscle strength (**C7**)

(vi)   Radiography for body composition (see **A4**)

(vii)   Environmental description (see **H**)

(c) Sampling:

The choice of sample naturally depends upon the object of the investigation—whether related to growth studies, or comparison of populations in different habitats, or on different dietaries. Where there are marked seasonal variations of activity or microclimate, these variations must first be documented by appropriate techniques (see **H**), and at least two studies of working capacity may be needed at appropriate times of the year.

Where the population unit is small enough for this to be feasible, it would be worthwhile considering testing all available adults of both sexes, and children from the age of adolescence onwards. In the more typical situation, however, the investigator must decide for himself what size of sample would be optimal or ideal for fulfilling the aims of his own study. This requires an estimate of the inter- and intra-subject variability, and of the expected differences in population means. A general formula and tables based on those parameters is given in the Technical Introduction, and from this an appropriate sample size can be devised.

In Canadian populations, the C.V. of aerobic power is about 16%. The difference in **mean** aerobic power between active and inactive groups is about 20%, and between sedentary and athletic groups about 100%. The minimum sample size to establish a difference of activity at a given age-group is thus about 16.

$$\text{s.e.} = \frac{16\%}{\sqrt{16}} = 4\%.$$
$$\Delta = 20 \pm 4\%.$$
$$t = 5.00$$

Having decided on this desirable sample size, the investigator would need to obtain an adequately representative sample of the population.

A comparison of random and arbitrary samples would be in order. In one study, only 35% of a random sample of children were prepared to participate in an extensive servies of observations when given the freedom of choice demanded by ethical standards.

Where time and facilities are limited, the investigator should in any case endeavour to study at least 50 male subjects between the ages of 20 and 30.

II. TECHNIQUES

(a) **Supervision of the subjects** (bicycle and step tests)

When the subject first attends, the medical examination should be carried out (see **F1**)

The subjects should wear light clothing during the test, preferably gym. clothes (only shorts and light rubber shoes) so that the larger part of the body is nude. This is necessary in order to facilitate heat exchange.

The test should be made **after at least an hour's complete rest.** During this period of rest, the subject should be made familiar with the apparatus for collecting expired air and for measuring heart rate (cardiac frequency). Cardiac frequencies should be measured every 15 minutes during the rest period, and oral temperature at the end of this period.

Subjects should be rejected from the test on the following criteria:

(i)   An oral temperature in excess of 99.5°F. (37·5°C).

(ii)   An f_h value at the end of the rest period above 100/min.

(iii) Evidence of an intercurrent infection, such as of the upper respiratory tract.

(iv)   When subjects above the age of 40 are to be tested, a resting ECG should be taken immediately before the work test, and should be examined by a physician. The slightest suspicion of irregularity should be taken as an indication to abandon the test.

The personnel in charge of the test should be instructed to recognise important symptoms and signs on the ECG which indicate cardiac insufficiency. Ventricular extrasystoles that become less with exercise can probably safely be ignored. A physician should be available at all times.

The subject should not be exposed to rapid chilling after the test.

(b) **Bicycle Ergometer Test**

During the preliminary period the necessary electrodes will have been fitted and a sufficient period of time must be allowed to familiarise the subjects with the work procedures involved. Wherever possible, it is recommended that the **12**-min. progressive bicycle test to be outlined is repeated at least twice to overcome the difficult problems of habituation and learning. This is of particular importance where sedentary subjects and/or primitive groups are to be studied.

(i) Choice of work rates

Four submaximal work rates should be chosen, the aim of the test being to span the f_h range of 110–165 beats/min.

The level of O_2 consumption at which the subject reaches a f_h of 165 beats/min. will vary directly in relation to the curve of his VO_{2max}. While the lower two of the 4 rates of exercise can be set at the same level for most subjects (except the very young and old), those for the upper two rates of work need to be adjusted approximately in relation to the probable VO_{2max}. (as judged from the subject's response to the 1st and 2nd work loads) in order to attain the desired cardiac frequency. A sequence of three 4-minute loadings may be preferable to four 3-minute loadings. Some investigators use three 6-minute loadings.

(ii) Typical bicycle ergometer test procedure

Time (mins)

0–60	Subject reports to the (field) laboratory and is prepared for the work test as outlined above.
60–63	Subject works at 300 kgm/min.
62–63	Expired air collected.
62·5	Measurement of f_h taken
63	Work load is increased to 450 or 600 kgm./min. depending on the response of the subject to the previous work load.
65–66	Expired air collected.
65·5	Measurement of f_h taken.
66	Work load is increased to 600, 750, or 900 kgm/min.
68–69	Expired air collected.
68·5	Measurement of f_h taken.
69	Work load is increased to 750, 900, 1050, or 1200 kgm/min.
71–72	Expired air collected.
71·5	Measurement of f_h taken.

A von Döbeln-type upright bicycle ergometer should be used for the test. The subjects should pedal at a set frequency of either 50 or 60 revolutions/min. in time with a metronome, the work load being controlled by the observer. The exact revolutions should be counted either by the observer, or recorded via a cyclometer attached to the bicycle during the last 2 minutes of exercise. This value should be used when computing the exact work load.

For female subjects, sedentary and older men, the most suitable work loads will probably be 300, 450, 600 and 750 gkm/min. For young healthy men, 300, 600, 900, and 1050 or 1200 kgm/min. may be found more appropriate. In very athletic subjects, a work load of 1800 kgm/min. may have to be included.

It should be appreciated that this procedure is only a guide to the type of work rates which will give a span of 100–165 beats/min. In practice the observer must work out for himself suitable work loads for a particular population under study if necessary in pilot investigations. The aim must always be to avoid overtaxing the indivual and at the same time being sure of obtaining sufficiently high levels of f_h to be able to extrapolate the f_h/VO_2 value without too great an error.

(c)   Step test

In difficult conditions where facilities are limited, a step test may be used as an alternative to the bicycle ergometer test described above. The pattern of the two tests is identical except that the double 9″ step (Master's type) replaces the bicycle ergometer as a means of producing a fixed rate of external work.

The test occupies 12 minutes and the work rate is increased every 3 minutes as in the bicycle test. The subject ascends the step with three paces—one foot on the middle step, then both feet **flat** on top and descends backwards with three paces, until both feet are **flat** on the floor. The rhythm is set by a metronome: a pattern of 10, 15, 20 and 25 ascents/min. for reasonably fit subjects, and 8, 12, 16 and 20 ascents/min. for those who are less fit, is usually adopted. This pattern, however, can be adjusted to meet the individual case as before, by observing carefully the subject's f_h response to the first and second work loads. Subjects are advised to support the ECG cable with the left hand to avoid tripping.

The progressive double step test has two particular advantages over the more conventional single step procedure because: (1) the height of the step (9″) is that commonly encountered in buildings, and (2) the use of three rather than two paces in making the ascents permits a steady rhythm at low work loads

Typical step test procedure

Time (mins),

0–60   Subject reports to the (field) laboratory and is prepared for the work test as outlined under (a) above.

60–63	Subject works at 8 or 10 ascents/min.
62–63	Expired air collected.
62·5	Measurement of f_h taken.
63	Work load is increased to 12 or 15 ascents/min., depending on response of subject to previous work load of 8 or 10 ascents/min.
65–66	Expired air collected.
65·5	Measurement of f_h taken.
66	Work load increased to 16 or 20 ascents/min.
68–69	Expired air collected.
68·5	Measurement of f_h taken.
69	Work load increased to 20 or 25 ascents/min.
71–72	Expired air collected.
71·5	Measurement of f_h taken.

(d) **Measurements:**

(i) **Cardiac frequency**

It is recommended that cardiac frequencies be measured by means of an electrocardiogram or similar device, as this reduces the observer error, and gives a permanent record.

The following detailed procedure is recommended when the ECG is used:
1. The skin must be cleaned with alcohol and prepared with electrode paste or jelly, or alternatively the usual electrode paper properly wetted could be used.

2. Three disc electrodes (obtainable (in the U.K.) from Beckman Ltd. or Devices Ltd.) or suction cup electrodes, should be fixed to the chest wall with adhesive, one below and to the right of the right nipple, one below and to the left of the left nipple, and one below and to the right of the left nipple (sternum). If disc electrodes are not available, the conventional plate electrodes may be used with a rubber strap sufficiently tight around the chest to prevent slipping of the electrodes, but not so tight as to be uncomfortable to the subject or to interfere with his chest movement.

3. The ECG terminals preferred for the above positions of the electrodes are those marked right arm, left arm, and right leg (=neutral, on back) respectively. The recordings are consequently made on Lead II.

4. In order to eliminate possible electrical interference the ECG should be properly earthed. This is particularly essential where ergometers are used, and these should also be earthed.

5. ECG function is to be checked as to the proper centering, the stylus temperature, and for interference, before the start of the test.

6. The record is taken for a period of at least 10 seconds during the last 15 seconds of the 6th minute of exercise.

7. All records are to be labelled, indicating work load, name and serial number of subject, time taken, and date.

8. The cardiac frequency should be calculated from the deflections over the entire 10-second interval, and not from 2–3 beats as usually recommended by the manufacturers.

Alternatively, cardiac frequency can be counted with reasonable accuracy by means of a stethoscope and stopwatch. The subjects should wear rubber bands around the chest at nipple level. The stethoscope (flat variety) is held firmly over the apex beat of the heart under this band. The count should be made for a full 30 seconds. The stopwatch should be running and the counting should be started immediately **AFTER** the second-hand has passed the zero mark and stopped immediately **BEFORE** it reaches the 30-second mark. It is preferable to count aloud to avoid distractions and the intrusion of extraneous noises. A match-stick can be picked up for each 10 counts and the number of these acts as a useful check of the number of 10's in the count. It is important to check the calibration of the stop-watches against each other about once a week, and to reset the rate mechanism in any watch that is inaccurate by more than 1 second in 1 minute. It would be preferable to use the type of stopwatch which is calibrated directly in terms of pulse-rate.

(ii) COLLECTION, SAMPLING, AND ANALYSIS OF EXPIRED AIR

(1) Collection

The standard Douglas bag method is recommended for the collection of expired air. The Douglas bags should be made of vinyl plastic or heavy duty polythene. They should be fitted with wide-bore light-weight taps and a flexible side-arm tube for sampling gas. Such bags are less permeable than rubber to O_2 and CO_2, offer a low resistance to flow, are easy to transport and use, and do not occupy much space. The subject wears a conventional noseclip and is connected to the Douglas bag via a low resistance Otis-Mekerrow or Rudolph valve and short length of corrugated, smooth internal bore, flexible tubing. The orifice of the mouthpiece should be at least 1″ diameter, and the tubing and wide bore Douglas bag taps $1\frac{1}{2}$″, in diameter. Before use the resistance of the system to air flow should be measured. It should not exceed 1·5 cm H_2O at a flow rate of 200 1/min. The dead space of the valve should also be measured. Ideally it should not exceed 50 ml and in any case it must be stated when reporting results. The Douglas bag taps should be opened as expiration terminates and inspiration begins, and closed at the same phase of the respiratory cycle. The time during which the collection is thus made is to be noted accurately and used in the calculation of the results (see (4) below).

In some groups the nose is flat and/or the alae of the nose rigid so that the usual nose clip cannot be applied satisfactorily with the result that the ordinary mouth-piece cannot be used. In these circumstances some workers have found that the Edwards' face mask fitted with light-weight valves (Max Planck valve-body and Draeger valves) is satisfactory. The valves, one on either side of the face, are connected to the Douglas bag by two lengths of flexible hose and a Y-piece. However, face-masks do tend to leak and the valve arrangement offers a high resistance to flow. They should be used with caution, with certain reservation for maximal work (see **C2**).

The expired gas volume is ascertained by emptying the contents of the Douglas bag through a gas meter. In the laboratory the bell spirometer is the instrument of choice but in the field use should be made of the dry bellows-type (Parkinson-Cowan, Ltd.) gas meter. Provided that the gas is pressed out evenly from the Douglas bag through the meter, fairly accurate results can be obtained. A Centigrade thermometer, accurate to 0.2°C, is placed in the exit port to measure the temperature of the gas. From this, and the barometric pressure, the measured volume is converted to volume at STP. Flow meters directly coupled to the expiratory or inspiratory channels are usually subjected to large fluctuations in error depending on the rate of flow. They also tend to increase ventilatory resistance.

Mouthpieces should be washed with soap and water; if they will not be damaged by boiling, it is recommended to insert the equipment in boiling water for 3–5 min. after use. When boiling is impossible, the use of a standard bactericide at the recommended dosage is advised. Nose clips need not be sterilised except following their use on a subject with nasal secretion. Valves and connections should be washed with soap and water after use. When using an open system, one need not wash the tubing past the expiratory valves, but they should be rinsed in water and dried before use. Most manufacturers provide sterilisation procedures for their equipment.

(2)   **Gas Sampling.**

Vinyl plastic bags of $1\frac{1}{2}$-litre capacity fitted with stopcocks or Spencer Wells forceps are by far the most convenient and satisfactory for this purpose in field work. Provided that the sample is analysed within 3 hours no appreciable loss of CO_2 will occur from these bags. When stored in sealed canisters, these plastic bags can be kept for 24 hours before doing the analysis. In addition, plastic bags have the technical advantage that they permit gas samples of exactly 10·00 mls to be drawn into the Haldane apparatus, thus eliminating computation. The bag should be flushed once with the air to be analysed before the collection proper. An alternative procedure is the use of 50 ml syringes lubricated with ethylene glycol, but these are more expensive. This method does eliminate the use of large amounts of mercury and is more convenient and simple than the conventional sampling tube procedure. Provided that the samples are analysed within 2–4 hours, there is no appreciable change in the air composition. If only glass tonometers are available, acidulated water may be used to replace mercury for sampling purposes in the field. Under these conditions the gas can safely be stored for 1–2 weeks.

(3)   **Gas Analysis**

Haldane or Scholander techniques for analysing expired air are still the most suitable for field work, as a stable electricity supply is not always available for paramagnetic or other types of analysers. The usual procedures and precautions should be taken to obtain the best results.

Should a stable a.c. power supply be available, then the Beckman Model E2 oxygen analyser can be recommended. The only model providing adequate accuracy is the limited (10%) range E2. This instrument operates most efficiently at a constant temperature, and it is advisable to have it switched on permanently. The gas to be analysed should be dried, and care should be taken to get a constant flow of air through the instrument. To achieve these ends, a glass U-tube filled with anhydrous magnesium perchlorate and topped up with a glass suction flask containing a small amount of water is mounted between the outlet of the analyser and the vacuum system. The latter provides a visual check on the flow rate through the apparatus.

The O_2 analyser could also be used to determine the CO_2 concentration. This is done by inserting another U-tube containing a CO_2 absorbing agent such as " Ascarite " in the system. The CO_2 concentration is then obtained by difference, using the following formula:

$$CO_2\% = \frac{\% \ O_2 \text{ with } CO_2 \text{ removed} - \% \ O_2}{\% \ O_2 \text{ with } CO_2 \text{ removed}}$$

The sampling procedure described above can be eliminated when using these analysers. A mixing box of at least 4 litres capacity could be inserted in the expiratory channels and the sample drawn from there through the analyser. Allowance should be made for the amount of air drawn off when measuring the expiratory volume.

(iii) **Calculations**

As all volumes are to be corrected to STP it is essential to record environmental temperatures and barometric pressures. Aqueous tension at existing room temperatures can be read off tables. The following calculations serve as an example:

> Room Temperature = 23°C
> Barometric Pressure = 630 mm Hg
> Aqueous tension at 23° = 21.09 mm Hg
> Volume of air expired (uncorrected) $\doteq$ 56·5 litre/min.
> CO_2 concentration in expired air = 4·0%
> O_2 concentration in expired air = 16·5%

Subtracting the sum of the O_2 and CO_2 values from 100 results in the concentration of nitrogen in expired air being higher than that found in the atmosphere and a correction is therefore necessary. By convention we correct for inspired air as follows:

$$\frac{O_2 \text{ in atmosphere}}{N_2 \text{ in atmosphere}} = \frac{x}{N_2 \text{ in expired air}}$$

$$\frac{20·93}{79·04} = \frac{x}{79·50}$$

$$= 21·07\% \ O_2 \text{ in inspired air}$$

$$\therefore \% \ O_2 \text{ taken up} = 21·07 - 16·50$$
$$= 4·57\%$$

$$CO_2 \text{ blown off} = 4·00 - 0·03$$
$$= 3.97\%$$

The volume of expired air should be corrrected to STP.

$$Vs = Vr \times \frac{T1 \times Pr - AT}{T2 \times Ps}$$

(Vs = Vol. under STP

(Vr = Vol. recorded

(T1 = 273

$$= 56 \cdot 5 \times \frac{273 \times 630 - 21 \cdot 09}{296 \times 760}$$

(T2 = 273 + Rm. Temp.

(Pr = Baro. Pressure

(Ps = 760 mm Hg.

(AT = Aqueous tension

$$= 41 \cdot 80 \text{ litres}$$

$\therefore O_2$ consumed $= \% \ O_2$ taken up $\times$ ventilation rate

$$= 1 \cdot 920 \text{ litre/min.}$$

(iv)   **Extrapolation for estimation of maximum aerobic power**

While the sub-maximal tests will be of value for comparison with other groups (using strictly standardised methods), the information gained can also be used to obtain an estimate by extrapolation of the maximal aerobic power. This requires a knowledge of the average maximal pulse rate for the group concerned. In most cases this means that a special investigation of a sub-sample will need to be carried out. The subjects comprising this sub-sample will need to work up to and at their maximal level (see **C2**) with a recording of the pulse-rate (the estimation of oxygen usage is not strictly necessary). For European populations, for example, the average maximal pulse rate is already established (Astrand, I., **Acta Physiol. Scand., 49,** suppl. 169:1, 1960).

When the four sub-maximum values of oxygen usage and cardiac frequency are plotted a regression line can be obtained which is to be extrapolated to the (group) maximum pulse rate to give the corresponding oxygen usage ($= VO_{2max}$).

(v)   **Ancillary observations:**

(1)   A general medical examination and record of medical cardio-vascular history will have been made as part of the preparation and supervision of the subjects (see II (a) above).

(2)   The assessment of occupational history and habitual activity is dealt with in **C6**. For the latter, the basic observation would be a 24-hour recording of pulse-rate, by tape-recorder, SAMI, or watch-recorder. For recording activity, the questionnaire method would need to be adopted.

(3)   Lung function tests are described under **C4**.

(4)   The anthropometric measurements are described under **C5** and **A1**. The essential observations here comprise height, weight, skin-fold thicknesses, muscle girths, and other measurements related to bone development, chest development, and length of limbs.

(5)   Radiography in the field should be carried out wherever possible, for estimation of bone, muscle and fat by X-rays of calf, upper arm, and thigh. Details are given under **A4**.

(6)   Environmental assessment is described in section **H**.

III.   DATA COLLECTING SHEET

Occupation:

Name:*

Height:

Serial number:

Weight:

Age:

Date of examination:

Sex:

Place of examination:

Test used: bicycle/step

Barometric pressure:

First/second testing of this subject:

WB temperature:

Ethnic and tribal origin

DB temperature:

(or nationality):

Name of Investigator:

ST

$\dot{V}_E$ ATPS (L/min)	$\dot{V}_E$ BTPS (L/min)	$\dot{V}_E$ BTPD (L/min)	$F_{E}O_2$ (%)	$F_{E}CO_2$ (%)	$F_{I}O_2$ (%)	R.Q.	$\dot{V}O_2$ STPD (L/min)	f (breaths /min)	f_h (beats /min)	LA (mM /L)	BP s	d

BMAXIMAL

ork ad gm/ in)												

XIMAL

ork ad m/ n)												

s:
ull details of the subject and his population group are to be entered in the **BASIC
DENTIFICATION SHEETS,** as laid down in the Technical Introduction.

C2. DIRECT MEASUREMENT OF MAXIMUM AEROBIC POWER

I. INTRODUCTION

    (a) General

    (b) Observations to be made

    (c) Sampling

II. TECHNIQUES

III. DATA COLLECTING SHEET (see C1)

I. INTRODUCTION

(a) General:

The direct measurement of maximum aerobic power (VO_{2max}) has the disadvantage of requiring from the subject exhaustive efforts. The direct maximal test should be carried out where possible in conjunction with the submaximal bicycle test (see **C1**) and in any case should always be started at submaximal rates of work. The criterion for maximal effort should be that VO_2 shows no further rise with increasing work load, i.e. at least 3 values of VO_2 at the plateau level should agree to within $\pm 5\%$.

(b) Observations to be made:

The observations to be made on the subject at rest and during exercise are the same as those outlined in **C1** with the addition that some teams may wish to collect pre-warmed finger-prick blood immediately following the cessation of work for the determination of lactic acid concentration. Maximum blood lactic acid values may be used as supplementary evidence of maximal performance but should never be used as a criterion of VO_{2max}.

The test should be stopped during the performance of any given work load if the following signs or symptoms occur:

(i)   Pains and symptoms characteristic of " ischaemic heart disease ".

(ii) Severe pains and symptoms from other organs.

(iii) Pathological ECG-changes such as ST-segment depression more than 0·2 mV, series of multifocal extrasystoles, supra-ventricular arhythmia, conduction abnormalities, and other abnormalities indicating insufficient myocardial nutrition.

(c) Sampling: (see C1.)

II. TECHNIQUES

It is unlikely that a treadmill will be available in the field. As in the case of submaximal tests (see **C1**) either the bicycle or the step test can be used for the direct estimation of maximum aerobic power. Each of these has its advantages and disadvantages (see **C1**). The investigator should naturally use the same method for the maximal as for the submaximal test.

From the results of the submaximal test, the observer will have a guide to the work load at which the VO_{2max} is likely to be obtained. The subject should be prepared for the test in a similar manner to that described in **C1**. If the VO_{2max} test is to be measured immediately following the submaximal test, at least 30 minutes' rest should be allowed.

The maximal test, using the **bicycle ergometer,** is begun with the work load set at approximately 70% of the subject's VO_{2max} (as judged from the submaximal test). The pedal frequency should be set at 60 revolutions/min. This pedalling rate will be satisfactory for most unfit male and female subjects. For more athletic individuals, however, the pedal frequency may be increased to 70–90 revolutions/min., especially at the higher work loads, in order to ensure that the VO_{2max} value is reached.

The subject is allowed to warm up for 2 minutes at this level and then the work load is increased to the expected maximum work load. This work load is maintained for a further 2 minutes, and thereafter the work load is increased every 2 minutes by approximately 200 kg/min. until complete exhaustion is reached. Expired gas is collected using the standard Douglas bag method (see **C1**) and cardiac frequency measured during the final minute of each work period, the aim being to make at least 4–5 measurements of VO_2 in order to establish whether the criterion for maximum effort previously outlined has been ascertained. If, upon subsequent anaylsis, 3 VO_2 points do not agree to within $\pm 5\%$ then efforts must be made to call the subject back at a later stage for retesting.

It is of the utmost importance that during the measurement of VO_{2max} the resistance to flow of the gas collection circuit is not allowed to exceed 1·5 cm H_2O at 200 1/min (see **C1**).

Maximal Step Test

The subject should be prepared for the test in the manner previously described (see **C1**). The double (two) step is turned round and the subject asked to climb the single step 18″ high with two paces. If necessary, the procedure should be demonstrated to the subject (ascent with two paces, one foot on step, two feet flat on top, descend backwards with two paces, both feet flat on floor).

The initial work load is set at 70% of the predicted VO_{2max}, the exercise intensity is then increased slightly at the end of each second minute. Expired air volume and gas samples, for the measurement of O_2 consumption, and cardiac frequency, are taken during the final 30 seconds at each intensity of exercise.

The stepping rhythm is controlled by a metronome at 80–140 paces per minute, the actual pace selected of course depending on the fitness of the subject.

III. DATA COLLECTING SHEETS

The data collecting sheets for the submaximal and maximal work tests are given under **C1**.

C3. ANAEROBIC POWER

I. INTRODUCTION

    (a) General

    (b) Observations to be made

    (c) Sampling

II. TECHNIQUE

III. DATA COLLECTING SHEET

I. INTRODUCTION

(a) General:

It is well known that the maximum muscular power output that can be reached in an exercise of long duration, when an aerobic state is attained, is appreciably less than the power output that can be sustained for only a few seconds. This is due to the fact that the splitting rate of the high-energy phosphate compounds (ATP + CP = phosphagen) which is the most direct source of energy for mechanical work, can take place at a much higher rate than phosphagen resynthesis from oxidative metabolism.

When one runs up a staircase at top speed, provided that the effort is maximal, a constant speed is attained in about 1–2 seconds, which is constant up to the 5th second, then declines. This exercise is a very convenient ergometric procedure, since it appears that the energy requirement for speed maintenance in running a given distance is independent of speed; for a given incline of the steps, the energy requirement depends only on the mechanical work as calculated from the body lift. The vertical component of the speed in metres per second also gives the mechanical power output expressed in kg. metres per kg. second. It is also known that the efficiency in this type of exercise approaches 0·25; in fact, running at an incline exceeding about 30%, the external work is given practically by the body lift alone, all other factors, such as the speed changes at each step, the impact of the body on the ground in the last phase of the step, etc., being negligible. The energy requirement is therefore easily calculated.

It will be necessary to obtain equipment˙suitable for use in the field, consisting of:

(1) A photoelectric beam circuit and electronic timing device modified so as to operate from a portable source of electricity. (A battery-operated

device should weigh no more than 10 kg., and a transformer with quartz resonator to provide a.c. about 12 kg. A fully transistorised battery-operated circuit could be constructed weighing less than 5 kg.)

(2) A strongly-built set of steps which can be erected securely, if necessary without other support. Due to the high gravitational and inertial forces to which this staircase is repeatedly subjected by the subject's running at top speed, it must be erected firmly on smooth ground, and should be so arranged that the subject reaching the end of the stairs at top speed will find a convenient horizontal surface to allow a deceleration as shown in Fig. C3/1.

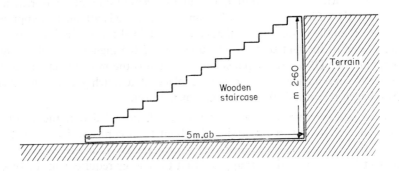

Fig. C3/1   Staircase for test of anaerobic power.

(b) **Observations to be made:**

Horizontal and vertical dimensions of step.
Time at taking off for 4th jump.
Time at taking off for 6th jump.
Body weight.

(c) **Sampling:**

A random sample consisting of 10–12 subjects per 10-year age-group is recommended.

II. TECHNIQUE

The subjects are invited to run at top speed up ordinary stairs, two steps (17·5 cm. vertical height each) at a time. No more than 2 m. sprint should be allowed before reaching the staircase. The time taken to cover an even number of jumps is measured with an electronic clock sensitive to 0·01 sec., driven by two photoelectric cells. The light beams run parallel to the steps, and are interrupted by the running subject. The reason for an even number of jumps is to have the subject intercept the beam of light while in the same position and in the same phase of his movement.

The vertical component of the speed is easily calculated by knowing the vertical dimensions of the step. By simply measuring the vertical component of the speed between the 2nd and 4th second of the run, when a constant speed level is reached, the maximum power value is obtained, thus avoiding the calculation of the energy employed for the initial acceleration.

For the measurement of the power, the time taken from the fourth to the sixth jump (70 cm.) is recorded.

Subject's name :*

Serial number:

Age: Weight (kg.) :

Sex:

Ethnic and tribal origin (or nationality) :

Occupation:

Date of examination:

Place of examination:

Dimensions of step:—horizontal (cm.) :
                     vertical (cm.) :
                        (recommended—17·5 cm.)
Time taken from 4th to 6th jump (sec.) :

Name of Investigator: . . . .

*Full details of the subject and his population group are to be entered in the **BASIC IDENTIFICATION SHEETS** as laid down in the Technical Introduction.

C4. FORCED EXPIRATORY VOLUME AND VITAL CAPACITY

I. INTRODUCTION

- (a) General
- (b) Observations to be made
- (c) Sampling

II. TECHNIQUES

- (a) Apparatus
- (b) Training of personnel
- (c) Technique of measurement
- (d) Recording of results

III. DATA COLLECTING SHEET

I. INTRODUCTION

(a) General:

Measurements of lung capacity are related on the one hand to the pattern of growth, bodily physique, habitual activity, and work capacity of the individual, and on the other to the influence of such environmental factors as high altitude and air pollution, including smoking. It therefore needs to be assessed by a well-standardised technique, while the data on the factors influencing it are obtained at the same time.

The principle of the method is simple. The subject first fills the lungs by inhaling to a maximal extent, then exhales into a spirometer which is either equipped with an automatic timing and volume measuring device, or arranged to record on a kymograph or chart recorder. The volumes expired during one second and after complete expiration are recorded.

(b) Observations to be made:

1. Respiratory observations.

(i) THE FORCED EXPIRATORY VOLUME (FEV) is the volume of gas which can be expired in a short time, during a forced expiration starting from full inspiration (i.e. total lung capacity). The time which is usually adopted is one second, when the index is designated $FEV_{1.0}$

(ii) THE FORCED VITAL CAPACITY (FVC) is the volume of gas which can be expelled during a forced breath from full inspiration to complete expiration. In normal subjects this differs little if at all from the vital capacity (VC) in which expiration is gentle and not forced, and the inspiratory vital capacity (IVC), in which the volume is measured during inspiration.

Forced Expiratory Volume ratio (FEV%) is the forced expiratory volume expressed as a percentage of the forced vital capacity, i.e. $(FEV_{1.0}/FVC) \times 100\%$

2. **Ancillary observations.**

(i)   General medical and nutritional examination, including respiratory symptoms and smoking habits (see **E1** and **F1**.)

(ii)   If possible, assessment of habitual physical activity. (see **C6**.)

(iii) Morphological observations. (Anthropometry, see **A1** and **C5**; Body composition, see **A5**)

(c) **Sampling:**

The minimum size of a sub-sample should be 20, but smaller groups, (e.g. 10) are suitable for some studies. For adults the sub-sample might comprise males or females in a 10-year age-group, and possibly be further classified in other ways. For children the age range should be much less, or height or weight used instead. The number of such groups will clearly depend upon the circumstances.

II.   TECHNIQUES

(a) **Apparatus:**

Equipment for making the measurement is available in most countries, but may have undesirable features; the following are minimal requirements for satisfactory results. They should be checked before the equipment is accepted for use.

The spirometer should be linear and record volume accurately to within 100 ml. over its whole range of movement which should be 9 1. The linearity of calibration may be checked over the whole range of excursion by the addition of known volumes of air from a calibrated tonometer (usually 500 ml.) by displacement with water. The corresponding deflections on the kymograph should not differ by more than 1 %. The factor for converting from the indicated reading to the volume displacement is obtained from these data.

The apparatus should have a low inertia and offer a low resistance to gas flow. For this purpose the diameter of the tubing should be not less than 3 cm. and of the mouthpiece not less than 2·5 cm. The combined effects of inertia and resistance may be assessed by measuring the back pressure in the tubing during the performance of the test. For a subject having an $FEV_{1\cdot 0}$ of at least 3·5 1. the back pressure should not exceed 5 cm. H_2O for longer than 30 milliseconds, and after that should not be more than 1·5 cm. H_2O.

1. **Apparatus incorporating a timing unit:** This should be self-contained, accurate to $\pm 1\%$, and capable of calibration under the conditions of use. During expiration the timing mechanism should be actuated after the exhalation of 100 ml. (range 75–150 ml.) of gas. An apparatus which meets these requirements is illustrated in Fig. C4/1, below, and is obtainable from

Garw Electronic Instruments Ltd.,

Pontyrhyl, Nr. BRIDGEND,

Glamorgan, WALES.

2. **Closed current apparatus incorporating a kymograph:** The minimum paper speed for measurement of FEV should be 4 cm./sec. and for vital capacity 5 cm./min.

The convention, which should be adopted when measuring the one-second timed period from the record on the kymograph (forced expiratory spirogram) is illustrated in Fig. C4/2, below.

A closed circuit apparatus should be tested for leaks; for this purpose the mouthpiece should be occluded and a 2 kg. weight placed on the bell. The kymograph should be left running for 20 min. during which time the change in volume should not exceed 15 ml.

When reading the scale on the apparatus or measuring the tracing on the kymograph the data should be recorded to the nearest 0·1 1.; if the reading is exactly half way between 0·1 1. divisions, the higher of these should be recorded.

(b) **Training of Personnel:**

The results of the test are influenced by the personality and exact procedure adopted by the operator. The latter can be standardised by learning from one who is experienced with the method. To this end two operators each make measurements on a group of subjects who are presented to them in random order; the observers should be in separate rooms which are some distance apart so that the sounds of their voices do not travel between them. If a systematic difference of more than 3% emerges from this preliminary study the new operator should receive further instruction and the trial be repeated.

(c)   Technique for Measurement:

Use of a nose clip

A nose clip is not normally required for these measurements, but its use is recommended as a few subjects continue to pass air through the nose when the mouth is open. The clip should close both nostrils completely, and be checked by the subject attempting to exhale with the mouth shut.

1.   Forced expiratory volume

The procedure should be explained in simple terms to the subject, who should then loosen any tight clothing. He should sit upright but comfortably in front of the apparatus.

The height of the tube between the apparatus and the mouthpiece should be adjusted to the height of the subject and the nose clip applied.

The subject is asked to take as full a breath as possible, then to insert the mouthpiece, close the lips around it and blow out as hard as possible. It is often helpful for the operator to give a demonstration using a detached mouthpiece.

During an initial practice attempt, the subject is observed for any faults (see below), then after explanation a second practice blow is made. Three further blows are then made, making at least five in all, with an interval of at least 15 seconds between them. This interval should be increased if the subject appears in any way distressed.

If, during any attempt, it can be seen that the performance is incorrect, the measurement should be rejected and repeated. The following faults in particular should be looked for:

The mouthpiece height may be incorrect, giving an uncomfortable posture.

The subject may not take a full inspiration. Often the reason is that he does not realise that there is no hurry to begin expiration.

There may be hesitation at the beginning of expiration. It should be emphasised that, once started, the breath must continue rapidly without any pause. A demonstration usually corrects this fault.

The mouthpiece may be incorrectly inserted and the lips not closed around it. A common fault is to purse the lips in front of the mouthpiece as if playing a trumpet. The usual reason is a loose upper denture.

2. Forced vital capacity (FVC) or vital capacity (VC)

(i) **Single breath procedures.** The procedure for forced vital capacity may follow on after that for the FEV, the subject being asked to continue the forced expirations until no more air can be exhaled. However, as this procedure may provoke coughing, most authorities recommend that the forced vital capacity or vital capacity be measured separately after the FEV. When this is done the subject is asked to make three further expirations starting from full inspiration and continuing until no more air can be exhaled. Expiration should be forced or gentle (not forced) depending on whether the forced vital capacity or vital capacity is required. The method adopted should be recorded.

(ii) **Closed circuit procedure.** The mouthpiece is placed in the subject's mouth and the kymograph operated at low speed. A baseline of quiet breathing is obtained and then the subject is instructed to inhale to a maximum extent. Additional encouragement is provided by the operator until the maximum inspiratory position is indicated on the kymograph by the trace flattening off to horizontal. The subject is then instructed to exhale, either forcibly or gently as required. During the manoeuvre the operator again provides encouragement until exhalation is complete as judged by a short horizontal trace on the kymograph. The subject then continues with normal breathing. The manoeuvres should be repeated at least three times.

Common errors : the faults encountered in measuring the FEV may arise. In addition, expiration may be incomplete either because of coughing or because insufficient time has been allowed for complete recovery from the previous test. Some subjects try to limit their inspiration or expiration to reduce coughing.

(d) **Recording Results:**

It is recommended that the values recorded for the forced expiratory volume and forced vital capacity or vital capacity are each the mean of three technically satisfactory results following two practice attempts at the FEV. Where the operator prefers to record the maximum value instead, this should be noted. The volumes should be reported at body temperature (see table C4/1 below) on a data sheet of the type illustrated. (See III. DATA COLLECTING SHEET, below.)

TABLE C4/1

Factors for conversion of volumes from ATPS to STPD and BTPS

Ambient temperature °C	Aqueous vapour pressure (mmHg)	Factor to convert to: STPD	BTPS
14	12·0	0·936	1·133
15	12·8	0·932	1·128
16	13·6	0·928	1·123
17	14·5	0·924	1·118
18	15·5	0·920	1·113
19	16·5	0·916	1·108
20	17·5	0·911	1·102
21	18·7	0·906	1·096
22	19·8	0·902	1·091
23	21·1	0·897	1·085
24	22·4	0·893	1·080
25	23·8	0·888	1·075
26	25·2	0·883	1·069
27	26·7	0·878	1·063
28	28·3	0·874	1·057
29	30·0	0·869	1·051
30	31·8	0·864	1·045
31	33·7	0·859	1·039
32	35·7	0·853	1·032
33	37·7	0·848	1·026
34	39·9	0·843	1·020
35	42·2	0·838	1·014
36	44·6	0·032	1·007
37	47·1	0·826	1·000
38	49·7	0·821	0·994
39	52·4	0·816	0·987
40	55·3	0·810	0·980

III.   DATA COLLECTING SHEET

Forced expiratory volume ($FEV_{1.0}$) and forced vital capacity (FVC).

Subject   Name:*   Sex: Occupation:

                  Subject no.:   Height: Ethnic and tribal

                  Date of birth: Weight: origin (or

                  Age: Bronchitis in   nationality):

                                    past 3 years: Yes/No

                  Date of   Place of

                    examination: examination:

                  Non-smoker/smoker: light/heavy cigarettes/pipe/cigar/other

Apparatus Serial no.:

                  Factor converting mm to l:

                  Calibration reading expected:

                                observed:

Readings   Time (24 hr. clock):

                  Barometric pressure (mmHg):

                  Apparatus temperature (°C):   (a)

                  Conversion factor to BTPS (table):   (b)

                  Overall correction factor (i.e. (a) x (b)):

Comment   Coughing during test: Yes/No

                  Co-operation satisfactory: Yes/No

                  Performance of test: Good/Fair/Poor

                  Hours since antispasmodic:

                  Hours since last smoked:

                  Other:

	$FEV_{1.0}$	FVC/or VC (state which)
Practice attempts:		
Sum of three satisfactory attempts:		
Mean:		
Corrected to BTPS:		
$FEV_{1.0}$% FVC:		

*Full details of the subject and of his population group are to be entered in the **BASIC IDENTIFICATION SHEETS,** as laid down in the Technical Introduction.

C5. MORPHOLOGICAL MEASUREMENTS IN WORK CAPACITY AND PULMONARY STUDIES

I. INTRODUCTION
(a) General
(b) Observations to be made

II. DATA COLLECTING SHEET

I. INTRODUCTION

(a) General:

Many studies of working capacity and pulmonary function have omitted to take full account of the physique and body composition of the subjects. Most investigators have been content to specify only height and weight. For comparative studies it is clearly important to take into account the body build and its components. As the most suitable measurements for this purpose have not been established, it is necessary to recommend here a list of measurements which may appear unnecessarily extensive. Nevertheless, the measurements suggested (under (b) below) should not take a practiced anthropometrist more than 10–15 minutes to complete.

It is highly desirable that, in addition to anthropometric measurements, more direct estimates of the body composition should be made. For this purpose, radiography of the limbs should be used, and wherever possible other techniques, for the assessment of fat, muscle, bone, body water, etc.

(b) Observations to be made:

1. Anthropometry (for Techniques, see A1)

The following is a suggested list of basic measurements, to which the investigator may wish to add additional measurements and skin-fold thicknesses as presented in **A1** (Other Measurements).

Weight

Stature

Sitting height

Total arm length

Upper arm circumference

Transverse chest

Antero-posterior chest

Chest circumference

Triceps skin-fold

Subscapular skin-fold

Wrist breadth

Bicondylar humerus

Biacromial diameter

Biiliac diameter

Suprailiac skin-fold

2. **Body composition** (for Techniques, see **A4**)

X-rays of the thigh (see **A4**) to give muscle thickness have been shown to correlate significantly with working capacity.

3. **Photography for somatotyping** (for Techniques, see **A3**)

4. **Body composition by underwater weighing** (for Techniques, see **A5**)

II. DATA COLLECTING SHEET

*For full details, see Individual
Identity Sheet (01).

IBP/HA Project ref. no.	1 ☐☐☐☐
Study number	5 ☐☐
Subject's name:* Serial number	7 ☐☐☐
Sex (M=1 ; F=2)	10 ☐
Place of examination: Age (years)*	11 ☐☐
Examination date (year + 3 decimals—see Table in Technical Introduction)	13 ☐☐☐☐☐
Procedure category	18 ☐☐

CODE FOR "NOT APPLICABLE"=X; CODE FOR "DATA NOT RECORDED"=Y

Weight (kg.)	20 ☐☐☐☐
Stature (mm.)	24 ☐☐☐☐
Sitting height (mm.)	28 ☐☐☐☐
Total arm length (mm.)	32 ☐☐☐
Upper arm circumference (mm.) (relaxed)	35 ☐☐☐
Wrist breadth (mm.)	38 ☐☐
Bicondylar humerus (mm.)	40 ☐☐
Biacromial diameter (mm.)	42 ☐☐☐
Biiliac diameter (mm.)	45 ☐☐☐
Transverse chest (mm.)	48 ☐☐☐
Antero-posterior chest (mm.)	51 ☐☐☐
Chest circumference (mm.)	54 ☐☐☐☐
Triceps skin-fold (mm.)	58 ☐☐☐
Subscapular skin-fold (mm.)	61 ☐☐☐
Suprailiac skin-fold (mm.)	64 ☐☐☐
Record of other investigations made:— Other anthropometric (yes=1 ; no=0)	67 ☐
Radiography for body composition (yes=1 ; no=0)	68 ☐
Photographs for somatotyping (yes=1 ; no=2)	69 ☐
Body composition by underwater weighing (yes=1 ; no=2)	70 ☐

Signature of Investigator: . . . .

C6. ASSESSMENT OF HABITUAL PHYSICAL ACTIVITY

I. INTRODUCTION

    (a) General

    (b) Observations to be made

II. TECHNIQUES

    (a) Questionnaire

    (b) Diary methods

    (c) Heart rate counters

    (d) Measurement of oxygen consumption

    (e) Assessment of food intake

    (f) Instruments

III. DATA COLLECTING SHEETS

    (a) Questionnaire

    (b) Diary

    (c) Heart rate counters

    (d) Measurement of oxygen consumption

I. INTRODUCTION

(a) General:

For a correct interpretation of the assessment of working capacity (see **C1** & **C2**), a knowledge of the subject's occupation and habitual activity is essential. In studies of calorie intake, also, the determination of the daily energy expenditure is important (see **E1** to **E3**.) A third application is in the investigation of the relation between physical activity and cardiovascular disease. Many methods for the assessment of habitual physical activity have been proposed.

The physiological problem is essentially simple, and valid methods for the measurement of oxygen consumption, and hence energy expenditure, have been in use since the introduction of Douglas bags in the early years of the century. There are two problems, however, which have been only partly solved. The first is to use methods which do not modify ordinary activity, and the second is to have techniques which can be applied to a relatively large number of subjects. The term used is ' habitual ' activity, so the duration of any assessment has to be decided. A minimum period of 24 hours may be taken, and it is important that the assessment is not confined to working hours. In some cases, such as agriculture, seasonal factors are so evident it is obvious that an assessment of one day in the year can scarcely be adequate. For many office workers, however, the activity pattern is so constant that one day may be quite sufficient. As a general guide, a survey should cover a period of 1 week, including the week-end, and wherever possible should be repeated at least once, e.g., summer and winter.

The amount of detail to be included will affect the method or methods which can be used, and will depend to some extent on the purpose of the study. In a nutrition survey, for example, the total energy expenditure per day or the average energy expenditure must be estimated to decide the level of food intake. From this point of view it does not matter how energy is expended. But such information may not be sufficient to decide important questions concerning the relationship between physical activity and the incidence of coronary heart disease or other chronic degenerative conditions. Two comparable individuals or groups of individuals may have similar overall energy expenditure, but the pattern of activity could be very different. On the one hand, there might be a steady level of energy expenditure with little variation from minute to minute, whereas the second group could have peaks of energy expenditure, lasting perhaps only a few minutes, with a lower steady level between peaks. Clearly, for some purposes it would be essential to have information about peak activities, their frequency, duration and intensity. Another example of different activities with comparable energy expenditure which may have important physiological or clinical effects is the posture adopted by the individual. In this context, the term ' posture ' should include not only body position but also static or rhythmic movements.

For some purposes, therefore, an overall measure of energy expenditure may be adequate, for others it may be essential to have a detailed account of activity on a minute-to-minute basis. The available methods and their limitations must be considered in the light of the questions asked by the investigator. Broadly speaking, these methods consist of observation, or measurement, or a combination of the two. At the present time, on the present information, the use of a heart-rate integrator combined with questionnaires appears to be the most suitable technique for the assessment of habitual physical activity.

(b) Observations to be made:

The following methods of observation are suggested, in order of simplicity, and will be described under II. TECHNIQUES, below.

    (1)   Questionnaire.

    (2)   Diary.   (This is definitely more difficult than the questionnaire, in that the successful use of the diary does depend upon having fairly sophisticated subjects.)

    (3)   Heart rate integrator.

    (4)   Time and motion study.

(5)   Direct measurement of energy expenditure and food intake. (The direct measurement of food intake is dealt with under Sections **E1, E2 & E3**. The direct measurement of energy expenditure would imply the use of the IMP, or the Max-Planck Respirometer.)

At the present time, it is considered that under most circumstances under field conditions, cinematography is not sufficiently validated to be of use as a method of observation by itself. It should probably only be employed in conjunction with one of the other methods.

Where no specialised technical support is available, it has been found that mechanical equipment is in general more reliable than electronic equipment over a prolonged period of field study in an isolated situation.

II.   TECHNIQUES

(a)   Questionnaires. *

Questionnaires may be self-administered or completed in reply to questions by an interviewer. They may cover details of activity for the previous days, weeks, months, or even years.

Some authors have tested the reliability of their questionnaires by comparing answers received at successive interviews, or by comparing the answers to a self-administered questionnaire with the answers obtained by an interviewer. Several workers criticise the use of questionnaires as they doubt the accuracy of recall, particularly when questions are asked about activity over a long period of time. It would appear that these criticisms come mainly from those who have assessed activity in other ways, including direct measurement, and who find a poor correlation between answers to questions and the results of measurements. There is some evidence that many subjects over-estimate the duration or the intensity of physical exertion.

The weight to be attached to these criticisms depends on the use to be made of questionnaires. The scoring system used to assess answers varies from grading individuals into categories of light, medium, and heavy work, or inactive, moderately active, and very active, to detailed scoring based on the use of tables of energy expenditure for various tasks. If all or the majority of subjects over-estimate their degree of physical activity, then the **grading** of

* Based upon a report by Karvonen, *et al* (1965), on the types of questionnaire in general use.

individuals would not be affected, although estimates made of the actual energy expenditure could be considerably in error.

This leaves the problem of the most appropriate questionnaire. It seems probable that questionnaires of any form are unlikely to be an appropriate method of study for communities living under primitive conditions, (and the diary technique would under these conditions of course also be unusable). For other groups, the most suitable design of questionnaire depends on the kind of group being studied.

In the " self-assessment " type of questionnaire (see example in III DATA COLLECTING SHEETS, below) the subjects are requested to answer questions relating to their level of activity in various pursuits, (e.g. walking, sport, gardening, etc.). Levels of activity are classified as ' very active ', ' fairly active ', ' average ', ' fairly inactive ', and ' very inactive '. If the subjects query the meaning of these categories, they are told to use their own judgement. They are also asked not to ponder the questions, but to answer according to their first impression. The questions are not asked consecutively in the course of the questionnaire, but are interspersed with other questions, to minimize the chances of responses to one question influencing responses to a subsequent one. This procedure also reduces any chance of a subject remembering his answers to any particular question at a later point in time.

A correlation of $+ \cdot 81$ has been obtained between a first and second administration of these " self-assessment " questions, and it seems possible that this technique of questioning may be comparable in validity to that of the recall interview.

(b)   Diary methods.

A variant of the questionnaire technique is for the subject to keep a diary of his daily activities for a particular period of time as determined by the form of the investigation. A diary should be devised in which activities are recorded using a simple code (see DATA COLLECTING SHEET). The code itself has to be designed for the particular group of subjects concerned, to cover the particular activities in which they are engaged. Activities such as lying, sitting, standing, and walking could be designated as L, S, St, and W, and would be included in all codes. For a housewife, activities such as shopping, cooking, and housework would have code letters; for a soldier, code letters would be needed for drill, marching, shooting, etc. In general, it has been found that some **fifteen code letters** can adequately cover the habitual activities of any particular individual.

Where such diaries have been used, the limit of time has usually been one week, and the variation from day to day appears to be sufficient to make one week's observation the minimum required. In any case, it is necessary to include week-end activities as well as working days.

This method requires the co-operation of the subject to a greater extent than the questionnaire technique, but those who have used the method have found that for many groups such co-operation can be obtained. In using the diary, the investigator collects the records daily, checks the entries with the subjects, and advises about difficulties experienced. The time spent in each activity is tabulated, and the energy expenditure calculated by applying standard figures for expenditure in the different activities. In many cases, the use of the diary card is supplemented by measurements of energy expenditure of the individual in particular activities, by the methods outlined in paragraph (d) below. If this is not possible, then " conventional " values for the different kinds of activity may be obtained from the tables provided by Passmore, R., and J. V. G. A. Durnin, **Physiol. Rev. 35**, 801–840, 1955.

A modification of this method is the direct observation of the subjects and recording of their activities by the investigator. This is sometimes known as the " time and motion " method. Briefly, the observer is equipped with a walkie-talkie radio set, and is in communication with a central recording station, where his observations are coded. In practice, this method is suitable where a group of subjects is carrying out a similar task, and can be observed as a group. It is, in general, too expensive in manpower when only single subjects can be followed. Activities are described in the simplest terms, similar to those used in the diary codes described above. In some surveys, a combination of diary recording and time and motion study has been used, employing the observers for group activities, and supplementing this with diaries when the subjects were engaged in separate activities.

The time and motion technique can be used to validate the records obtained on diary cards; (in studies of military personnel it was found that diary cards were accurately completed by men in the higher intelligence groups, but accuracy fell off considerably in the lower intelligence groups.)

The limitations of time and motion studies have already been indicated: use for groups only, and expensive in manpower. It is, however, an objective and reliable method in terms of accurate information about the time spent in different activities.

(c)   Heart rate counters

In the individual subject at any one time there is a highly significant relationship between heart rate and energy expenditure. This relationship varies considerably between individuals, and can vary also in the individual depending on his state of physical fitness. It is also obvious that many factors other than physical work can affect heart rate, including changes in body temperature and emotional stimuli. There can, however, be little doubt that continuous measurement of heart rate is a most important tool for the assessment of habitual activity, and a number of devices have been evolved for making this measurement.

The use of sophisticated electronic equipment in the field will of course only be practicable in those cases where either the work is carried out within easy reach of an electronic workshop, or a skilled electronics technician, familiar with the apparatus to be used, is a member of the field team.

At present, the following instruments appear to be most suitable for field use; (see also (f) below).

(1)   The first consists of a small, rugged, self-contained heart-beat counter, which is activated by the R-wave of the ECG. The instrument is coupled to a wrist-watch in which the balance-wheel has been removed and replaced by a specially designed relay armature. The ' time ' displayed by the watch is an indication of the cumulative number of heart-beats during the elapsed time.

(2)   A different method of recording the heart rate and storing the data has been developed by Wolff, who uses an electro-chemical system. This instrument (the SAMI) derives its input signal from two adhesive chest electrodes, which will maintain satisfactory contact for 48 hours, with minimal skin irritation, even under very unfavourable conditions. The signal is amplified and converted into a constant charge pulse which is applied to the electro-chemical integrator (' E-cell '). At the end of a period of measurement the E-cell is removed, and is then reset in a replay machine which provides a digital read-out of the quantity of charge stored in the E-cell. From this, the number of heart-beats can be calculated. A more complex instrument is available, containing three E-cells and additional circuits to sort the incoming signals into three rate levels. (See detailed note under (f) below.)

(3)   A more detailed, but much more expensive method of heart rate

recording is by means of a small portable electro-cardiograph amplifier and tape recorder, using parasternal leads. An accelerated play-back device with digital counter and printing mechanism provides a permanent record of the pulse rate for alternate minutes of a 24-hour day.

(d)   Measurement of oxygen consumption

There are several techniques available: the Douglas bag for the collection of expired air and its subsequent analysis, the Max-Planck respirometer, which measures the volume of expired air and collects an aliquot sample for analysis, and the Integrating Motor Pneumotachograph (IMP) which incorporates a flow-meter and sampling device.

The Douglas bag method has the advantages of simplicity and reliability. All the expired air is collected during the sampling period; the volume can be accurately measured and analysis of the air is, of course, identical whatever procedure is used. The limitations are the interference with normal activity due to the general need to carry the large Douglas bag on the back, and the short sampling period   Usually a nose-clip and mouthpiece are used and there are objections by subjects to their continued use.

The Max-Planck (Kofranyi-Michaelis) respirometer is also carried on the back; it is light and of limited size (28 × 20 × 12 cm), so interference with habitual activity is not as marked as with the Douglas bag. It has been successfully used in a wide variety of tasks. The limitations are that the work of the respirometer is done by the force of expiration, and at high ventilation rates the resistance or back pressure increases substantially.

The IMP is an electronic instrument with the flow meter attached directly to a face-mask. The recording and sampling equipment can either be carried in a pack on the back or be stored in two separate pockets. It has the advantage that an integrated sample of expired air can be collected over periods of 2–3 hours and interference with activity is minimal. It has been used successfully in a wide variety of tasks and situations, including surveys in polar regions. The disadvantage of the instrument is the need for expert maintenance and servicing.

These three instruments all have their place, and their suitability will depend largely upon the type of activity it is intended to study.

In many surveys, as already indicated, the diary method as well as time and motion studies may be combined with measurements of oxygen consumption.

When standard figures are used for the estimation of energy expenditure, considerable errors can be introduced because of the marked individual variation that is found in the oxygen consumption for particular tasks. A procedure which has proved satisfactory and is not too time-consuming is to measure the oxygen consumption of tasks such as sitting, standing and walking, over short periods of time (10–20 min.). Since these three activities, combined with lying, will cover the greater part of the day, calculation of energy expenditure from the time and motion study and these individual metabolic measurements will be of considerable accuracy. Unusual tasks, if carried out for a substantial period of time, may also require metabolic study. But it is worth remembering that if a task occupies only a few minutes in the day a large error in estimating the energy expenditure will have an insignificant effect on the estimate for 24 hrs.

An alternative to this technique (sometimes called the ' menu ' system) is to measure oxygen consumption continuously throughout the day. With present methods this is an impossible ideal since either a face-mask or a mouthpiece has to be worn and must be removed at least during meal times. However, using the IMP it is possible to make measurements for up to 20 hr per day, the missing time consisting of meal times and rest periods. The IMP is worn for approximately 2-hr periods and removed for 10–15 min. throughout the day, apart from meals. Since activities during the period of measurement are varied, an integrated value for energy expenditure is obtained rather than the value for a particular activity. Measurement continued during the hours of sleep confirms that the convention of using the BMR value for the hours of sleep is accurate, and this obviates the need to make direct measurement during sleep. In such surveys time and motion studies (see (b) above) should be made throughout the day, so comparisons can be made of direct recording of energy expenditure with the results of calculation from the time and motion figures. Although the two are significantly related there is a considerable scatter. If it is accepted that the direct measurements with the IMP are accurate, the individual calculations from the time and motion study might show marked differences from the direct measurements, although calculations based on a group of six or more subjects would be closely similar to values obtained from direct measurement.

Over a wide range of ventilation volume the extraction of oxygen is relatively constant, and the error involved in calculating oxygen consumption from ventilation volume alone appears to be of the order of $\pm 10\%$. Such a error may be quite acceptable in many studies, and the technique is considerably simpler than measuring oxygen consumption. A flow meter attached to a face mask or mouthpiece is all that is required, including of course a recording system. The IMP can be used in this way, but the flow meter designed by Wright is simpler and more convenient. (See (f) below.)

(e) Assessment of food intake

Energy intake balances energy expenditure, except in those cases where body weight is changing rapidly. In the absence of marked weight changes it may be assumed that intake will be identical with expenditure, so measurement of food consumption could be substituted for other means of assessing habitual activity. There are some necessary reservations. In many cases calorie balance is only achieved over a period of a week; where subjects lead a standardised existence, however, it may be that a shorter period than a week can be used for measurement of food intake. Weight changes or the absence of weight change are not inevitably related to calorie balance as there can be marked alterations in the proportions of total body water. It may be concluded that food intake measurements continued over a week are likely to be similar to the week's energy expenditure but, of course, provide no information about the pattern of habitual activity.

The assessment of food intake is described in detail under **E1, E2,** and **E3.**

(f) Instruments

(1) Watch recorder:

HT–62A Heartbeat Totalizer, manufactured by:
The Waters Company,
P. O. Box, 529,
Rochester,
Minnesota, U.S.A.

Specifications:

(wrist-watch indicator)	Thickness–$\frac{3}{8}''$
	Diameter–$1\frac{1}{4}''$
	Total weight–$2\frac{2}{5}$ oz.
(Power supply – amplifier)	Dimensions: $2\frac{1}{2}'' \times \frac{3}{4}'' \times \frac{3}{8}''$
	Weight–$\frac{3}{4}$oz.

Also required: 2 miniature 1·35 v. mercury batteries (Mallory 4RM–625R)

The above apparatus available from the Manufacturers, or:

Picker Nederland,
Graaf Lodewijkstr. 63,
Nieuwerbrug a/d Rijn,
Holland.

The recorder runs for 72 hours without changing the batteries: the watch however needs to be wound every 24 hours.

(2)   Wolff ' SAMI ' recorder:

Available from:

TEM Sales, Ltd.,
Gatwick Road,
Crawley,
Sussex, England.

The simplicity of operation and data recording with the SAMI (Socially Acceptable Monitoring Instrument) make it possible to carry out measurements simultaneously on large groups of subjects with a small staff of investigators. Typically, two investigators can keep 20 instruments in the field 7 days a week, changing subjects every 2 days, and dividing the day into 3 recording periods. The subjects are issued with 6 E-Cells and suitable pre-printed envelopes and carry out the change of E-Cells at times coincident with the start of their working, leisure, and sleeping periods.

A temperature SAMI (SAMI/T) is also available. This can be set to give any one of three possible measurements:

1. A mean temperature.

2. The integral or dose in terms of degree-minutes of heat stress above a pre-set level.

3. As above, but for cold stress.

A variety of thermistor sensors can be employed for environmental skin or body temperatures.

SAMI's for noise and posture are in preparation.

Full operating details for the SAMI are provided with the instrument.

(3) A small portable **electrocardiograph amplifier and tape recorder** is available from:

Avionics Research Products Corporation,
6901 West Imperial Highway,
LOS ANGELES, California, U.S.A.

(4)   The **Wright spirometer** is available from:
British Oxygen Company,
Medical Department,
Spencer House,
St. James' Place,
LONDON S.W.1.,
England.

Overall dimensions; $2\frac{1}{2}'' \times 2\frac{1}{4}''$
Weight of instrument: 5 oz. approx.
Minimum steady flow response: 2 litres/min.
Maximum permissible flow: 300 litres/min.

(5)   The **IMP** is available from:
Hook and Tucker Ltd.,
301, Brixton Road,
LONDON S.W.9.
England.

(6)   The **Max-Planck (Kofranyi-Michaelis) respirometer** is available from:
Zentralwerkstatt Göttingen Gmbh,
34, Göttingen, Postfach 624,
Bunsenstr. 10,
W. Germany.

The price of the Model 59, with valve, is approximately £85. It is advisable
to make provision for 2–3 spare valves, (approx. £5 each.).

III. DATA COLLECTING SHEETS

(a) Questionnaire:

The following is an example of a "self-assessment" type of questionnaire (Yasin)·

Name:*   Ethnic group (or nationality):

Subject no.:   Occupation:

Age: Place:

Sex: Date:

                                         Name of investigator:

1. General Physical Activity:

Thinking of the things you do and have done in your spare time which involve physical activity, whether *light, moderate, or strenuous,* which category in the scale below best describes how physically active you have been *for most years of your adult life?* (CIRCLE ONE ONLY)
very active/fairly active/average/fairly inactive/very inactive

2. Walking:

Which category in the scale below best describes how active an outdoor walker you have been *for most years of your adult life?* (CIRCLE ONE ONLY)
very active/fairly active/average/fairly inactive/very inactive

3. Gardening:

Which category in the scale below best describes how active a gardener you have been *for most years of your adult life?* (CIRCLE ONE ONLY)
very active/fairly active/average/fairly inactive/very inactive

4. Strenuous sports:

Which category in the scale below best describes how active you have been in strenuous sports and games *for most years of your adult life?* (CIRCLE ONE ONLY)
very active/fairly active/average/fairly inactive/very inactive

5. Spare-time physical work:

Think of the things you do and have done in your spare time which involve *physical work,* e.g. household chores, repair and maintenance work to house, furniture, car, etc., *other than sedentary work, walking, gardening, and sports.* Which category in the scale below best describes how active you have been with spare-time physical work *for most years of your adult life?* (CIRCLE ONE ONLY)
very active/fairly active/average/fairly inactive/very inactive

III.   DATA COLLECTING SHEETS (continued)

(b) Diary method:

1.   Activity proforma for each individual
(To be printed as a conveniently small card or booklet to be kept in the pocket)

Name:	Occupation:
Serial number:	Ethnic group or nationality:
Age:	Place of examination:
Sex: M/F	Date of this record:
Observer's name:	Day of week:

Fill in details of your activities for all your daytime hours using the abbreviations given. This daily diary form covers 24 hours, and has a *square for every minute*.

Try to estimate the duration of each activity to the nearest minute.

Carry this form with you with a pencil or pen all day. If in doubt about anything, please ask the observer.

ABBREVIATIONS

Sample portion of proforma:

A	Ablutions	I	Ironing
BM	Bed-making	K	Kneeling
C	Cooking	L	Lying
DS	Dressing	R	Running
FC	Fieldcraft	S	Sitting
FS	Floor-sweeping	SL	Sleeping
		ST	Standing
		W	Walking

TIME 0 1 2 3 4 5 6 7 8 9

06:00
06:10
06:20
06:30
06:40
06:50
07:00

For other activities, use the code provided by the observer.

2. Estimation of daily physical activities

(From: F. J. Bonjer, Netherlands Institute for Preventive Medicine, Leiden, Holland)

The following proforma is a suggested way of recording all the different daily activities classified under 7 major headings, and given in terms of minutes spent in the different activities. The total is of course 1440 minutes.

Name:

Serial number:

Age:

Sex: M/F

Observer's name:

Occupation:

Ethnic group or nationality:

Place of examination:

Date of this record:

Day of week:

TIME-BUDGET OF DAILY ACTIVITIES

1. Night's rest: (mins.)

2. Bathing, dressing, eating: (mins.)

3. Transportation to and from work:

walking— (mins.)

driving private car— (mins.)

travelling by bus or rail— (mins.)

cycling— (mins.)

4. Work posture:

sitting— (mins.)

standing— (mins.)

walking— (mins.)

5. Physical effort during work:

light (2–3 kcal/min)— (mins.)

moderate (3–4 kcal/min)— (mins.)

heavy (4–5 kcal/min)— (mins.)

6. Leisure time posture:

sitting— (mins.)

standing— (mins.)

walking— (mins.)

7. Physical effort during leisure time:

light (2–3 kcal/min)— (mins.)

moderate (3–4 kcal/min)— (mins.)

heavy (4–5 kcal/min)— (mins.)

Note should be taken of time, number and total duration of all peak loads in day.

III. DATA COLLECTING SHEETS (continued)

(c) and (d) Energy expenditure by pulse-counting and by measurement of oxygen consumption:

Name:*

Serial number:

Age:

Sex:

Occupation:

Ethnic group or nationality:

Date(s) of examination:

Place of examination:

Name of investigator:

ACTIVITY (see IIa)	Average pulse rate/min. (see IIc)	Duration of activity per day (mins.) (see IIb and IIIb)	Equivalent gross energy expenditure (kcal/min) (see IId)	TOTAL WORK PER DAY (kcal)		Notes
				From pulse rate (see IIc)	From activity (see IIa/b)	

*Full details of the subject and his population group are to be entered in the **BASIC IDENTIFICATION SHEETS,** as laid down in the Technical Introduction.

C7. TESTS WITH DYNAMOMETERS

I. INTRODUCTION
   (a) General
   (b) Observations to be made
   (c) Sampling

II. TECHNIQUES
   (a) Cable tensiometer tests
   (b) Strain-gauge dynamometer tests
   (c) Equipment

III. DATA COLLECTING SHEET

I. INTRODUCTION

(a) General:

For the measurement of muscle strength, many modifications of the spring-balance principle have been suggested, the spring-balance being substituted by dynamometers of mechanical or electrical design. These tests may be carried out either using the relatively simple techniques of cable tensiometry, or with strain-gauge dynamometers. The results are expressed in kg. push or pull, or (if strain-gauge equipment is used), in kg. × cm. —i.e. torque— when the muscle strength of a single joint with a well-defined axis of rotation is to be measured. Dynamometers which measure torque have the advantage that, with proper placement of the joint (i.e. co-axial with the dynamometer), trick movements will have no influence on the result.

The ideal muscle test would be one that in one trial measured the maximum tensions throughout the whole range of movement of the joint(s) and could be adapted to any muscle or muscle group. In practice, this is difficult for several reasons, partly technical, and partly because a maximum exertion of a muscle throughout its whole range of shortening would induce fatigue so that the last part of the contraction would not be maximal. An attempt has therefore been made to select the tests so that movements of everyday life are represented as widely as possible. This means that the tests will be to a high degree functional, involving movements in more than one joint.

A common feature of the strain-gauge dynamometer methods is that the strength of the muscles is usually measured during isometric or nearly isometric contractions. This necessitates strict definitions of the positions of the limbs and the trunk during the tests, as changes in both leverage and muscle length will influence the results. In the strain-gauge techniques, all forces or torques are measured by means of the deformation of a steel rod, the form and dimensions of which can be varied so that it best fits the case. The deformations are recorded by means of strain-gauges glued to the steel rod, a Wheatstone bridge, and a recording potentiometer, after amplification.

Tests of strength using strain-gauge equipment, however, can only be carried out under laboratory conditions. Similar consideration applies to the use of many of the techniques employing cable tensiometry, since a completely stable support is necessary. One example of such a support is the Hettinger Strength Chair, which, although it is moveable, is bulky and of heavy construction, and would require three or four men to carry it. It would therefore obviously be unsuitable in many field situations.

It is however possible to improvise a satisfactory technique for immobilising the subject during a number of the cable tensiometer strength-test procedures. This involves the use of a sturdily-constructed table (see (c) Equipment, below), with a hole cut in the middle, through which the cable passes, to be attached to a hook at the bottom of the table. A limited range of tests using the techniques of cable tensiometry are thereby made feasible for field use.

If such a table is not available, the tests which can be performed in the field are limited to hand-grip (which can be tested by the Smedley adjustable dynamometer, the simple Collins dynamometer (Fig. C7/1 facing this page), the Ikai hand-grip dynamometer, or the Stanley Cox grip dynamometer), and backward extension of the trunk and knee extension (leg lift), which are measured with a platform dynamometer.

(b) Observations to be made:

Hand-grip

Both hands should be tested. This test can be carried out by cable tensiometry or with the use of a strain-gauge dynamometer (Asmussen's Dynamometer II), or a simple hand-grip dynamometer.

Backward extension of the trunk

This test can be carried out by cable tensiometry or with the use of a strain-gauge dynamometer (Asmussen's Dynamometer IV) or by a simple platform dynamometer.

Leg extension

This test can be carried out on each leg separately by cable tensiometry or with the use of a strain-gauge dynamometer (Asmussen's Dynamometer V).

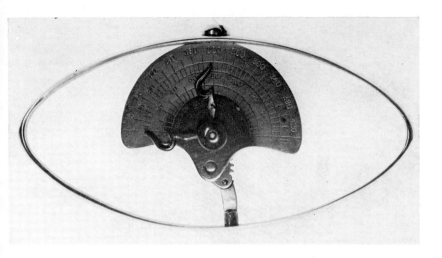

Fig. C7/1   Collins hand-grip dynamometer.

The testing of both legs together is suggested as an additional test using Asmussen's Dynamometer V.

Knee extension (leg lift)
This test can be carried out by cable tensiometry (on the table—see Techniques below), or by using a simple platform dynamometer.

Forward flexion of trunk
This test can be carried out using cable tensiometry; it is suggested as an additional test using Asmussen's Dynamometer I.

Horizontal push
This test can be carried out by cable tensiometry; it is suggested as an additional test using Asmussen's Dynamometer IV.

A number of further tests can be carried out using both techniques. For those using cable tensiometry, reference should be made to Clarke, H. Harrison, and D. H. Clarke, **Developmental and Adapted Physical Education.** Englewood Cliffs, New Jersey: Prentice-Hall Inc., 1963, pp. 73–97, and Clarke, H. Harrison, **Application of Measurement to Health and Physical Education:** Prentice-Hall, Inc., 1967, Ch. 7. For other tests using strain-gauge dynamometers, reference should be made to Asmussen, E., K. Heeboll-Nielsen, and Sv. Molbech; ' **Methods for Evaluation of Muscle Strength** ', Communication No. 5 of the Testing and Observation Institute of the Danish National Association for Infantile Paralysis (1959).

Ancillary observations
The recommended morphological observations are described in **C5.**

(c) Sampling:
Strength tests are of interest in population studies in relation to the growth and development of children, bodily physique, working capacity, and nutritional status.

The sample size will therefore be determined by the investigations conducted for any of these purposes. It is clear that with well-standardised instruments, the large individual scattering on a test is not due to the measuring technique to any appreciable extent, but to physical and physiological differences in the subject. For children, for example, Asmussen has shown that age, body type, and state of sexual development are important factors in determining the larger part of the observed inter-individual differences. Tests with strain-gauge equipment have shown standard deviations of ± 15–20% of the mean. Sample size should therefore be adjusted accordingly. Asmussen has suggested various ways of calculating standards. For children, he recommends a grouping according to stature, using a 10 cm. increase in height per group. The average values in each height group are determined and plotted on a double-logarithmic system. When plotted in this way, the curves become straight lines, and are therefore easier to use. Samples may also be grouped according to sex and age, and possibly body type.

In any case, a ' realistic ' sample size to aim for in a field study would be at least 100 individuals of each sex in each 10-year age-group if possible. An age-limit of 45 for the cable tensiometer tests is recommended.

II. TECHNIQUES

In the tests described below, standardisation of the body position in which movements are made is of the utmost importance. Subjects must in all cases be exhorted to do their best. It has been shown that results obtained using the ' shout ' technique of exhortation (in which the tester encourages the subject with vigorous calls of ' Go, Go, Go ', or other appropriate words) may exceed the results when this exhortation has not been used by as much as 20%.

It has been shown that the difference between muscle groups on the right and left sides of the body is about 5–10% of the strength of the stronger side, with a standard deviation of about 4–11%. This difference is most pronounced in the lower extremities.

(a) Cable tensiometer tests:

(1) Grip strength (hand-grip):

This test can be carried out using the Smedley dynamometer, which is adjustable to the size of the subject's hand, or the Collins dynamometer, a less expensive instrument which is not adjustable, or the Ikai hand-grip dynamometer. A further alternative instrument is the Stanley Cox grip dynamometer, manufactured by Rank Medical Equipment. This is non-adjustable.

Using the Smedley instrument, the dynamometer is adjusted so that the second joint of the fore-finger flexes on the gripping-bar of the dynamometer at a right angle. The instrument should then be adjusted to a comfortable grip. The scale reading before gripping should be half the distance from the tip of the thumb to the tip of the fingers; the handle must be locked after rotation. The subject is allowed to try the apparatus, and then the best of three readings is taken to the nearest 100 g. with the subject gripping as he flexes the forearm. The test is performed on each hand in turn. A note is made of which hand is dominant.

(2) Back strength (backward extension of trunk):

The subject stands on the base of the back strength dynamometer with legs extended and back bent 30° forward. The standardisation of this position is of the utmost importance. The subject pulls the dynamometer handle, and the best of three trials is recorded. **Leg lift (knee extension)** can also be tested with this dynamometer. Full instructional details for the Stanley Cox Back and Leg Dynamometer are given in catalogue B.L.D. issued by Rank Medical Equipment, Welwyn Garden City, Hertfordshire, England.

(3) Horizontal push and pull:

Both these tests are performed with the subject lying in the supine position on the table (see c. below), with the hips and knees flexed comfortably, and the free hand resting on the chest. For **flexion,** the upper arm is held close to the side, and the forearm is held at 90° mid-prone (palm facing inwards). The harness of the cable tensiometer is placed mid-way between the shoulder and the elbow joints, and the attachment of the cable is vertically below. An assistant should prevent lifting of the shoulders and hips. For **extension,** the upper arm is elevated to 90°, with the forearm directed across the body, and the cable tensiometer is hooked above the subject's head. The assistant prevents elevation and adduction of the shoulder.

(4) Leg extension:

The subject sits in a backward-leaning position, with his arms extended to the rear, and his hands grasping the sides of the table. The knee to be tested is extended to 115°. The collar is fitted around the leg, mid-way between the knee and ankle joints, and the other end of the cable is attached to a hook on the underside of the table. An assistant exerts pressure to prevent lifting of the buttocks and flexing of the arms.

(5) Knee extension:

The subject sits in a backward-leaning position, arms extended to the rear, hands grasping the sides of the table, and the knee on the side to be tested in

115° extension. A strap is attached to the leg midway between the knee and ankle joints, and the pulling assembly is attached to the hook at the lower end of the table. An assistant prevents lifting of the buttocks and flexion of the arms. Knee extension can also be tested using the back-strength dynamometer.

The above arm and leg strength tests should be carried out on each limb in turn, and all the results, in kg. to the nearest 100 g., (the best of 3 trials in each case) should be recorded in the Data Sheet.

(6)   Trunk flexion:

The subject lies in the supine position with the upper part of the back over a slit in the table. The legs are straight together, and the arms folded on the chest. The trunk strap is fitted around the chest close under the armpits, with the opposite end of the cable attached to the cross-bar of the table immediately below. An assistant prevents raising of the legs by pressure on the hips.

Trunk extension may also be tested in this way, with the subject in the prone position, with his arms clasped behind his back.

The result (the best of 3 trials) is to be recorded in kg. to the nearest 100 g. in the Data Sheet.

(b)   Strain-gauge dynamometer tests:

These tests are fully described in recent Communications of the Testing and Observation Institute of the Danish National Association for Infantile Paralysis, Copenhagen, Denmark. Full details of the dynamometers and ancillary electrical measuring equipment required are also contained in these publications, and also in Asmussen, E., **Sartryk ur Försvarsmedicin, 3:** 152–155, 1967.

(c)   Equipment (for cable tensiometry techniques).

(1)   Table

A padded table, approximately 6′ 6″ long, 2′ 9″ wide, and 2′ 6″ high is required for placing the subject in the correct position for most of the tests. In order to permit attachment of the pulling assembly directly below the subject in trunk (and hip) tests, a slit 20″ × 7″ should be cut lengthwise in the centre of the testing table, beginning 10″ from one end. Appropriate hooks for attaching the pulling assembly are placed in a frame under the table.

Hand-grip dynamometer (Stanley Cox)

(In the U.K.) Manufactured by:
Rank Medical Equipment Ltd.,
Bessemer Road,
Welwyn Garden City,
Hertfordshire.

Price: £6. 6s. 0d.

Ikai dynamometer (hand-grip)

Information available from:

Dr. Toshiro Ishiko,
School of Health Sciences,
The University of Tokyo,
3–1, 7-chome, Hongo, Bunkyo-ku,
Tokyo, Japan.

Price: Approx. $10.00

Smedley's dynamometer

Information available from:
C. H. Stoelting Co.,
424, N. Homan Ave.,
Chicago, Illinois 60624.
U.S.A.

Price: Approx. $100.00

Back-strength dynamometer

Available from:

(in U.K.) Rank Medical Equipment Ltd., (Manufacturers)
Bessemer Road.
Welwyn Garden City,
Hertfordshire.

Price: £64. 0s. 0d.

(in U.S.) Narrangsett Gymnasium Equipment Co.,
Centralia,
Missouri.

Cable tension equipment

The cable tensiometer and all other related equipment, including a tensio-meter calibrator stand (which should be used regularly to calibrate all cable tension equipment) are available from:

> Pacific Scientific Co., Inc.,
> 6280 Chalet Drive,
> City of Commerce
> California 90022,
> U.S.A.
> Prices on application.

(Calibration factors for cables of a defined thickness (e.g. 1/16″) are shown on the lid of the box. On no account should boxes be interchanged, or the wrong cables used. Results for all tests should be recorded after conversion to kg.)

III.   DATA COLLECTING SHEET

Name:*

Serial number:

Age:

Sex:

Place of examination:

Date of examination:

Occupation:

Observer:

Weight (kg.):

Height (mm.):

Ethnic and tribal origin

(or nationality):

Record to nearest 100 g. the best of 3 trials

Grip strength (left hand):

Grip strength (right hand):

Dominant hand:

Instrument used for grip strength:

Horizontal arm push (left):

Horizontal arm push (right):

Horizontal arm pull (left):

Horizontal arm pull (right):

Trunk flexion:

Back strength:

Knee extension (left):

Knee extension (right):

Trunk extension:

Leg extension (left):

Leg extension (right):

*Full details of the subject and his population group are to be entered in the **BASIC IDENTIFICATION SHEETS,** as laid down in the Technical Introduction.

C8. SIMPLE PERFORMANCE TESTS

I. INTRODUCTION
   (a) General
   (b) Observations to be made
   (c) Sampling

II. TECHNIQUES

III. DATA COLLECTING SHEET

I. INTRODUCTION

(a) General:

A very great variety of simple tests are in use amongst physical educationalists, sports instructors, and others interested in the rapid assessment of 'physical fitness '. The value of these tests is not to be underestimated, for example, by their use quite a striking difference in fitness between British, American, and South African school-children has been demonstrated. Variations related to age, sex, training, and physique, have also been shown.

A well-known battery of tests of motor fitness is that proposed by the American Association for Health, Physical Education, and Recreation (AAHPER) (1958). In addition, the Harvard step-test has also been widely used. It seems useful therefore to include here details of these tests.

(b) Observations to be made:

(1)   Harvard step-test.
(2)   The 7-battery AAHPER test:
      (a)   Pull-ups
      (b)   Sit-ups
      (c)   Shuttle-run
      (d)   Standing broad-jump
      (e)   50-yd. dash
      (f)   Soft-ball throw for distance
      (g)   600-yd. run-walk

(3) Ancillary observations

As in all studies of work capacity (see **C1** & **C2**) and strength tests (see **C7**) these performance tests should be accompanied by adequate studies of the morphological characteristics of the subjects (see **C5**). The subjects would also be given a basic medical (see **F1**), and wherever possible nutritional (see **E1**) examinations.

(c) Sampling:

For the purposes of population comparisons, it is suggested that the recommendations on sampling laid down for children and adults in **A1** should be followed as a general guide.

Samples should include not less than 100 of each sex, in every 10-year age group of adults or 1-year age group of children. Where practicable samples of this size should be included for different racial, occupational, or income groups.

II. TECHNIQUES

(1) Harvard step-test

This test is performed by the subject stepping on and off a bench 20″ (=50·8 cm.) high 30 times a minute for 5 minutes, or until he is unable to maintain the pace. Standardisation of the test conditions is important. The Harvard step test should not be performed within 3 hours after a heavy meal. The subjects should wear light gymnastic costume (no long trousers or skirt). Stepping should be in time to a metronome beating at half-second intervals, stepping up with one leg on the first beat, up with the other leg on the second beat, down with the first leg on the third beat, and down with the other leg on the final beat of the cycle. It is permissible to change step from time to time. The subject must stand erect at each step on to the bench; if he crouches or fails to keep up with the metronome the observer must immediately encourage him to do better. If the faulty posture or timing is maintained for 15 seconds the exercise is stopped and the duration of exercise recorded to the time of stoppage.

A 20″ (=50·8 cm.) bench is suitable for adult men, 17″ (=43·2 cm.) for adult women, 18″ (=45·7 cm.) for boys 15–18 years old, and 16″ (=40·6 cm.) for girls 15–18 years old.

The Rapid Fitness Index (RFI) is derived from the duration of exercise (up to 5 min.) and a single post-exercise pulse-count, viz:

$$RFI = \frac{\text{duration of exercise (seconds)} \times 100}{5.5 \times (\text{pulse-count } 1\text{--}1\frac{1}{2} \text{ mins. after exercise})}$$

(2)   AAHPER tests

The American Association for Health, Physical Education, and Recreation, gives the following detailed instructions for the performance and scoring of each of the 7 tests. For ease of comparison with previous results, the following sequence should be maintained: pull-up, sit-up, shuttle-run, standing broad-jump, 50-yard dash, soft-ball throw for distance, 600-yard run-walk. In this sequence, the first three or four tests are conveniently performed indoors.

Fig. C8/1   Pull-ups.

(a) Pull-ups

The pull-up for male subjects is performed hanging from a bar high enough for the feet to be clear of the floor when the arms are fully extended. The overhand grasp is used. (See Fig. C8/1). The subject raises his body by his arms until his chin is above the bar and then lowers himself to the starting position. No swinging of the body or kicking of the legs is permitted. The exercise is repeated as often as possible without resting, and the score is the number of complete pull-ups achieved.

(**Modified Pull-up.** In the modified pull-up for female subjects a horizontal bar, set at about chest level, is grasped with both hands, using an overhand grasp. The subject extends her legs under the bar and extends her arms fully. (See Fig. C8/2). The arms should form an angle of 90° with the straight trunk and legs, which should form an angle of 45° with the floor. The heels should be braced (for instance against the scorer's feet) to prevent slipping. From

Modified pull-up

Fig. C8/2   Modified pull-ups (for girls).

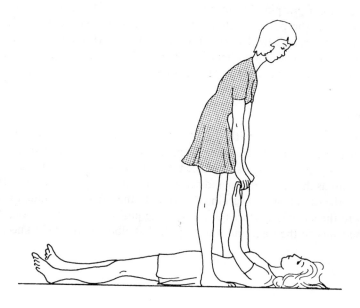

Fig. C8/3 Straddle chinning.

this position, keeping her body straight, the subject raises herself by her arms until the chest touches the bar and then returns to the starting position. No resting is permitted. The score is the number of completed pull-ups to a maximum of 40.

In some groups it may be found that the majority of female subjects are able to complete 40 modified pull-ups with little difficulty, and therefore the following alternative test has been proposed by the AAHPER, which has the advantage that there is no arbitrary maximum score.

Flexed arm hang

The subject pulls herself up with an overhand grasp on a horizontal bar at her own standing height, until her chin is above the level of the bar. The score is the number of seconds that this position can be maintained.

A second alternative to the modified pull-up for female subjects is **Straddle Chinning.** The subject lies supine with her partner standing astride of her, and the subject grasping her partner's hands. (See Fig. C8/3). Keeping her body straight, she pulls herself up by her arms until her trunk touches the inside of her partner's thighs—in this position her arms should be parallel with her trunk—and then lowers herself to the starting position. The exercise is repeated as often as possible and the score is the number of complete straddle chinnings achieved.)

(b)   Sit-ups

The sit-up is performed with the subject supine on the floor with the legs extended and feet about 2 ft. (60 cm.) apart. The hands are placed on the back of the neck with the fingers interlaced and the elbows against the floor. A partner holds the ankles down and acts as scorer, (see Fig. C8/4). To perform the test, the subject sits up turning the trunk to the left and touching the right elbow to the left knee, returns to the starting position, and then sits up turning the trunk to the right and touching the left elbow to the right knee. The

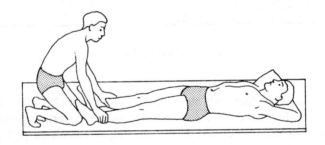

Fig. C8/4   Sit-ups.

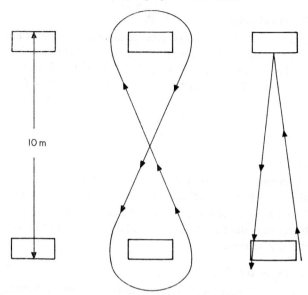

Fig. C8/5 Shuttle run.

exercise is repeated, alternating sides. In scoring, one point is given for each complete movement of touching elbow to knee. No score is counted if the fingertips do not maintain contact behind the head, if the knees are bent when the subject lies on his back, or when he begins to sit up, or if he pushes up off the floor with an elbow. The original test specifies a maximum score, but to abolish this arbitrary limit it is recommended that the maximum number of sit-ups which can be performed in 1 minute is scored.

(c) Shuttle-run

For the shuttle-run two parallel lines are marked on the floor 30 ft. (9·2 m.) apart, and two small blocks of wood (2″ × 2″ × 4″ (5 × 5 × 10 cm.)) are placed beyond one of the lines. Starting from behind the other line the subject runs to the blocks, picks one up, runs back to the starting line, and places the block behind the line, runs back and picks up the second block, and runs back with it across the starting line. (See Fig. C8/5). At least two scorers should be available with stop-watches so that at least two subjects can run at the same time. Two trials are allowed, with a rest between. The score is the shorter of the two times, to the nearest tenth of a second.

(d)   Standing broad-jump

For the standing broad-jump the subject stands with feet apart and toes just behind the take-off line. Preparatory to jumping the subject swings the arms backwards and bends the knees (see Fig. C8/6). The jump is accomplished by simultaneously extending the knees and swinging the arms forward. The jump is measured to the heel or other part of the body that touches the floor nearest the take-off line. Three trials are allowed and the score is the longest of the three jumps measured to the nearest centimetre.

(e)   50-yard dash

This test is performed by two or more subjects at a time, depending on the number of timers with stop-watches available. The starter drops his arm on the command ' go ', to give the timer a visual signal. This test is performed once only and the score is the time taken to run 50 yards (46 m.) measured to the nearest tenth of a second.

(f)   Soft-ball throw for distance

A standard 12″ (30·5 cm.) circumference soft-ball is used. Starting from in front of a line 2 metres behind the take-off line, the subject throws the soft-ball overhand from behind the take-off line as far as possible. The throw is

Fig. C8/6   Standing broad-jump.

measured from the point of landing to the nearest point on the take-off line. Three throws are allowed, and the score is the furthest of the three throws, measured to the nearest 25 cm.

(g)   600-yard run-walk

The score for this test is the time taken for the subject to cover 600 yards (551 m.) measured if possible with a stop-watch to the nearest tenth of a second. The test is performed once only.

Reliability of tests

This battery of 7 tests has been used extensively in the USA and in Great Britain, and all the tests have proved intrinsically reliable, as indicated by a highly significant test-retest correlation. The following points, however, are to be noted:

(i)   Results for the **Pull-ups** are very reliable with very little improvement shown in mean scores between the first and the fourth trials. Only one or two practice trials appear necessary in order to produce very stable results.

(ii)   Untrained subjects appear to require four or more practice trials in **Sit-ups** and **Shuttle-run** tests, before satisfactorily stable results can be obtained.

(iii)   Two or three practice trials seem to be necessary in order to produce good reliability in the **Standing broad-jump, 50-yard dash,** and **600-yard run-walk.**

(iv)   In the **Soft-ball throw** test, the first trial score was highly reliable, and apparently is as good an estimate of the subject's true scores as scores made on subsequent test days.

(From: Brown, S. R., and A. Field: " Reliability and Errors of Measurement of the AAHPER Youth Fitness Test ". Abstracts of the Canadian AHPER. Aug. 1966. Vol. 1., No. 1)

Measures of total fitness from simple performance tests.

If tests with an arbitrary maximum score are excluded from the test battery a general criterion of athletic fitness may be derived by converting the raw scores of each test to standard scores (T-scores, sigma scores) and adding these. Unfortunately T-scores (or percentiles) are valid only for the group or groups being tested but, if suitable fitness tests are used, standard scores may be derived for any combination of groups and thus enable comparisons of ' total fitness ' to be made between the individual groups.

III. DATA COLLECTING SHEET

Name:*   Height:

Subject no.:   Weight:

Age: Observer:

Sex: Ethnic and tribal origin

Place: (or nationality):

Date: Occupation:

---

1. Harvard step-test:

Duration of exercise.................sec.

Pulse-count after exercise ..../30 sec. (from 1–1$\frac{1}{2}$ min. after
exercise)

2. AAHPER tests:

(a) Pull-ups or modified pull-ups:
   No. of pull-ups or modified pull-ups achieved .....
   Time flexed arm hang maintained...............(secs.)
   No. of straddle chinnings achieved..............

(b) Sit-ups:
   No. of sit-ups achieved (in 1 minute)............

(c) Shuttle-run:
   1st trial ....
   2nd trial ....
   Best time ....sec.

(d) Standing broad-jump:
   1st trial ....
   2nd trial ....
   3rd trial...............
   Longest jump ....m.............cm.

(e) 50-yard dash:
   ....sec.

(f) Soft-ball throw for distance:
   1st throw ....
   2nd throw.............
   3rd throw ....
   Farthest throw ....m...........cm.

(g) 600-yard run-walk:
   ....sec.

*Full details of the subject and his population group are to be entered in the **BASIC IDENTIFICATION SHEETS,** as laid down in the Technical Introduction.

D. CLIMATIC TOLERANCE

D1   Whole body cold tolerance sleeping test
D2   Whole body cold tolerance waking test
D3   Cold-induced pressor test
D4   Cold-induced vasodilation test
D5   The controlled-hyperthermia heat tolerance test
D6   The multi-stress heat tolerance test (multiple exposures)
D7   The multi-stress heat tolerance test (single exposure)
D8   A mobile hot-room for field use
D9   Salt and water studies
D10   Sweat-gland counting
D11   Thermal comfort assessment
D12   Morphological measurements in relation to climatic studies

D1. WHOLE BODY COLD TOLERANCE SLEEPING TEST (8-HOUR TEST)

I. INTRODUCTION
   (a) General
   (b) Observations to be made
   (c) Sampling

II. TECHNIQUES
   (a) Outline of method
   (b) Preparation of subjects and test procedure
   (c) Equipment

III. DATA COLLECTING SHEET

I. INTRODUCTION

(a) General.

Both the 'prolonged' (8-hour sleeping test) and an intermittent multi-temperature 'acute' test (see **D2.**) are entirely suitable for the study of whole-body exposure, in that these tests certainly give complementary information. Both tests should be carried out in standardised mobile cold rooms, so that various sources of error (as well as inconvenience) in past tests would be eliminated.

The '8-hour sleep test' was evolved by several investigators, and has already been used for comparing the responses of many ethnic groups exposed to the same standardised cold stress. Emphasis is placed on exploring differences in heat production, heat loss, and heat storage. Recognising that any differences which might exist between ethnic groups will be small, the exposure to thermal stress must not be so severe as to mask the small difference.

Two important differences must be considered when comparing the results from the prolonged moderate cold exposure with results from the intermittent multi-temperature acute test. First, in the 8-hour test, the temperatures of the human body are approaching a steady state, and thus minimising the effects of subject variation in heat capacity and variation in heat content prior to the test. Second, the regulatory stimulus derived from a rapidly falling skin temperature is minimised in the prolonged test, whereas it is very important in the acute test, especially in the extreme cold air temperatures.

The night-time is the period of lowest heat production in man, the longest continuous period without side variations in heat production, and is the time of lowest environmental temperatures. Night, therefore, is likely to be the time of greatest cold exposure in ethnic groups lacking a highly developed thermal technology. Although sleep during the night may alter some aspects of temperature regulation and the response to cold, a long (8-hour) moderate cold exposure at night offers one useful standard cold stress for man.

Since sleep is important for the welfare of man, assaying the amount of sleep during the period of cold exposure at night is essential in a comparative study of ethnic groups.

(b) **Observations to be made:**

It is recommended that in both tests, the basic measurements should always include:

1. Physiological:
    (i)   Skin temperatures at the agreed 10 sites (see below) to give average skin temperature.
    (ii) Toe and finger temperatures to give information on peripheral blood flow.
    (iii) Rectal temperature as ' core ' measurement.
    (iv) Oxygen consumption by continuous sampling.
    (v)   Shivering by EMG (where possible).
    (vi) Brain activity by EEG.
    (vii) Urine output.

In both tests, essential ancillary measurements should include:

2. Anthropometry:
    (i)   Skinfold thicknesses at 10 sites. (See **A1.**)
    (ii) Other measurements of physique. (See **A1.**)

The following examinations should also be included:
    (i)   Medical examination. (See **F1.**)
    (ii) Nutritional assessment. (See **E1.**)
    (iii) Assessment of habitual physical activity. (See **C6.**)
    (iv) Environmental assessment. (See **H.**)

(c) **Sampling:**

Because the number of man-hours required to obtain a minimum of thermal physiological data on one individual is so great, the number of individuals studied cannot be as great as may be required by geneticists and physical anthropologists, but must be sufficient to apply small sample statistics. The results on even a small indigenous sample of, say, twenty individuals of the same sex and age group, i.e. 10–15 years, 20–50 years, over 60 years, will gain greatly in interpretative value if similar studies are made at the same time, or on a subsequent occasion, on a matched control group, not habituated to the local conditions. A realistic sample size in some of the most interesting ethnic groups, e.g. Indians of Tierra del Fuego, Ainu, Kalahari Bushmen, might be as low as ten. The use of a controlled cold chamber will make such comparisons far more reliable.

II.   TECHNIQUES

(a)   Outline of method: (See Fig. D1/1.)

The subject lies for 9 hours at night inside a standard blanket bag (insulation = 1·7 clo*) on a canvas cot with his head in a ventilated plastic hood. The cot stands inside an environmental chamber. For the first hour the subject is kept warm by providing additional insulation. After the first hour, the additional insulation is removed so that the subject is left inside the blanket bag exposed to 5°C for 8 hours. The oxygen consumption and carbon dioxide production are determined for successive intervals throughout the night by measuring the volume, pO_2 and pCO_2 of the air ventilating the hood during each interval. The rectal temperature and 10 skin temperatures are measured by thermocouples attached to the body and read regularly throughout the night by potentiometer. Brain activity is regularly recorded from electrodes adhering to the scalp and leading to an electroencephalograph (and, if possible, muscle activity is recorded from electrodes adhering to the skin over large muscle masses, and leading to an electromyograph). Two-way communication is available to the investigator and the subject at all times by means of a microphone speaker in the ventilated hood.

(b)   Preparation of subjects and test procedure:

(i)   Preparation of subjects

6:00 PM   The subjects are given a standard European meal, high in carbohydrate.

$$* 1 \text{ clo} = 0.18 \frac{°C}{\text{Kcal/sq.m./hr.}}$$ The insulation of the blanket may be determined by placing a sample piece on a flat, horizontal heat flow meter; it includes the insulation of the overlying still air.

9:00 PM   Subjects are weighed and measured for height. The skinfold thickness at 10 places (cheek, chin, chest (juxta-nipple), subscapular, suprailiac, abdominal, triceps, forearm, above knee, median calf) is obtained with a skinfold caliper. (See **A1**.)

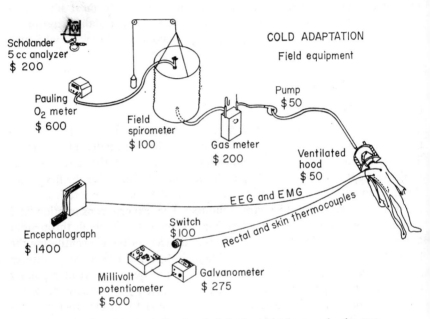

Fig. D1/1   Apparatus for the whole body cold tolerance sleeping test.

Needle or cup electrodes are attached to the scalp with collodion and adhesive tape. If an electromyograph is to be used, needle electrodes are inserted and taped over muscle masses on the chest, arms, and thighs. All leads are securely taped to the body and assembled into a group at the shoulder where they leave the body. The subject is covered with a blanket during this procedure.

Next, the subject is asked to lie on his side on a blanket, outside but along-side the sleeping chamber. Again he is covered with a blanket while the thermocouples are attached. The rectal thermocouple is inserted 15 cm or more with the aid of a lubricating jelly. The lead is taped to one cheek of the buttock. The skin thermocouples that end with a copper disc are taped to the skin with a 2″ × 5″ strip of adhesive tape. The disc is centered on the tape. The tape over the disc is first pressed onto the skin, and moving away from the disc toward the two free ends the tape is pressed securely to the skin. Skin thermocouples that terminate with a ring are attached to the skin with a thinned contact cement. Skin thermocouples are placed on: the dorsum of the foot; outside the mid-calf and thigh; chest above the nipple; back over the scapula; lateral side of the mid-upper arm; back of hand; side of neck; abdomen and forehead. All leads are securely taped down with small strips of tape and assembled into a group at the shoulder where they leave the body.

The naked subject (except for shorts or loin cloth) now enters the blanket bag on the cot in the chamber. He passes his head into the hood and the free end of the rubber sleeve is rotated and stretched over the fixed ring of the hood. The sleeve should be rotated sufficiently to effect a seal about the neck but not so much as to choke or irritate the sleeping subject. Talcum powder applied to the neck reduces irritation.

The leads from the muscle and scalp electrodes are plugged into a junction box lying beside the hood. The subject is asked to open his eyes, close his eyes, and to blink his eyes to check for proper function of the brain potential leads.

(ii) **Test procedure**

9–10:00 PM In addition to subject preparation, instrument calibrations and preparations are part of the routine procedure. These include:

(1) Ice (if available) is cracked and placed with water in a thermos flask. All the reference junctions (including rectal, skin, auxiliary, and air thermocouples) are inserted to the middle of the ice-water mixture. The water level in the flask should be below the ice level. This will insure that, during

one night's run, the level of warmer, dense water will not rise to the level of the cold junctions.

(2)   The auxiliary warm junction is placed with a standard thermometer in a warm bath at about 38° C. This junction (as well as all the other thermocouples on the subject) may be calibrated or checked.

(3)   The drying agent in the U-tubes for drying air samples entering the O_2 meters is replaced. It is advisable to use one of the indicating type agents for which the exhausted drying agent changes colour.

(4)   The O_2 meter is calibrated by reading the meter with dry outdoor air at several manometric pressures in the meter. It is advisable to have the O_2 meters on continuously, day and night, when a series of night tests is anticipated. This means only that the magnetic analysis unit is maintained at the operational temperature (140°F, 59·4°C) at all times and costs very little in additional power. Experience has shown that minor fluctuations in the calibration factor are reduced in this way.

(5)   The pumps for ventilating the hoods are turned on and warmed up and adjusted to flow 35 to 40 litres/min.

(6)   The spirometers and the Douglas bags are flushed with ventilated hood air and then emptied in preparation for the start of the metabolic measurements.

(7)   The $\frac{1}{2}$-cc Scholander analyser is checked by analysing outdoor air. The analysis is found satisfactory if it is within $20·93 \pm 0·02\%$ for oxygen; and $0·03 \pm 0·02\%$ for carbon dioxide. Sometimes there is an unexplainable consistent error in these analyses. In this case, the analysis of the sample of ventilating air from the hood is subtracted from the analysis of outdoor air rather than 20.93% to obtain the $\triangle \%O_2$ for calculating the R.Q. and oxygen consumption.

(8)   The compressor and evaporator blower and one auxiliary blower are turned on for one hour or more to dry out the air in the chamber.

The details for making the measurements are as follows:

1. **Measurement of oxygen consumption and carbon dioxide production.**

A. Ventilating hood.

The hood is constructed entirely of plastic, or at least its upper surface and sides must be of clear plastic. Outdoor air enters either through a port in the back, or through a series of small holes around the inside of the head opening. Air flows over and around the head, and out through a port in the back.

The head is sealed in the hood by means of a large flexible sleeve made of thin rubber dam. One end of the sleeve (35 cm. in diameter and about 50 cm. long) is permanently attached to a ring on the outside surface of the front of the hood. The other free end of the sleeve is cemented to an elastic rubber ring whose diameter is a little less than the ring on the hood. After the head is passed through the sleeve and into the hood, the elastic rubber ring is stretched over and sealed in a groove around the outside of the ring on the hood. The elastic rubber ring and the free end of the sleeve are then rotated half-a-turn or so, until a suitable seal is obtained around the neck. Talcum powder applied to the rubber ring and the groove permits the rubber ring to rotate freely.

The hood is ventilated at the rate of about 35 litres/min., or sufficient to maintain the CO_2 level at about 1 %. Since the fresh air is drawn through the hood by a pump on the outflow side of the hood, the hood is under a slight negative pressure which ensures that no respired air escapes from the hood except through the outflow port. The large air intake port is joined to a large diameter (75 cm.) flexible hose, which leads to fresh outdoor air. Care must be taken, especially on gusty nights, to place the free end of the hose in an open window in such a way that the pressure of the wind does not blow air down the hose, and blow respired air by the neck seal. Fluctuating ambient pressures may also be avoided by attaching the air intake hose to the bottom of a 5-gal. can, which is open at the top, and into which an excess of outdoor air is pumped.

A small pillow is placed in the hood for the comfort of the subject, and a speaker-microphone is installed on an upper surface of the hood for communication.

B. Ventilating pump.

A noiseless air pump with an outflow adjustable between 25 and 100 litres/min., but otherwise constant after adjustment, is desirable for this purpose. Unfortunately, no such pump is available. There are two suitable compromises: the Reciprotor pump, type 606G (see (c) below), or a pump constructed from either a squirrel-cage blower or a vacuum-cleaner blower (see (c) below).

C.   Dry Gas Meter.

Any one of several makes is suitable for this purpose. The capacity of the meter should cover the range of 20–100 litres/min. without significant error. The meters should be checked frequently against a good spirometer. A manometer and a thermometer in the air stream of the gas meter are desirable. An inexpensive flowrater may be used to monitor the flow.

D.   Sample collection.

Two methods are suitable:

1.   All the ventilated air of a metabolic period may be collected in a Scholander field spirometer (Scholander P. F., and H. Jensen. Bag spirometer **Scand, J. Clin. and Lab. Invest. 10,** 225, 1958) or in a Darex Sounding Balloon (see (c) below), rendered gas-tight by ' cooking ' in water at 90°C for 30 minutes, without moistening the inner surface. Unless two spirometers or balloons are available for each subject, the ventilating air cannot be sampled all the time, since some short time is required to withdraw samples for gas analysis and to empty the spirometer. It is practical, however, to collect ventilating air for 15 to 17 minutes of each 20-minute period, leaving 3 to 5 minutes for sample taking and emptying the spirometer. With two spirometers, all ventilating air may be continuously collected in alternate spirometers. The advantage of this method is that there is no possibility of failing to obtain a representative sample for analysis.

2.   A small fraction of the ventilating air may be continuously collected alternately in one of two Douglas Bags. The bulk of the ventilating air is exhausted into the atmosphere after passing through the gas meter. The preferred way to achieve this method of sampling is to flow all the air, after it leaves the gas meter, through an adjustable resistance valve. A small side tube is joined to the valve between the resistance and the gas meter; i.e. on the upstream side of the valve. This side tube is then connected alternately to the Douglas bags. A small amount of air (the fraction depends upon the resistance setting of the valve) will now leave the main stream and flow continuously into the Douglas bag, while most of the air passes through the

valve. The fraction of the ventilating air that is sampled is to a good approximation independent of the rate of ventilation. The advantage of this method is that it allows a continuous sampling of the metabolic rate while requiring less laboratory space.

E.   Gas Analysis.

Several methods are available for gas analysis, but only two will be detailed since these have been used extensively in field investigations, and they serve to illustrate the methodology.

1.   Scholander $\frac{1}{2}$-cc. analyser.

Two 10 cc. syringes are flushed and filled with gas from either the spirometer or the Douglas bag, according to the method by which samples were collected as described under D, above. By keeping the syringe vertical, the weight of the plunger will keep the contained gas under positive pressure and free from contamination. Analysis for $\%O_2$ and $\%CO_2$ should be completed according to the method described by Scholander. (Scholander P. F. Analyser for accurate estimation of respiratory gases in one-half cubic centimetre samples. **J. Biol. Chem., 167,** 233, 1947). Long storage times should be avoided where possible. Analysis may also be accomplished with the Haldane apparatus with about the same accuracy, working time, and skill.

2.   Pauling meter. (See also (c) below).

Rapid and highly accurate analyses of pO_2 may easily be achieved using the Pauling type meter, based on the high paramagnetic susceptibility of oxygen compared with the other common respiratory gases. Several details must be carefully followed to achieve the high accuracy (± 0.05 mm. Hg.) required by the ventilated hood method for metabolic rate determination.

(a)   To obtain a true difference in partial pressure of oxygen between outdoor air and mixed ventilatory air, the partial pressure of water vapour in both samples must be the same. This is best achieved by drying all gases entering the analyser. Therefore unknown gas samples as well as outdoor air are passed through small U-tubes containing Drierite (anhydrous $CaSO_4$), one tube for the unknown sample, and one for outdoor air.

(b)   Samples are drawn through the oxygen meter, drying tube, and tubing leading from the spirometer or Douglas bag by means of a small vacuum pump which will draw at about 200–300 ml/min. Readings of the oxygen meter are made only after the flow is stopped

and the pump is disconnected so that the pressure in the meter is
barometric pressure.

(c)   Several readings of the pO_2 of outdoor air should be made throughout
the night to correct for any drift in the barometric pressure or any
possible instrument drift; (the latter is usually negligible).

(d)   It is recommended that a calibration curve be drawn for each instrument at the beginning or end of every night run. This is easily
accomplished by installing an accurate water manometer in the
outdoor air hose. After flushing the meter with fresh outdoor air,
and then reading the pO_2 at barometric pressure, a clamp (haemostat)
is placed on the rubber hose between the source and the manometer.
Air is drawn through the hose leading from the O_2 meter until the
pressure falls a few cm. H_2O. This hose is also clamped and the gas
in the meter, hose and manometer is allowed to equilibrate. The pO_2
of the gas in the O_2 meter is read and the manometer is read. The
pressure is reduced again and another set of readings is taken, and so
on for several points down to about 75 cm. H_2O pressure below barometric pressure. The scope of the linear curve obtained in this way
(see Fig. D1/2), is the calibration factor for the O_2 meter for the night
run ahead. More frequent calibrations have proved unnecessary, but
less frequent checks may affect the accuracy of the metabolic determinations by as much as 1–2%.

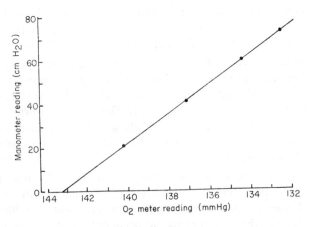

Fig. D1/2   See text.

10:00 PM   The first metabolic period and the first body temperature measurements of Subject A are started. At exactly 10:00 PM the Douglas valve, which directed the ventilating air from the gas meter to exhaust, is turned to direct the air into the spirometer. At the same time, the volume reading of the dry gas meter is obtained and recorded. The barometric pressure and the gas meter temperature are recorded.

10:05 PM   The first metabolic period and the first body temperatures of Subject B are started.

10:16 PM   End first metabolic period of Subject A by turning Douglas valve from spirometer to exhaust—at the same time reading and recording gas meter. Dry sample air is drawn from the spirometer through the O_2 meter for one minute and thirty seconds to purge all parts thoroughly. Flow is stopped, the O_2 meter is returned to barometric pressure and the partial pressure of oxygen in the sample is read and recorded. A sample is also drawn into two 10 ml. syringes for analysis in the Scholander analyser. The spirometer is emptied.

10:20 PM   The second metabolic period of Subject A is started by reading and recording the gas meter, and temperature readings are taken.

10:21 PM   The first metabolic period of Subject B is ended. The gas in the spirometer is analysed in the O_2 meter for Subject B and also a sample is removed for analysis in the Scholander analyser. The spirometer is then emptied.

10:25 PM   The second metabolic period of Subject B is started by reading the gas meter and turning the Douglas valve to the spirometer. Temperature readings are also started.

10:36 PM   Second Subject A period ends.

10:40 PM   Third Subject A period begins.

10:41 PM   Second Subject B period ends.

10:45 PM   Third Subject B period begins.
            So it continues throughout the night.

11:00 PM   The air temperature in the chamber is dropped from 20°C to 5°C and held at 5°C for eight hours of moderate cold exposure.

Several times throughout the night, the partial pressure of oxygen in dry, outdoor air is recorded. At the same time, barometric pressure and gas meter temperature are recorded.

Once every hour for each subject, gas samples are removed for analysis in the Scholander analyser.

All data are recorded on the standard forms. (See Data Collecting Sheets.)

EEG and EMG Routine

When two two-channel recorders are available, one recorder is operated continuously throughout the night at slow speed with one channel connected to the muscle leads of A, and the other connected to the muscle leads of B. These leads provide a continuous record of the ECG as well as the intermittent EMG recordings of shivering or other muscle activity.

The other recorder has EEG amplifiers installed. One channel is connected to one of two pairs of scalp electrodes (frontal or occipital) of Subject A, and the other channel is for one of two pairs of head electrodes of Subject B. For ten seconds of each ten minutes throughout the night, the recorder is turned to fast speed to record the brain activity.

II.   Metabolic Rate

A.   The gas meter flow rate is

$$\dot{V}_m = \frac{Vfinal \quad - \quad Vinitial}{\text{time of metabolic period in minutes}}$$

The flow rate reduced to standard temperature and pressure dry is

$$\dot{V}_{STPD} = \frac{B.P. - pH_2O}{760} \times \frac{273}{27 + 3T_m} \times \dot{V}_m$$

where B. P. = barometric pressure in mm Hg.

pH_2O = water vapor pressure of air through gas meter. We guess this to be 10 mm Hg or about half saturated at gas meter temperature.

T_m = gas meter temperature.

B. Oxygen Consumption

The rate of oxygen consumption may be calculated for each metabolic period from measurements of pO_2 of the ventilatory gas collected in the spirometer, of pO_2 of dry, outdoor air, flow rate and R.Q. as follows:

$$\dot{V}O_2 = \frac{(pO_2 \text{ air} - pO_2 \text{ sample}) K_m}{B.P.} \times \frac{\dot{V}_{STPD}}{1 - (1-R.Q.) \times 0.2093}$$

pO_2air   = partial pressure of oxygen in outdoor air in mm Hg.

pO_2 sample = partial pressure of oxygen in spirometer air in mm Hg.

K_m = calibration factor of oxygen meter.

           = slope of calibration curve of manometer reading in cm H_2O (ordinate) versus O_2 meter reading in mm Hg (abscissa) $\times$ 10 $\times$ 0.2093 divided by 13.54.

R.Q.   = respiratory quotient, obtained from hourly determinations by Scholander analysis. Otherwise, it may be assumed to be 0.80 for a man on a mixed diet in a near post-absorptive state.

C. Rate of Heat Production

Assuming an R.Q. = 0.80 so that the calorific value of a litre of oxygen of 4.8 Kcal/litre may be used:

Heat Production in Kcal/kg/hr $= \dfrac{\dot{V}O_2 \times 4.8 \times 60}{Wt.}$

where Wt. = weight in kg.

BODY TEMPERATURES

(a) Rectal and individual skin temperatures:

The millivolt readings obtained from the potentiometer for each thermocouple are converted to °C. Small corrections for the thermocouple wire in use should be applied if required.

(b) Average skin Temperature:

An average skin temperature may be computed according to the method of Hardy which weights the skin temperature of a given part by the ratio of the skin area of that part to the total surface area of the body. For the ten sites at which skin temperature is measured as recommended above, the weighting factors are:

Foot, 0.07; Calf, 0.13; Thigh, 0.19; Pectoral, 0.13; Scapula, 0.12; Abdomen, 0.12; Arm, 0.15; Hand, 0.05; Neck, 0.03; Forehead, 0.04.

(c) Mean Body Temperature

Using total calorimetric data on man in the Russel Sage Calorimeter, Hardy determined that the proportions of core and average skin temperatures which best agreed with the mean body temperature were:

$$\text{M.B.T.} = 0\text{·}7\ T_{rectal} + 0\text{·}3\ T_{avg.\ skin}.$$

EFFECTIVE TISSUE CONDUCTANCE

A rough estimate of the effects of the vascular response of the body to cold exposure upon the thermal characteristics of the body may be obtained by calculating a term called Body Tissue Conductance. Assuming a simple physical model for which heat flows from the core at T_{rectal} to the surface at $T_{avg.\ skin}$ through a surface area equal to that of a man, then

$$\text{Body Tissue Conductance in Kcal/m}^2/\text{hr/}^\circ C = \frac{\text{Rate of heat loss through surface}}{(T_{rectal} - T_{avg.\ skin}) \times \text{S. A.}}$$

where   Rate of heat loss through skin surface =
Rate of heat production $- 8\%$ of rate of heat production $+$ rate of change of heat content.
Here it is assumed that 8% of the heat produced is lost through insensible loss from respiration.

T_{rectal} and $T_{avg.\ skin} =$ the average values for the interval for which conductance is calculated.

S.A. =   Surface Area in metre^2. To be measured for each individual, if possible. Otherwise surface area may be computed from the Dubois Formula as

S.A. $= W^{0\cdot425} \times H^{0\cdot725} \times 0.0007184$
where   W = weight in kg; and H = height in cm.

The rate of change of heat content $(T_{rectal} - T_{avg.\ skin})$ may be roughly determined for each metabolic interval by estimating the slope of the curve of mean body temperature versus time and multiplying by weight in kg. and by specific heat (0.83).

LEAN BODY MASS AND BODY FAT (see also A5)

From the thickness of ten skinfolds less 40 mm (the skin thickness of ten skinfolds), the body fat content and lean body mass may be calculated from the empirical relationship obtained by Allen, *et al.*, **Metabolism**, **5**:346, 1965.

(c) **Equipment:**

I. ENVIRONMENTAL CHAMBER

The specifications are outlined below. Note that a training period would be required, and acceptance tests or runs would have to be carried out.

Dimensions:

Present Hammel chamber:
Length 102″.
Width 86″.
(to accommodate 2 beds).
Height 96″.
(to accommodate step-rest)

Item

(i)	Box-(room)	Dimensions: I.D. (clear) 102″ × 86″ × 96″(h)
		Insulation: $3\frac{11}{16}$″ or 4″ nominal + (wall thickness) Polystyrene or equivalent.
		Interior: White paint—moisture proof.
		Exterior: Aluminium recommended—indifferent.
		Door: Indifferent.
		Lights: 30-watt fluorescent.
(ii)	Refrigeration Unit.	Air conditioning + control
		Performance: +5°C to +50°C in environments −5°C to +35°C.
		Tolerance: ±2°C — Room load + 4000 BTU/hr.
(iii)	Air flow.	Air movement: continuous—uniform—120 ft/min linear in working area ± 40.
		Air renewal: 2 c.f.m./person (**dry**) maximum —3 people.

This chamber was designed specifically for the 8-hour night-time cold exposure test. Details of its construction are shown in Fig. D1/3. The internal dimensions are such that two men can be studied simultaneously

throughout the night. The chamber is designed to maintain under load an
internal temperature between 3 and 5°C in an ambient environment of 20°C.
Heaters are also installed to maintain any internal temperature up to 30°C.

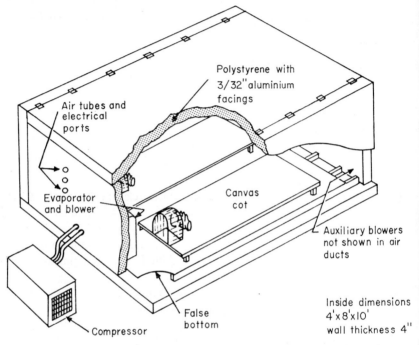

Fig. D1/3   Design of environmental chamber. (Full description in text.)

The chamber is assembled from 4′ × 10′ or 4′ × 8′ sections of 4″ thick
polystyrene bonded between two $\frac{3}{32}$″ hardened aluminium sheets. The
top and bottom are assembled from two 4′ × 10′, sections joined edge-to-edge
in a double mortise and tenon joint. The outer edges are protected with a
$\frac{1}{16}$″ aluminium sheath.   The ends are 4′ × 8′ sections joined to the top and
bottom by aluminium strips overlapping the joint. Metal screws pass through
holes in the strip and are screwed into the metal surface on the end sections.
The 4′ × 10′ side sections are doors hinged at the top to allow easy access to
the interior of the sleeping chamber.

At one end of the chamber rests an enclosed evaporator unit with its
blower below. A false bottom of $\frac{1}{2}$″ plywood is supported 4″ above the
inside bottom of the chamber. The spaces between the supporting 2″ × 4″ 's

and the two bottoms serve as return air ducts. After passing through the ducts beneath the false floor, the air is blown up over the evaporator fins and cooled. It then passes out of the top of the evaporator unit and back through the environmental chamber to enter the floor ducts again. Three auxiliary blowers are installed in the lower back of the chamber. One blower blows air down the middle floor duct and the other two blow air down the outermost floor ducts. A 1000-watt heater is mounted in the discharge stream of each of the three auxiliary blowers. Each heater may be thermostatically controlled.

A performance curve of the chamber with a 300-watt load simulating two men shivering vigorously is shown in Fig. D1/4.

Two ports are in the end of the chamber through which pass the liquid and gas refrigerant lines to and from the compressor-condenser unit outside the chamber. This unit is enclosed in its shipping crate with the ends removed to permit free ventilation of the condenser.

In addition, three ports on either side of the evaporator unit permit air tubes to pass to and from the hood, and all electrical connections to and from the subject pass through the third port.

II.   COTS, SLEEPING BAGS, AND NIGHT LIGHTS

2″ nylon webbing stretched across a framework of $\frac{3}{4}$″ aluminium pipe, speed-rail tees, elbows and corners serve as the cot. The cots are supported on short legs resting on the false floor so that the webbing is 12″ above the floor, as shown in Figure D1/3.

The sleeping bag is made by folding lengthwise a single woollen blanket, trimming one end of the folded blanket to a taper and sewing together all free margins except the end which is to remain open. The blanket is thus formed into a mummy case and encircles the subject as he lies on the cot.

A small night lamp and a urinal are provided for the convenience of the subjects.

III.   VENTILATING PUMP

The Reciprotor pump (type 606G) is available from Reciprotor, A/S, Copenhagen, Denmark. It is adjustable, has a nearly constant outflow, and is rather quiet if the outflow does not exceed 35 litres/min. Its maximum capacity is 45 litres/min. An alternative type of pump which has proved satisfactory can be fabricated by enclosing either a squirrel cage blower or a vacuum-cleaner blower inside a can or suitable container with an in-port and an out-port provided. The motors of these blowers must have brushes (or be, otherwise, non-synchronous motors), so that they may be plugged in to a variable d.c. source or into an auto-transformer which provides adjustable a.c. voltage. This type of pump may have a high capacity, and the accompanying whine is not noticeable in the hood at flows of 25–50 litres/min. provided the pump is placed in the circuit after the gas-meter. The flow of these pumps is dependent upon the ambient pressure at the intake and the outflow of the entire system. In order to reduce the effects of a variable load upon the rate of air flow, a speed control unit may be used which maintains essentially constant speed characteristics with varying torque requirements. Such a circuit is described in Silicon Controlled Rectified Hobby Manual; (available from General Electric, Rectifier Components Dept,. West Genesee St., Auburn, New York).

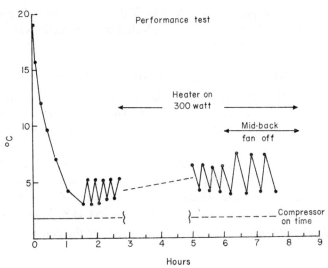

Fig. D1/4 (See Text).

IV   DAREX SOUNDING BALLOONS (for sample collection).

These are available from Dewey and Almy Chemical Division, W.R. Grace Co., Cambridge 40, Mass., U.S.A. Type J 11–10–300 will contain 2,400 litres inflated.

V PAULING METER

The Model C or Model E, Beckman Instruments Oxygen Analyzer (range 120–160 mm. Hg) has proved to be a very accurate and rugged instrument for field use.

CONVERSION TABLE

This must be constructed, to read from degrees Centigrade to millivolts, with a range of –10°C to 60°C.

III. DATA COLLECTING SHEET (1)

Name:*
Serial no.:
Age:
Sex:
Height (cm.):
Weight (kg.):

Surface area (sq. m.):
Ethnic group or nationality:
Occupation:
Place of examination:
Date of examination:
Name of Observer: (1)

OBSERVATIONS ON VENTILATION AIR

Time of observation	Exposure temp. (°C)	Gas meter reading (litres)	pO$_2$ Outdoor air (mm. Hg) (Pauling)	Bar. press. (mm. Hg)	Temp. of gas meter air (°C) (T$_m$)
0 min. 16 min.	(20) (20)				
20 min. 36 min.	(20) (20)				
40 min. 56 min.	(20) (20)				
60 min. 76 min. 80 min. 96 min. 100 min.	(5) (5) (5) (5)				

Exposure at 5°C continues for 8 hours.

*Full details of the subject and his population group are to be entered in the **BASIC IDENTIFICATION SHEETS** as laid down in the Technical Introduction.

Signature of Observer: ....

III. DATA COLLECTING SHEET (2)

Name:*   Surface area (sq. m.):
Serial number: Ethnic group or nationality:
Age: Occupation:
Sex: Place of examination:
Height (cm.):   Date of examination:
Weight (kg.):   Name of Observer: (2)

COLLECTION OF SAMPLE AND GAS ANALYSIS

Interval of collection	16 min. vol. (litres)	$\dot{V}_m$ rate (l/min)	STPD	$\dot{V}_{STPD}$ (l/min)	$pO_{2air} - pO_{2sample}$ mm Hg
0–16 min.					
20–36 min.					
40–56 min.					
60–76 min.					
80–96 min. etc.					

(Continued)

Table—continued

COLLECTION OF SAMPLE AND GAS ANALYSIS

	% O_2 sample (Scholander $\frac{1}{2}$cc) **	% CO_2 sample (Scholander $\frac{1}{2}$cc) **	R.Q. **	$\dot{V}O_2$ STPD (ml/min) **
0–16 min.				
20–36 min.				
40–56 min.				
60–76 min. etc.				

*Full details of the subject and his population group are to be entered in the **BASIC IDENTIFICATION SHEETS** as laid down in the Technical Introduction.

** Analysis of % O_2 and % CO_2 by Scholander $\frac{1}{2}$ cc analyser—make once every hour.

Signature of Observer: . . . .

III. DATA COLLECTING SHEET (3)

Name:**

Serial number:

Age:

Sex:

Height (cm.):

Weight (kg.):

Surface area (sq. m.):

Ethnic group or nationality:

Occupation:

Place of examination:

Date of examination:

Name of Observer: (3)

(Suggested weighting factors for average skin temperature are given in brackets)

TEMPERATURE RECORDING

Time	Air temp	Rectal temp	Dorsum foot (0·07)	Outside mid-calf (0·13)	Outside mid-thigh (0·19)	Juxta-nipple (pec-toral) (0·12)	Scapu-la (0·12)	Abdo-men (0·11)	Outside mid-upper arm (0·14)	Back hand (0·05)	Side neck (0·03)	Fore-head (0·04)	Av. skin	*MBT
0 min. — mV ——°C														
20 min. —														

(Continued)

Table—continued

40 min.															
60 min.															
80 min.															
100 min.															
120 min.															

*Mean Body Temperature $= 0.7\, T_{rectal} + 0.3\, T_{avg.\ skin}$.

Full details of the subject and his population group are to be entered in the **BASIC IDENTIFICATION SHEETS as laid down in the Technical Introduction.

Signature of Observer: ....

III. DATA COLLECTING SHEET (4)

Name:*

Serial number:

Height (cm.):

Weight (kg.):

Age:

Sex:

Surface area: (sq. m.)

Ethnic group or nationality:

Occupation:

Place of examination:

Date of examination:

Cheek skin-fold:

Chin skin-fold:

Chest (juxta-nipple) skin-fold:

Subscapular skin-fold:

Suprailiac skin-fold:

Abdominal skin-fold:

Triceps skin-fold:

Forearm skin-fold:

Above knee skin-fold:

Medial calf skin-fold:

Name of Investigator:

Time	VO_2 (ml/min)	Heat production (Kcal/hr)	−8% heat production (Kcal/hr)	Storage (Kcal/hr)	Surface heat loss (Kcal/hr)	Surface heat loss (Kcal/m²/hr)	Rectal-skin temp. gradient (mean for each period) (°C)
16 min.							
36 min.							
56 min.							
76 min.							
96 min.							
etc.							

(continued)

Table—continued

Time	Skin-air temp. gradient (°C) (mean for each period)	Body conductance (Kcal/m²/hr/°C)	Air conductance (Kcal/m²/hr/°C)	Heat production (Kcal/m²/hr)	Heat production (Kcal/kg/hr)
16 min.					
36 min.					
56 min.					
76 min.					
96 min.					
etc. etc.					

* Full details of the subject and his population group are to be entered in the **BASIC IDENTIFICATION SHEETS,** as laid down in the Technical Introduction.

D2. WHOLE BODY COLD TOLERANCE WAKING TEST

I. INTRODUCTION

    (a) General

    (b) Observations to be made

    (c) Sampling

II. TECHNIQUES

III. DATA COLLECTING SHEET

I. INTRODUCTION

(a) General:

It is of interest to compare the reaction to cold of peoples who are subjected to different degrees of cold exposure in their daily lives. In order to compare the results of studies in different parts of the world it is essential to have a standard experimental procedure which will be used by all investigators. A comparison of the cold tolerance sleeping test (8–hour test), (see **D1**), and the present test, is reported by Wyndham *et al*, in ' Human Adaptability and its Methodology ' (Ed. H. Yoshimura and J. S. Weiner, Japan Society for the Promotion of Sciences, Tokyo, 1966), pp. 18–35.

Rationale of the 2-hour exposures at air temperatures ranging from 27°C to 5°C involves the construction of a temperature response curve of the organism over the range of its normal regulation. The 2-hour exposures are conducted at air temperatures of 27°C., 20°C., 15°C., 10°C., and 5°C. This enables the 'critical' air temperature to be established, and the relation of fall in air temperature to increase in metabolism and decrease in surface temperature as a result of vasoconstriction, to be determined.

(b) Observations to be made:

A. Preliminary and ancillary investigations:

1. General medical examination. (See **F1**).

2. Occupational history and habitual activity. (See **C6**).

3. Anthropometry, (skin-fold thickness, height, weight, surface area, and other measurements of physique; see **C5** and **A1**); tests of muscle strength. (See **C7**).

4. Environmental assessment. (See **H**).

B. Cold exposure test:

The essential physiological observations are the following:

1. Skin temperature at 10 sites to give average skin temperature.
2. Toe and finger temperatures to give information on peripheral blood flow.
3. For ' core ', the rectal temperature always.
4. Oxygen consumption by continuous sampling.
5. Urine output for water diuresis.
6. Shivering, by inspection. (In addition, where resources are available, shivering by electromyograph.)
7. Heart rate by pulse-counting, and, wherever possible, by ECG.

In addition, where possible:

8. Blood flow measurements by plethysmography.
9. Blood pressure, (See **F3**).

(c) **Sampling:**

A sufficient number of subjects is needed to determine, with confidence, the inter-individual variances at the five different levels of the independent variable, so that the appropriate mathematical curve, (polynomial, exponential, etc.) can be fitted, and the goodness of fit tested, statistically. Differences between populations can be tested statistically by calculating appropriate confidence limits to the curves.

Because the number of man-hours required to obtain a minimum of thermal physiological data on one individual is so great, the number of individuals studied cannot be as great as that which may be required by geneticists and physical anthropologists, but must be sufficient to apply small sample statistics. The results on even a small indigenous sample of, say, 10 male subjects, or at the least 5, at each of the 5 test conditions, will gain greatly in interpretative value if similar studies are made at the same time or on a subsequent occasion on a matched control group, not habituated to the local conditions. The use of a controlled cold-chamber will make such comparisons far more reliable.

II. TECHNIQUES

Subjects are exposed to five separate tests, each of two hours duration, at air temperatures of 27°C., 20°C., 15°C., 10°C., and 5°C. Air movement should be 100—150 ft./min. For this purpose the chamber described in **D1** is relatively inexpensive and mobile. The standard pre-experimental conditions are as follows:

(a) Post-prandial state for 12 hours.

(b) In field—activity reduced to camp chores.

Subjects have one hour of absolute rest before commencing the study. At the start of the experiment, wearing only thin cotton shorts, the subjects lie on stretchers which have canvas supporting strips at the heels, buttocks, shoulders, and occiput. (See also **D1**). An effort is made to ensure that the subjects lie fully extended with legs spread apart and arms away from the body. Fingers are spread, and toes directed towards the air flow. Rectal and skin temperatures are measured just before the start of the experiment, and every 30 minutes during the two hours of exposure.

Oxygen consumption measurements are performed in the same way as in the whole body cold tolerance sleeping test (see **D1**), using an open circuit system, drawing air from a ventilated hood in which the head of the subject is sealed by means of a large flexible sleeve. The hood should be ventilated at a rate to maintain the expired oxygen or carbon dioxide difference at 1 % or less. The calculation is made with the appropriate corrections for pressure, temperature, and moisture, by multiplying the flow rate by the absolute difference in oxygen content of the intake and exhaust air.

In the Douglas bag and mask method, the oxygen consumption measurements are made by determining the volume and gas concentrations of gas collected during the last 5 minutes of each half-hour. The samples of expired air can be analysed on electronic analysers, or by chemical methods.

The skin thermocouples are taped down in the same positions as in the 8-hour exposure test. (See **D1**). Rectal temperatures are recorded with a thermocouple in a small silver pellet ($\frac{1}{2}''$ long, $\frac{1}{8}''$ in diameter) covered with a 12″ long vinyl tube, which is inserted 8″ into the rectum. On a number of occasions the rectal temperatures are recorded before and immediately after the exposure, to check the recordings made by the thermocouple.

Ten 36-gauge copper-constantan thermocouples are taped to the following skin sites: chest, forehead, finger, hand, upper arm, back, lateral thigh, medial thigh, foot and toe. In addition one thermocouple is inserted into the rectum, as described above. A Tinsley vernier potentiometer is used, with distilled water and melting ice in a thermos flask as the cold junction. Temperatures are recorded continuously. The temperatures which are recorded each half-hour are used for the comparisons.

III. DATA COLLECTING SHEET

Name:*

Subject no.:

Age:

Sex:

Height:

Weight:

Ethnic group or nationality:

Occupation:

Date:

Place:

Barometric pressure:

Name of investigator:

Record temperatures to the nearest 0·1 °C in the following table:

Areas:	Chest	Fore-Head	Finger	Hand	Upp. Arm	Back	Lat. Thigh	Med. Thigh	Foot	Toe	Rec-tum	Mean
Time (mins) (27°C)												
0												
30												
60												
90												
120												
(20°C)												
0												
30												
60												
90												
120												
(15°C)												
0												
30												
60												
90												
120												
(10°C)												
0												
30												
60												
90												
120												
(5°C)												
0												
30												
60												
90												
120												

(continued

III. DATA COLLECTING SHEET (continued)

Oxygen uptake at each temperature condition:
(l/min.)

Test conditions	Time:			
	25–30	55–60	85–90	115–120
27°C				
20°C				
15°C				
10°C				
5°C				

*Full details of the subject and his population group are to be entered in the **BASIC IDENTIFICATION SHEETS,** as laid down in the Technical Introduction.

D3. COLD-INDUCED PRESSOR TEST

I. INTRODUCTION
   (a) General
   (b) Observations to be made
   (c) Sampling

II. TECHNIQUES

III. DATA COLLECTING SHEET

I. INTRODUCTION

(a) **General:**

Acute severe cold exposure of homeothermic animals results generally in an increase of the arterial blood pressure due to reflex vasoconstriction. Immersion of one hand into cold water, for example, is a painful stimulus which produces such a vasopressor response. The increased blood pressure is caused primarily by an increased peripheral resistance although in some cases elevation of cardiac output, due to increased heart rate, could account for this response. A marked drop in skin temperature and in blood flow rate is observed not only in the immersed hand, but also in the contralateral hand. Blood pressure increase and skin temperature change in the extremities provide simple and adequate measurements of responses to a cold water test. In man, it has been demonstrated that people habituated to life in the cold have a lower pressor response than non-habituated subjects. Thus, such groups as Gaspé fishermen, fish-filleters, Eskimos, and University students, have been shown to exhibit significantly reduced responses to this test. It has also been shown that repeated severe appendage cooling results in a reduced vascular reaction, such as lowering of the arterial pressure. Furthermore, in addition to the reduced vascular reaction with acclimatisation, one also finds less pain and discomfort upon severe cold exposure.

There is evidence that the reduced vascular reaction which comes with acclimatisation ('habituation') is due to a central mechanism rather than a change in the local affector or effector mechanism.

This physiological evidence forms the basis for the 'Cold Pressor' test, which has been used to measure man's tolerance to cold.

(b) **Observations to be made:**

The essential observations to be made in this test are the changes in blood pressure and pulse rate during and after exposure of the hand to cold.

(c) **Sampling:**

It is suggested that at least 30–50 individuals of either sex and within narrow age limits should make up the sample, but as this test is fairly simple, larger numbers could be tested.

II. TECHNIQUE

(a) **Preparation of the subject for the test:**

It is essential for the validity of the test to have the subject under strictly defined conditions with regard to thermal body state, physical activity, emotional state, etc. The following recommendations for handling the subjects prior to the test should be considered.

(1) Rectal temperature should be within the range of 36.5°C–37.5°C. Skin temperature should not be below 32°C.

(2) The subjects should be in a post-absorptive state, having rested for at least two hours in a thermally comfortable room before the measurements.

(3) Care is to be taken in the handling of the subjects in order to minimise emotional reactions prior to and during the test. It is recommended that the subjects be familiarised with the experimental procedure before the actual testing. The subject should be told that even if the water feels painfully cold, no freezing of the tissues need be feared, since the temperature of the bath is always above 0°C.

(b) **Experimental procedure:**

(1) A temperature-regulated room should be used, ambient temperature being 20°–25°C, relative humidity 40–60%, and air movement reduced to a minimum so that it is insensible to the subject of the experiment. The subject should wear light clothing.

(2) The subject is in no way to be disturbed by environmental factors, and should be alone in the test room.

(3)   Instructions to the subject during the test should be either by light signals, or by inter-room loud-speaker communication. In some field conditions this may not of course be possible, and instructions will then have to be given to the subject directly.

(4)   The subject is to be seated in a comfortable chair during the test.

(5)   A well-stirred ice-water bath (water at 4°C) is used to create acute severe cold exposure, one opened hand being immersed in the water to the wrist joint. The cold water bath can be a 4-litre beaker or any other container. If equal volumes of crushed ice and water are used, the temperature of the bath will be kept close to 4°C for the whole duration of the test.

(6)   For a period of at least 30 minutes the subject is seated in the experimental chair preceding the immersion of the hand in the ice-water during which period measurements (see below) are taken at regular intervals in order to secure " base-line " measurements. No smoking should be allowed at this stage.

(7)   Continuous hand cold exposure in the ice-water bath for $2\frac{1}{2}$ minutes. **The subject should not be aware of the exact time for cold-water exposure in order to prevent the effect of increased alertness.**

(8)   The measurements are continued during a post-experimental period in order to see if, and after how long a period, the pre-experimental " base-line " values are regained.

(c)   **Measurements:**
The following measurements are taken;

(1)   **Systolic and diastolic arterial blood pressure.**
Pressure readings are made by means of the indirect auscultatory method, the pressure cuff being applied to the upper arm. If several tests are done on the same subjects, it is preferable that blood pressure measurements should be made by the same observer.

These measurements are made at least three times in the pre-experimental period, and the test should be postponed until constant values are obtained, in order to establish the " base-line ". Regular readings should be taken in the same way in the post-experimental period.

During cold-water exposure, pressures should be measured at the end of every half-minute after immersion in the water-bath.

The period of the test is sufficient to evaluate the response of the subject since the maximum increase in blood pressure is observed between the first and second minutes. The test could be extended for longer periods, but the values obtained between 0 and 2 minutes are those that should be used for evaluating the response.

(2)   Heart rate.

Heart rate should be continuously recorded (if possible with an integrating heart frequency machine).

(3)   Skin surface temperatures.

Continuous recording of skin surface temperature on the pad of the third finger, both on the cold exposed hand, and on the other hand, should be made.

(4)   Pain caused by the test.

Means of subjectively evaluating the pain caused by the test are not very definite. However, it may be possible for a group of subjects to give a comparative estimation of the test if they are submitted to many of these over a period of time. It is also worth while to record the opinions of all the subjects as to whether the test was extremely, moderately, or slightly painful.

III.   DATA COLLECTING SHEET

Name:*   Occupation:

Subject no.:   Ethnic group or nationality:

Age: Place:

Sex: Date:

                                    Name of Investigator:

	Before immersion			During immersion					After immersion		
	Readings:			$\frac{1}{2}'$	$1'$	$1\frac{1}{2}'$	$2'$	$2\frac{1}{2}'$	Readings:		
	(1)	(2)	(3)						(1)	(2)	(3)
Systolic press.											
Diastolic press.											
Pulse rate											
Ts immersed hand											
Ts other hand											
Notes on pain (record severity as: 0, +, ++, +++)											

*Full details of the subject and his population group are to be entered in the **BASIC IDENTIFICATION SHEETS,** as laid down in the Technical Introduction.

D4. COLD-INDUCED VASODILATATION TEST

I. INTRODUCTION

- (a) General
- (b) Observations to be made
- (c) Sampling

II. TECHNIQUES

III. DATA COLLECTING SHEET

I. INTRODUCTION

(a) General:

This well-established test still holds its position in the study of acclimatisation and tolerance to cold. Its chief disadvantage is that it is very painful (at least to non-acclimatised subjects), and that some experiments must be stopped because the subject is on the verge of fainting. The information obtained by this test would be enhanced if it were combined with a test for cold pressor response. (See **D3**).

(b) Observations to be made:

The essential observations to be made in this test are the skin temperature changes of the digits. In addition, where resources are available, hand plethysmography should be included.

(c) Sampling:

It is suggested that at least 30–50 individuals of either sex and within narrow age limits should make up the sample, but as this test is fairly simple, larger numbers could be tested.

II. TECHNIQUES

(a) Apparatus:

(1) A vacuum-flask calorimeter of 3000 ml. volume with a crushed-ice/water mixture subjected to the standardised vigorous stirring. Alternatively, the cold-water bath can be a 4-litre beaker, or other similar container. If equal volumes of crushed ice and water are used, the temperature of the bath will be kept close to 4°C for the whole duration of the test.

(2)   Thermocouple/potentiometer assembly which allows an accuracy to within $\pm 0.1°C$, and continuous recording or reading of three channels at least at each half-minute.

(b) **Procedure:**

The subject is studied in the reclined position, sitting in a comfortable chair in the thermally comfortable environment as described in **D3**. One arm hangs relaxed by the subject's side, with the palm turned inwards. Around the wrist, in a plane at right angles to the long axis of the extremity, a line is drawn at the lower border of the radial styloid process to mark the level of immersion:

Skin temperature measurements are best obtained with small thermocouples. these are attached as follows:

(1)   The recommended placement is the index fingernail bed, that is, the mid-line of the dorsal aspect of the distal phalanx, just proximal to the nail-fold.

It is also desirable to use the following sites:

(2)   The centre of the ball of the third finger. (It has been shown that the finger-pad is consistently warmer than the nail-bed during cold-induced vasodilatation.)

(3)   Over a prominent wrist vein 3 cm. above the line marked around the wrist.

These thermocouples are kept in place with small strips of waterproof adhesive tape covering the junctions. This method will not give absolute skin temperatures, but if the temperature of the water-bath is kept constant, the variations in the thermocouple temperature will be directly related to changes in cutaneous temperature.

Before the test, skin temperatures of both index finger tips are measured, until constant values are obtained.

When pre-test conditions are satisfactory, one opened hand is immersed up to the wrist into the water-bath (at 4°C), and is kept there for 10 minutes. Attention should be paid that the hand is not partially withdrawn, and that no movement of the fingers takes place. Temperature measurements of both index fingers are made at half-minute intervals throughout the experimental period, and for 3 minutes afterwards. Water-bath temperature is recorded simultaneously. This test will give an indirect evaluation of the blood-flow in the extremities, and will indicate the magnitude as well as the time of onset of the cold-induced vasodilatation.

III. DATA COLLECTING SHEET

Name:*   Occupation:
Subject no.:   Ethnic group or nationality:
Age: Place:
Sex: Date:
                                          Name of investigator:

Note any fainting reaction during test:
Record pain severity as 0, +, ++, +++:
Record temperatures to 0·1°C.

	IMMERSED HAND			OTHER HAND			water temp.
	Index finger	3rd finger	wrist vein	Index finger	3rd finger	wrist vein	
Before immersion Readings for "steady state"							
(1)							
(2)							
(3)							
During immersion after: 30″							
1′ 00″							
1′ 30″							
2′ 00″							
2′ 30″							
3′ 00″							
3′ 30″							
4′ 00″							
4′ 30″							
5′ 00″							

(continued)

III. DATA COLLECTING SHEET (continued)

5′ 30″							
6′ 00″							
6′ 30″							
7′ 00″							
7′ 30″							
8′ 00″							
8′ 30″							
9′ 00″							
9′ 30″							
10′ 00″							
After immersion after 30″							
1′ 00″							
1′ 30″							
2′ 00″							
2′ 30″							
3′ 00″							
Further readings							
(A)							
(B)							
(C)							
(D)							
(E)							
(F)							

(continued)

III. DATA COLLECTING SHEET (continued)

(A) —Lowest temperature before spontaneous rewarming.

(B) —Minutes after start at which lowest temperature reached.

(C) —Minutes after start at which spontaneous rewarming begins.

(D) —Maximum temperature reached during spontaneous rewarming.

(E) —Minutes after start at which maximum temperature reached.

(F) —Average temperature during 10 minutes' immersion.

Readings A, B, C, D and E can be taken from graphs constructed from the data in the table above.

*Full details of the subject and his population group are to be entered in the **BASIC IDENTIFICATION SHEETS**, as laid down in the Technical Introduction.

D5. THE CONTROLLED-HYPERTHERMIA HEAT TOLERANCE TEST

I. INTRODUCTION

    (a) General

    (b) Observations to be made

    (c) Sampling

II. TECHNIQUE

    (a) Preparation

    (b) Instructions for test procedure

    (c) Equipment

III. DATA COLLECTING SHEET

I. INTRODUCTION

(a) General:

This test measures the functional efficiency of the thermo-regulatory system.

It uses portable equipment to provide a controlled climate 'hot-room' facility in the form of an air-conditioned bed. It is suitable for field work. The equipment is relatively light (< 150 kg.), cheap (component cost approximately £500), and robust; it is self-contained and requires only electricity (2–3 kW, 240 V, 50 cyc. a.c.) and a water supply to operate.

The heat tolerance test has four principal objectives;

1 To test the set-points for temperature regulation: (a) measuring the normal level for body temperature regulation, (b) measuring the body temperature required to initiate the heat dissipating response of sweating.

2. To test the efficiency of the sweating mechanism: (a) measuring the rate of sweat secretion produced by a given rise in deep body temperature, (b) measuring the rate of decline in sweating at a fixed level of body temperature (i.e. sweat suppression).

3. To test the heat transport efficiency of the cardiovascular system by: (a) measuring the temperature gradient between the core and the periphery of the body with body temperature normal, and after raising it to 38.0°C, (b) measuring the skin blood flow at normal and raised body temperatures.

4. To provide sweat samples for the analysis of electrolytes and other constituents.

(b) Observations to be made:

1. The following observations are recorded during the test:

(a) The sweat rate in response to elevating deep body temperature to 38°C.

(b) The rate of sweat suppression.

(c) Sweat samples are collected for analysis.

(d) The deep body temperatures (ear and rectal) and skin temperatures and pulse rates of the subjects while resting in a neutral environment and again at the onset of sweating.

(e) The relationship between skin temperature and deep body temperature at the end of one hour of controlled hyperthermia to provide evidence of the efficiency of cardiovascular heat transport. If equipment is available, the peripheral blood flow in hand and forearm should be measured while resting in the neutral climate, and during the hour of controlled hyperthermia.

(f) The subject is asked to assess whether the climate in Stage I is thermally neutral or whether for maximum comfort he would prefer it slightly warmer or slightly cooler.

(g) If equipment is available, the subject's energy metabolism should be measured in the neutral climate and again when body temperature is raised.

2. The following ancillary and preliminary observations should be made:

(a) General medical examination (see **F1**).

(b) Assessment of habitual physical activity (see **C6**).

(c) Measurement of fitness, if possible (see **C1** and **C2**).

(d) Measurement of physique. (For anthropometric techniques see **A1**.)

(e) Environmental assessment (see **H**).

(c) **Sample Size:**

It is suggested that the sample size should generally not be less than 20 individuals. If both men and women are studied, they must be treated as separate samples. The initial sample should be fit young adults (age range 18–30 years).

Further details of the controlled hyperthermia technique and the rationale for this test are to be found in the following publications:

Fox, R. H., Goldsmith, R., Kidd, D. J. and Lewis, H. E. (1963) **J. Physiol.,**
166: 530–547.

Fox, R. H., Goldsmith, R., Kidd, D. J. and Lewis, H. E. (1963) **J. Physiol.,**
166: 548–562.

Bradbury, P. A., Fox, R. H., Goldsmith, R. and Hampton, I. F. G. (1964)
J. Physiol., 171: 384–396.

Fox R. H. (1965) Heat. In **The Physiology of Human Survival** (ed. Edholm
and Bacharach), Academic Press.

Fox, R. H. (1966) Human temperature regulation and adaptation to climatic
stress. In **Penguin Science Survey B,** 1966 (Ed. Allison), Penguin
Books.

Fox, R. H., Goldsmith R., Hampton, I. F. G. and Hunt, T. J. (1967) **J. Appl.**
Physiol., 22: 39–46.

Fox, R. H., Crockford, G. W., Hampton, I. F. G. and MacGibbon, R. (1967)
J. Appl. Physiol., 23: 267–275.

*Fox, R. H., Crockford, G. W. and Löfstedt, B. (1967) United States Public
Health Service: Technical Report No. 44, pp. 115–167.

*Fox, R. H. (1967) United States Public Health Service: Technical Report
No. 44 pp. 267–328.

II.   TECHNIQUE

The test is divided into the four stages as shown in Fig. D5/1.

I.   An initial 30-minute period during which the subject is exposed to a
pre-determined neutral thermal environment (air to suit 30°C); physiological responses (body temperature and pulse rate, etc.) are measured
at the beginning, after 20 minutes and again at the end of this period. A
short period of pre-treatment may be required if the subject starts the
test too warm or too cold (see below).

* Copies of this report can be obtained from either the United States Public Health Service,
National Center for Urban and Industrial Health, 1014, Broadway, Cincinnati, Ohio
45202, USA, or from Dr. R. H. Fox, National Institute for Medical Research (Hampstead
Laboratories), Holly Hill, London, N.W.3, England.

II.   A period of slow body heating (air to suit 45°C) which continues until sweating starts, at which time the physiological response is again measured.

III. A period of rapid heating (air to suit 55°C) to raise body temperature to the target level (38°C).

IV.   A period of 1 hour of controlled hyperthermia at 38°C with measurements at 15-minute intervals of sweat rate, skin temperature, deep body temperature and pulse rates. The 15-minute measurements of sweat rate permit the rate of sweat suppression to be calculated.

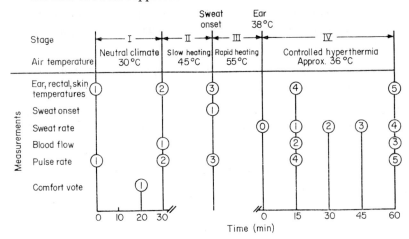

Fig. D5/1   Procedure for the controlled-hyperthermia heat tolerance test.

PROCEDURE

(a) **Preparation:**

It is best to perform the test on the nude subject, but to preserve modesty the briefest and lightest non-asborbent bikini may be worn. The bikini and a bra can be fashioned from thin black PVC sheeting cut into a double triangle, and moulded to form cups, respectively. This has little or no effect on the sweat measurement.

The subject is prepared for an experiment by first placing the thermistor thermometers in both ears. The skin temperature sensing elements (ST1) and electro-cardiograph electrodes are fixed to the skin, and a rectal thermometer is inserted. (See **D1** and **D2**.) The subject then dresses in a thin PVC vapour-barrier suit which seals at the neck with a soft rubber diaphragm and from which the total body sweat loss is collected into measuring vessels by suction through tubes at the feet.

After dressing, the subject lies on the bed and the air is sucked out of the suit to test that a negative pressure of 10 ins. Hg can be maintained. The second skin temperature measuring harness (ST2) is then applied by slipping the thermistor thermometers into the pockets on the outside of the vapour-barrier suit. The subject is wrapped in the air distributing layer, two blankets, an aluminised sheet, and then an insulating quilt is placed over all to insulate the subject from the environment. The head is enclosed in a heavily insulated hood. The air to the bed is switched on and the experiment begins.

(b) **Instructions for test procedure:**

Stop-watch 1	Stop-watch 2	Stage	Procedures
0		I	**Neutral Climate** Set air temperature at 30°C as soon as subject is covered by bedclothes. Record all temperatures and pulse rate. Provided skin temperature (ST2) is between 32 and 35°C, start first stopwatch. Record air, skin, and ear temperatures at 2-minute intervals. Suction on suit less than 1″ Hg. Pretreatment is required if the skin temperature (ST2) is outside the range 32–35°C at the start. The subject is too warm if the mean skin temperature is above 35°C at the outset of the test, or the subject is sweating; the air temperature to the bed should be lowered to 25°C and maintained there until the skin temperature has fallen to 33°C. The subject is too cold if the mean skin temperature is below 32°C at the outset of the test; the air temperature should be raised to 40°C

Stop-watch 1	Stop-watch 2	Stage	Procedures
			and maintained at this level until the skin temperature has risen to 34°C. Following the pretreatment to cool or warm the subject, the air temperature is returned to 30°C and the half-hour of Stage I begins.
20			Record all measurements and ask subject for comfort vote. (The subject is asked whether the temperature of the bed is exactly right or whether he would prefer to be a little warmer or a little cooler.)
30			Record all measurements.

II Sweat Onset

Commence slow heating (air temperature to bed raised to 45°C). Sweat detecting starts. (Apply iodine sweat detecting paper to forehead for 20 secs. once every 30 secs. or 1 minute.) Continue recording air, skin, and ear temperatures at 2-minute intervals until sweat onset. Record all measurements and note time of sweat onset.

III Rapid Heating

Raise temperature to 55°C. When ear temperature reaches 37·5°C, lower air temperature to 40°C, and raise suction to 10° Hg. If body temperature continues rising rapidly past 37·8°C, lower air temperature to 30°C. If the rate of rise is slowing down as it passes 37·8°C, lower air to 35°C. If the rate of rise is very slow, leave air at 40°C.

Target Temperature

When ear temperature reaches 37·9°C or thereabouts, start the second stopwatch for the beginning of the hour of controlled hyperthermia, and switch from collecting

Stop-watch 1	Stop-watch 2	stage	Procedures
			bottle 1 to collecting bottle 2. Record all temperature measurements. Lower suction pressure to less than 1″ Hg.
			Deep body temperature is maintained at 38·0°C during the hour of controlled hyperthermia by small alterations in the air temperature to the bed. The air temperature should be modulated within the range 30–40°C, except for a few individuals who require an air temperature 1 or 2°C lower. The aim is to find the air temperature which keeps the subject's body temperature poised at 38·0°C. The technique is quickly learnt, and after a couple of training sessions, almost anybody can keep the body temperature within $\pm 0·2$°C of target, and after a little experience within $\pm 0·1$°C. The beginner usually makes the mistake of altering the air temperature too often and too much.

		IV	**Hour of Controlled Hyperthermia**
	10		Raise suction to 10″ Hg.
	15		End collection 1 and record all measurements. Lower suction.
	25		Raise suction to 10″ Hg.
	30		End collection 2. Lower suction.
	40		Raise suction to 10″ Hg.
	45		End collection 3. Lower suction.
	55		Raise suction to 10″ Hg.
	60		End collection 4. Record all measurements.

(c)   Equipment:

The test equipment, sub-divided into its component units, is shown schematically in Fig. D5/2, and the bed is shown in use in Fig. D5/3. The air conditioning equipment, mounted on a lightweight frame, is slung below the bed, as shown in Fig. D5/4.

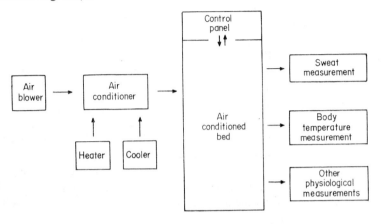

Fig. D5/2   Diagram of test bed.

(i) **Air blower**

The air pump is a standard industrial unit capable of delivering more than 40 cu.ft. of air/min. against a pressure of 1-2lb./sq. in. It is mounted in a heavily insulated box to ensure good sound insulation. The air is filtered and drawn through a car exhaust silencer. A throttle is provided on the air intake to adjust the air flow to the chosen rate, and the rate is measured by a differential pressure gauge across an orifice at the inlet to the bed.

(ii) **Air conditioning system**

The system is shown schematically in Fig. D5/5. Air from the blower is partitioned by adjustable dampers between hot and cold water heat exchangers and a bypass duct. There are two pairs of dampers and each pair is operated by a rod from the control panel. One pair of dampers controls the proportion of air cooled and the other controls the proportion of air heated. The two dampers of each pair are mounted at right angles to each other on a spindle so that rotation of the spindle through 90° will divert the air flow from the heat exchanger to the bypass duct or *vice versa*. With the damper settings illustrated in Fig. D5/4, all the air is passing through the hot water heater, but with movement of the hot air and then the cold air control rods through their full

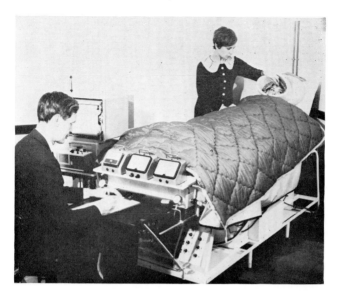

Fig. D5/3   Test bed in use.

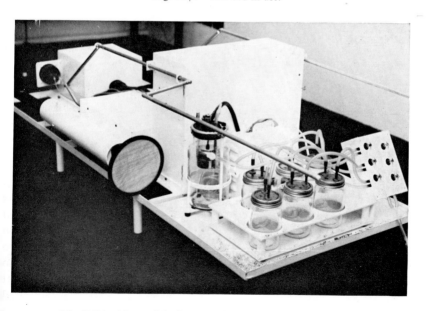

Fig. D5/4   Air-conditioning equipment installed below test bed.

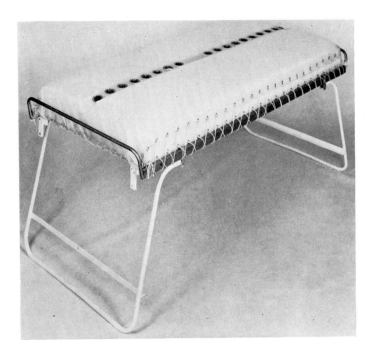

Fig. D5/6   Test bed stripped to mattress.

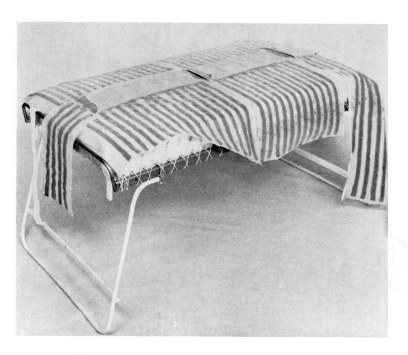

Fig. D5/7 Test bed with ventilated layer plugged in.

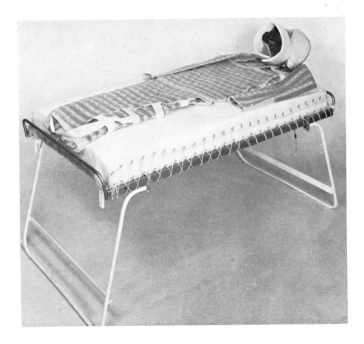

Fig. D5/8   Ventilated layer as it would appear wrapped around a subject.

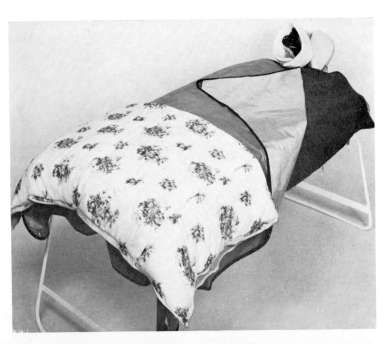

Fig. D5/9   See text

ranges the air flow is progressively diverted to the bypass duct and then to the cooler.

The unit has two heat exchangers on the cooling side. In most operating conditions a water supply with a temperature below 25°C is likely to be available and cooling would then be simply achieved by connecting the heat exchangers to the water supply. If the temperature of the water supply is too high, or for experiments on cold exposure, the available water supply would be passed through the first heat exchanger and cold water from a melting ice heat sink would be circulated through the second heat exchanger.

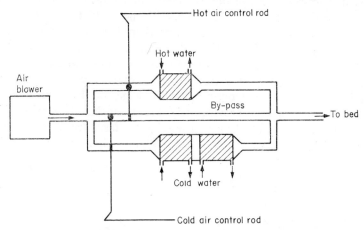

Fig. D5/5   Diagram of air-conditioning system.

(iii)   Heating and cooling units

The closed circuit hot water supply unit comprises a small electrically-driven water circulating pump, a thermostated 2-kilowatt immersion heater, and an adjustable cartridge-type thermostat operating a relay to control the power supply to the immersion heater. The thermostat on the immersion heater is set to operate slightly above the controlled level for the water temperature and acts as a safety device. The water temperature is set so that the air temperature can rise only a few degrees above the maximum of 50°–55°C required for rapid body cooling.

The closed circuit cold water supply unit utilises an identical water circulating pump. The water is circulated through a heat exchanger coil in a melting ice container. If ice is not available, a small refrigerator cooling a volume of water in a tank is required.

(iv)   Ventilated bed.

The complete bed with a subject being tested is shown in Fig. D5/3. The bed is a standard Danish design with a light-weight metal frame and folding legs. The mattress is specially constructed from PVC and foam plastic with a central air duct running the length of the bed and communicating through ports with the ventilated section above and the air conditioner below. The bed is shown stripped to the mattress in Fig. D5/6, with the ventilated layer plugged in (Fig. D5/7), and with the ventilated layer wrapped around as it would be on a subject in Fig. D5/8. The lowest of the three layers of foam plastic is a complete sheet on the bed-springs and forms an insulated floor for the mattress duct. The conditioned air is led into the mattress duct through a flexible coupling to the heat exchanger unit. The edges of the three PVC layers forming the mattress are provided with eyelets so that the mattress can be firmly tethered to the bed frame. The subject is insulated from the environment above by blankets, an aluminised sheet, and a quilted cover (Fig. D5/9).

The air distribution layer plugs into the ports on the upper surface of the ventilated mattress and encloses the whole body except for the head.

(v)   Sweat collecting system

The sweat collecting system is shown schematically in Fig. D5/10. The subject is dressed in a thin PVC suit which completely encloses the body and limbs and is sealed to the neck by a soft rubber diaphragm. The rubber diaphragm is sufficiently elastic to allow the subject to step into the suit from the head end. A port fitted with a removable rubber bung, through which the ECG and the thermocouple or thermistor skin temperature (ST1) leads pass, provides an airtight seal for electrical connections to the interior of the suit. Sweat is sucked out of the suit from both feet; perforated tubes running up the backs of the legs, the trunk, and down the arms help to ensure that the sweat is removed effectively. The suction applied to the suit is shown on a gauge on the control panel and is regulated by a needle valve. A drip chamber enables the operator to watch the sweat flow. The sweat is collected into five separate measuring cylinders or sample bottles; one bottle is used to collect all the sweat secreted prior to the hour of controlled hyperthermia, and the remainder are used to collect the four 15-minute samples. Suction is provided by a portable pump with a release valve set to operate just above 10″ Hg.

At the beginning of an experiment the system is checked to ensure that the suit is sealing sufficiently to give a 10″ Hg suction pressure and then the pressure is lowered to ½ to 1″ Hg for the initial stages of the experiment. The pressure is raised to 10″ Hg for the last five minutes prior to each of the four collections during the hour of controlled hyperthermia (see Fig. D5/10). For the collection at the beginning of the hour of controlled hyperthermia the moment to raise the pressure can be judged from the rate of rise of body temperature.

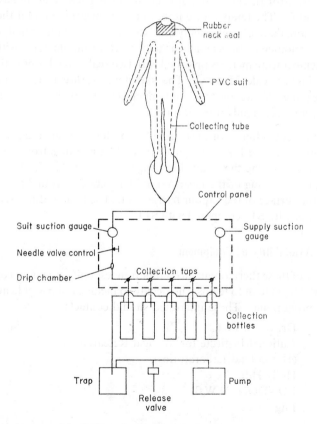

Fig. D5/10 Sweat-collecting system.

Sweat samples (20 ml) for subsequent analysis are taken from the initial collection and from the 15–30 minute and 45–60 minute collections. A few drops of toluene are added to each sample as a preservative.

(vi)   Temperature measuring system

The essential temperature measurements are deep body, skin, and the conditioned air supplied to the bed. Deep body temperature is measured in the external auditory meatus close to the tympanic membrane following the technique described by Bradbury *et al.*, **J. Physiol., 171:** 384–396, 1964.

The thermistor thermometers for measuring ear temperature have a range from 35–40°C. The temperature in both ears is measured and if the two ears differ by more than 0.2°C it usually indicates malfunctioning or malpositioning of one thermometer. In general, ear temperatures should agree within 0·1°C. The air temperature meter is provided with two scales, the lower scale 15–40°C and the higher scale 35–60°C. The skin temperature meter (ST2) gives a direct reading of the mean skin temperature from 30–40°C. The rectal temperature meter reads from 35–40°C.

Two different systems for measuring ' skin ' temperature are provided with this equipment. The first (ST1) gives individual readings from the skin sites chosen for measuring the mean skin temperature (see **D1**.) The second (ST2) gives a direct reading of the mean ' skin ' temperature from 8 predetermined sites on the surface of the vapour barrier suit. The temperatures recorded are a little lower with ST2 compared with ST1.

(vii)   Availability of Equipment

A number of these thermoregulatory function test units are under construction and available on loan to teams who decide to include a study of heat tolerance in their programme. Those interested should contact:

> Dr. R. H. Fox,
> National Institute for Medical Research
> (Hampstead Laboratories),
> Holly Hill,
> LONDON, N.W.3,
> England.

III. DATA COLLECTING SHEET

Name :*   Occupation :
Serial number :   Height (mm.) :
Age :   Weight (kg.) :
Sex :   Place of examination :
Ethnic and tribal origin   Date of examination :
  (or nationality) :   Name of Investigator :

Time at start of experiment :

Record temperatures to 0·01 °C.

STAGE I

Record sweat volumes in ml.

	Right ear	Left ear	Rectal	Skin	Pulse rate/min.
Initial					
Start					
20 mins.					
30 mins.					

STAGE II

Sweat onset					

STAGE IV

1st collection					
4th collection					

(continued)

Table—continued

SWEAT COLLECTIONS   0 : . . . .

                                    1 : . . . .

                                    2 : . . . .

                                    3 : . . . .

                                    4 : . . . .

                      Total 1st–4th : . . . .

Ear used to control body temperature : right/left

Average temperature of control ear over hour of hyperthermia :

Time (**mins.**) spent more than 0·1 °C from target :

Time (mins.) spent more than 0·2°C from target :

Mean skin temperature over last half-hour :

Mean bed air temperature over last half-hour :

Comfort vote in Stage I : too warm/neutral/too cool

COMMENTS :

D6. THE MULTI-STRESS HEAT TOLERANCE TEST

I. INTRODUCTION
(a) General
(b) Observations to be made
(c) Sampling

II. TECHNIQUES

III. DATA COLLECTING SHEET

I. INTRODUCTION

(a) General:

A heat tolerance stress test to be used in human adaptability investigations on a population basis should throw light on the following two questions:

1. The way in which different populations, living under different heat stresses in various parts of the world, make use of man's temperature regulatory mechanisms.

2. The limits of environmental heat stress for the different populations working at a moderate rate (i.e. at an oxygen consumption rate of 1·0 litre/minute or a metabolic rate of 5 Kcal./min.)

Both of these aims can be achieved by means of a multi-temperature test. In this test different samples of the population in question are exposed for three hours at a moderate rate of work in different environmental heat stress conditions. These are chosen to give Effective Temperatures of 78°, 82°, 86°, and 90°F. A mobile climatic room suitable for providing these test conditions is described in **D8**.

(A shortage of time and personnel may make it impossible to undertake this test. A shortened alternative, which gives similar results, is the US Public Health Service Test I, described in 'Comparative Methodology of Heat Tolerance Testing', Occupational Health Research and Training Facility, 1014, Broadway, Cincinnatti, Ohio, U.S.A. August, 1967. See also *op. cit.* p. 233).

(b)   Observations to be made:

Ancillary and preliminary observations.

1. General medical examination. (See **F1**).
2. Assessment of habitual physical activity. (See **C6**).
3. Anthropometric measurements. (See **A1**).
4. Measurement of fitness, if possible. (See **C1** and **C2**).
5. Environmental assessment. (See **H**).

Observations during test.

1. Sweat rate.
2. Deep body temperature.
3. Skin temperature.
4. Pulse rate.
5. Oxygen cost of work.
6. Sweat rate/body temperature relationship.

(c)   Sampling:

As this procedure involves four separate test conditions, it would not generally be possible to work on a very large sample. These should be of one sex, and chosen within a narrow age-range, probably in the first instance young adults.

Analysis

For the analysis, use was made of the Handbook of Statistical Tables by Donald B. Owen, and in particular of the graphs on page 44 showing the sample sizes needed for a test comparing the means of two normal distributions with unknown, but equal, standard deviations. These graphs were for two-sided tests at a significance level of 5%.

In the following tables are shown the difference between population means which we would be **90% certain** of showing up with samples of 10, 20 or 30 when working with a significance level of 5%. The differences are shown for different values of the unknown standard deviations.

Table 1

Rectal Temperature (°F)

n	Standard deviation							
	·3	·4	·5	·6	·7	·8	·9	1·0
10	·49	·65	·81	·97	1·14	1·30	1·46	1·63
20	·33	·44	·55	·66	·77	·88	·99	1·10
30	·26	·34	·43	·51	·60	·68	·77	·86

Table 2

Heart Rate (*beats/minute*)

n	Standard deviation							
	11	12	13	14	15	16	17	18	19
10	17·9	19·5	21·1	22·8	24·4	26·0	27·7	29·3	31·0
20	12·1	13·2	14·3	15·4	16·5	17·6	18·7	19·8	20·9
30	9·4	10·3	11·1	12·0	12·9	13·7	14·6	15·4	16·3

Table 3

Sweat Rate (*litre°*)

n	Standard deviation							
	75	100	125	150	175	200	225	250
10	122	163	203	244	285	326	366	407
20	82	110	137	165	192	220	247	275
30	64	86	107	129	150	172	193	250

In one study, the standard deviation in the 3rd hour of work in heat, varied from about 0·6 to about 1·0°F for unacclimatised men, and was as low as 0·35°F for some acclimatised men.

For unacclimatised men the standard deviation in the 3rd hour of work in heat varied from about 13 to about 19 beats/min. while for acclimatised men it could be as low as 11 beats/min.

Second hour sweat rates had standard deviations varying from about 75 to about 250, and in general those for acclimatised groups were smaller than those for unacclimatised groups.

II.   TECHNIQUE

(a)   Measurements at rest:

The test subjects should arrive at the laboratory after having had no more than a light meal. They are then weighed in the nude and thereafter provided with a pair of light shorts. It has been noted that most men prefer to work while wearing socks and rubber shoes, while the remainder work barefoot. The heights of the subjects are usually measured on another occasion, e.g. when they come for a medical examination (see **F1**.). While the ECG electrodes are being strapped down, thermistors are inserted into the rectum, mouth, and ear cavity. After connecting the appropriate leads to the Sanborn ECG and the potentiometer, the skin of the subject is marked with an ink pencil at six anatomical sites. This technique ensures uniformity of measurements, as it allows the temperature of the skin to be measured each time at exactly the same site.

The resting measurements of skin and body temperatures are made over a period of 1 hour, with the subject lying in the coolest environment that can be provided.

Each test subject is exposed to each of the four test conditions A–D, given below.

The sequence at which each subject is exposed to the various temperature conditions is according to a latin-square arrangement. At all temperature conditions the rate of work is kept constant at 1560 ft. lbs/min., (=215·3 m.kg./min.), and the rhythm of stepping on and off the step is 12 steps/min.

Condition	Dry-Bulb Temperature	Wet-Bulb Temperature	R.H.	V.P.
A	93	90	88	35
B	91	88	88	33
C	88	84	85	29
D	82	78	84	$23\frac{1}{2}$

The work consists of stepping on and off a wooden stool adjusted to a set height calculated by means of substituting body weight into the following formula:

$$\text{Stepping Height (ins.)}^* = \frac{1560}{\text{Body Weight (lbs)}}$$

The pace of stepping involves 12 steps on and 12 steps off the stool per minute and is indicated by a sound metronome set to ring 24 times per minute.

(b) Main study in heat:

On entering the climatic room the subjects remove their shoes, socks and pants and are weighed on a platform scale (assumed accuracy of ± 10 gm.) Then follow measurements of skin temperatures at the six anatomical points made by means of a constant pressure skin thermocouple. After taking a resting measurement of the heart-rate in the erect position the stepping is commenced in the heat at the rate of 12 steps per minute, on and off the stool.

During the first hour of exposure, measurements of the different temperatures (rectal, mouth, and ear cavity) and heart rate, are made every 5 to 10 minutes. However during the second and third hours they are made every 15 minutes. During the first hour expired air is collected (Douglas bag technique with mouth-piece) for three minutes for analysis of oxygen, CO_2, and nitrogen. The results of these analyses are used to calculate the metabolic rate of the men during their work in heat. Sweat rates are calculated from hourly body weight changes and incorporating water taken in and urine passed during hourly intervals.

* Stepping height (cm.) $= \dfrac{1794}{\text{Body weight (kg)}}$

The mean skin temperature should be calculated from the six skin temperature sites, using the following weighting factors:

cheek	0·14
chest	0·19
back	0·19
forearm	0·11
palm	0·05
thigh	0·32

Two criteria are rigidly employed for withdrawing a subject from the heat study:

(i)   A rectal temperature of 39·5°C. (103·1°F).

(ii) A heart rate of 180 beats/minute, if sustained for two successive counts within 30 minutes.

Drinking water is warmed to the test temperature, given a fruit flavour, and kept in a vacuum container. This preventive measure ensures that drinking water does not cool the mouth tissues and thereby affect the mouth temperature. Nevertheless, drinking water is always given at such a time that the mouth tissues can regain their original temperature. On the other hand drinking water is allowed *ad libitum*.

Aliquot samples of expired air are analysed in duplicate for oxygen content (e.g. on a Beckman oxygen analyser, Model E2.)

The data obtained in these tests should be expressed in terms of:

(a)   Body temperatures at each test condition.

(b)   Sweat rate at each test condition.

(c)   Heart rate at each test condition.

(d)   The sweat rate/body temperature relationship.

Analysis along these lines is discussed in detail by Williams and Wyndham in ' Comparative Methodology for Heat Tolerance Testing: A Cooperative International Study ', (1967) United States Department of Health, Education and Welfare, Public Health Service, National Center for Urban and Industrial Health.

II.   DATA COLLECTING SHEET

Name:*   Ethnic group or nationality:
Serial no.:   Occupation:
Age: Height (cm.):
Sex: Weight (kg.):
                                           Place of examination:
                                           Date of examination:

Temperature conditions of coolest
environment for resting measurements: DB: °C
                                         WB: °C
                                         w/v: m./min.
Stepping height (see p. 381):   cm.

RESTING MEASUREMENTS

Skin temperatures: cheek: forearm:
                   chest: palm:
                   back: thigh:
                   mean skin: (see p. 382)
Body temperatures: rectal: oral: ear:
Heart rate: /min.

MEASUREMENTS IN HEAT   (record all temperatures to 0·1°C)

Test condition: (A, B, C or D. See p. 381)

On entering climatic room, and at end of 1st, 2nd and 3rd hours, record the following:

	Body wt.	Water intake	Urine pas'd.	Heart rate	Chest temp.	Cheek temp.	Back temp	Fore-arm temp.	Palm temp	Thi' temp	Mean skin temp.
On entering											
End of 1st hr.											
End of 2nd hr.											
End of 3rd hr.											

During 1st hour, record the following:
              Expired air: O_2%:
                           N_2%:
                           CO_2%:
                           O_2 usage (l/min.):

(continued)

Table—continued

Every 5 min. during the 1st hour, and every 15 min. thereafter, record the following:

Min. of test	5	10	15	20	25	30	35	40	45	50	55	60	75	90	105	120	135	150	165	180
Rectal temp.																				
Oral temp.																				
Ear temp.																				

Record also : Maximum rectal temperature reached :
            Maximum oral temperature reached :
            Maximum ear temperature reached :

*Full details of the subject and his population group are to be entered in the **BASIC IDENTIFICATION SHEETS,** as laid down in the Technical Introduction.

Name of investigator: . . . .

D7. THE MULTI-STRESS SINGLE EXPOSURE HEAT TOLERANCE TEST

I.   INTRODUCTION

(a) General
(b) Observations to be made
(c) Sampling

II.   TECHNIQUES

(a) Test procedure
(b) Equipment—A portable test chamber (tent)

III.   DATA COLLECTING SHEET

I. INTRODUCTION

(a) General:

The U.S. Public Health Service method for heat tolerance testing (P.H.S. II) is a work-in-heat test which incorporates:

(1) A single test session;
(2) A constant environmental heat load;
(3) A step-wise increase in work rate.

Because only one temperature condition is prescribed, the test can be carried out in the field using a portable climatic chamber (see **D8**), or a tent, (see (b) Equipment, below). The test can of course also be carried out by bringing subjects to an existing hot-room, in cases where there is not sufficient time to carry out the multiple exposure test (**D6**). Because this form of multi-stress test using one temperature condition and three work levels has not been fully compared with the conventional test (**D6**), it is probably best used where a number of different groups are to be compared simultaneously.

(b) Observations to be made:

These are the same as those given in **D6**. They are:

Ancillary and preliminary observations:

1. General medical examination (see **F1**)
2. Assessment of habitual physical activity (see **C6**)
3. Anthropometric measurements (see **A1**)
4. Measurement of fitness if possible (see **C1** and **C2**)
5. Environmental description (see **H**)

Observations during test:

1. Sweat rate.
2. Deep body temperature.
3. Skin temperatures.
4. Pulse rate.
5. Oxygen cost of work.
6. Sweat rate/body temperature relationship.

(c) **Sampling:**

Samples should aim to include 20 individuals of each sex at each stress condition for every 10-year age group over the range 10–69 years. A minimal sample size would include 10 subjects of each sex at each stress condition, with at least some subjects in the 20–29 and the 40–49 age groups.

II. TECHNIQUES

(a) **Test procedure:**

Before selection for participation in the test, each subject is given a medical examination, including ECG, urine analysis, blood chemistry, blood counts, and a chest X-ray, in addition to the usual physical examination and medical history. Only those individuals with essentially negative findings are invited to participate in the test.

Name, height, weight, age, and other personal details are recorded for each subject accepted.

Then:—

1. Insert rectal catheter and tympanic thermocouple.
2. Attach chest electrodes for heart rate.
3. Mark places on skin where skin temperatures will be taken.

The test itself consists of one 30-minute warm-up period at comfort temperature, and three 45-minute work periods in a climate-controlled room held at 39°C (103°F) DB and 28·6°C (84°F) WB. The work is accomplished by stepping on and off a step 12 times a minute during the warm-up period,

8 times a minute for the first work period in the heat, 12 times a minute for the second work period, and 16 times a minute for the third work period. The height of the step is maintained constant at $10\frac{1}{4}''$ (26·1cm.) so that the energy cost of the work is proportional to body weight, and is relatively the same for all individuals when expressed as mkg./kg. body weight/min.

Oxygen consumption is measured from expired air samples collected for a five-minute period from the 20th to the 25th minutes of each work period.

Pulse rate, and rectal and tympanic temperatures are monitored continuously and read at 15-minute intervals.

The subjects are weighed to ± 10 gm. at the end of the warm-up period, and at the end of each work period. Drinking water is permitted *ad lib*, but is to be consumed only immediately after weighing. The amount is measured. Urine may be passed only immediately after weighing, and the amount is measured. Sweat production is calculated for each work period from the differences between change in body weight and quantity of water ingested.

Skin temperatures are measured at the end of the warm-up period and at the end of each work period. The six sites are; cheek, chest, back, forearm, thigh, and palm; the temperatures are measured by thermocouples.

Under field conditions, pulse rates could be determined with a stop-watch; rectal temperatures, with a clinical rectal thermometer; and body weights with a portable scale accurate to ± 10 gm (see **A1**). The work rate could be controlled by using a wooden stool $10\frac{1}{4}''$ (26·1 cm.) high, and pacing the number of steps per minute with a metronome or a string pendulum of suitable length.

(b) **Equipment—A Portable Test Chamber (Tent):**

The general requirements for the controlled climate room for this test are that it should be inexpensive, easy to erect and dismantle, light-weight, readily transportable, and simple to operate. It should be large enough to accommodate two subjects doing step exercises, and two observers. The air-conditioning system for the room should be capable of maintaining the desired test conditions over the range of ambient conditions likely to be encountered in most natural environments. The equipment described below has been designed to satisfy the test conditions of 39°C (103°F) DB and 28·6°C (84°F) WB. (25 mm. Hg. vapour pressure).

Construction Details

The test room would consist of a tent 8 ft. wide and 10 ft. long (2·44 ×
3·05 m.), with a centre height of 8½ ft.(2·59 m.) and a side-wall height of 5½ ft.
(1·68 m.). The tent should have an inner and outer skin supported on a
collapsible aluminium frame. The outer skin would be of suitable weather-
proof fabric. The inner skin should be fabricated of 1″ (2·5 cm.) fibreglass
batting captured between two layers of cloth to provide suitable thermal
insulation.

The floor of the tent should consist of a heavy ground cloth covered with
plywood. Provision must be made for attaching the edges of the ground
cloth to the tent walls to make the enclosure as tight as possible. Floor insulation could be provided by laying the ground cloth over a thick layer of dry
straw or similar material which may be available, or suitable insulating
material could be permanently attached to the underside of the plywood
sheets.

The entrance should be provided with a slide fastener (zipper) or other
device which would assure a tight closure. If the room is to be used extensively
at low ambient temperatures, a vestibule type of entrance would be desirable.

When the tent is exposed to direct solar radiation, a canvas fly located at
least one foot above the top of the tent should be used to reduce the solar
load and improve temperature control within the space. Such a fly would
also provide protection from rain, and it could be extended to protect the
auxiliary equipment.

Tents constructed as outlined above are described in a publication of the
U.S. Army Laboratories, Natick, Massachusetts. A portable test room of
similar construction has also been described by the Applied Sciences Laboratory, Johannesburg, South Africa. (see **D8**).

Air Conditioning System

As indicated above, the test condition for the room would be maintained at
39°C (103°F) DB and 28·6°C (84°F) WB temperature (25 mm. Hg vapour
pressure). This condition can be attained in most natural environments by
the processes of adiabatic saturation and sensible heating. A simple system
which would accomplish this is shown diagrammatically in Fig. D7/1.

Recirculated air from the test space is mixed with the desired amount of make-up air which enters at (M), and the mixture passes through the humidifier where its vapour pressure is raised to the required level. The humidified air then passes over electric heaters (H) which raise the air temperature as required to maintain the specified test conditions. Excess air is exhausted to the outdoors through the self-adjusting damper (D2). A centrifugal type fan is used to move the air through the system.

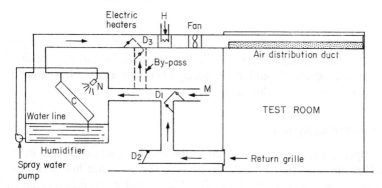

Fig. D7/1   Air-conditioning system (see text).

Humidifier

The humidifier as shown in Fig. D7/1 consists of a porous mat (C) which is wetted by a water spray from the low-pressure nozzles (N). Water and air flow in the same direction through the pad, the water then falls back into the sump below, and the air leaves through the outlet duct. Spray water is supplied to the nozzle by the small recirculating pump.

As an alternate design, the mat (C) could be placed in a vertical position and wetted by trickling water over it from a perforated trough.   This would require a smaller pump since both the water quantity and the discharge head would be reduced.

The mat in the humidifier can be of almost any material that will provide a large wetted contact area and offer a low resistance to air flow. The mats used in commercial evaporative coolers would be satisfactory. They are inexpensive and can be readily replaced when necessary. For the inclined mat or cell as shown in Fig. D7/1, a more permanent unit can be constructed of metal or plastic rods or tubes assembled parallel with the air flow and confined by a metal frame. The glass-fibre cells commonly used in capillary air washers are not recommended as they would probably disintegrate because of the rough travel and handling to which they would be subjected in this application. Eliminators should not be necessary on the downstream side of the mats, if the air velocity through the mats is less than 300 ft/min. (ca. 100 m./min.)

Heaters

The electric heaters should consist of several elements connected in parallel and individually controlled. One unit, having about 50% more capacity than each of the others, should be connected through a variable-voltage auto-transformer to provide close control.

Air Distribution System

It is important that the air supplied to the test space be distributed in such a way that air velocities throughout the occupied zone are low and uniform. Although this can probably be achieved in several ways, it is recommended that the air be supplied through one or two porous ducts running along the roof of the tent. A single duct could be located along the centre of the tent, or two smaller ducts could be located as shown in Fig. D7/2. The top half of each duct would be made of an air-tight fabric, and the bottom half of an open nylon fabric which would permit the passage of the required air volume without excessive pressure drop. If necessary, porous areas immediately over the subjects could be sealed to prevent excessive air velocities on the heads of the subjects. Such a system would provide uniform air distribution with a low initial velocity, and would add very little to the bulk or weight to be transported. The return air connection could be located near the floor at any convenient point.

System Controls

Control of the system shown in Fig. D7/1 can be accomplished manually or by conventional automatic control devices. For maximum portability and ruggedness manual controls should be used insofar as possible. With a reasonable amount of practice a skilful operator will be able to maintain the desired dry- and wet-bulb temperatures in the test space to within 1°F.

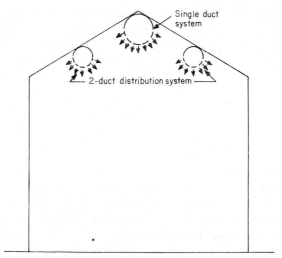

Fig. D7/2   Air distribution system (see text).

Control of Vapour Pressure

Humidity or vapour pressure may be controlled by any of three methods:

  a.   Adjust mixing dampers (D_1) so that the air leaving the humidifier will be at the desired vapour pressure.

  b.   Control the temperature of the spray water by means of an electric heater. The water heater is not shown in Fig. D7/1 but could be located either in the sump or in the pump discharge line. A variable-voltage auto-transformer would be used to vary the power input to the heater. It should be noted that if control is to be accomplished by heating the spray water, a spray nozzle must be used for wetting the mat. Trickling will not provide sufficient water flow for this type of control.

  c.   The vapour pressure leaving the washer might also be controlled by an air heater at the washer inlet but is the least desirable method for this application.

  If automatic control of the vapour pressure is desired the simplest method would be the on-off control of the spray water heater. This could be controlled by a humidistat or a wet-bulb thermostat located in the test room or the return duct. With heated spray water, the air leaving the humidifier will approach saturation at approximately the water temperature. The success of this approach will depend upon the effectiveness of the humidifier. Therefore, the heater might also be controlled by a thermostat located either in the air stream leaving the humidifier or in the spray water circuit. In these locations it would have to be set to compensate for the humidifier effectiveness. It would also require resetting for different internal latent heat loads.

Control of Dry-Bulb Temperature

The dry-bulb temperature would be controlled by proper adjustment of power to the electric heaters (H). As previously mentioned, several heating elements, each with its own manual switch should be installed. One of the elements should also be provided with a variable-voltage auto-transformer. Manual control would be obtained by turning on the required number of elements and by adjustment of the variable-voltage transformer.

If automatic control is desired, a thermostat would be located in the test room or the return duct to provide on-off control for the transformer-controlled heating element. The required number of elements would be turned on manually and the variable-voltage transformer would be set manually at a point where slight over-heating would occur, thus transferring control to the thermostat.

Control with By-Pass around the Humidifier

If electrical power requirements must be held to a minimum, some slight reduction in the size of air heaters (H) can be made by installing a by-pass around the washer and providing additional mixing dampers (D_3) as shown by dotted lines in Fig. D7/1.

With this design, damper D_1 would be roughly adjusted and manual control of the vapour pressure would be obtained by adjustment of damper D_3, or by control of power to the spray water heater as described above. If automatic control is desired it would be obtained by a humidistat or wet-bulb thermostat located in the conditioned space or in the return duct. Dry-bulb control, either manual or automatic, would be obtained as described above.

In the above discussion of controls the use of automatic damper operators has not been mentioned. Although excellent control can be obtained by automatic damper modulation, the equipment required is considered too expensive and complicated for this application.

Equipment Assembly.

It is recommended that the air-conditioning equipment and an engine-generator set of suitable capacity be permanently mounted in a truck. The truck could then be backed up to the tent and supply and return duct connections made with short lengths of light-weight flexible duct.

In cooler environments the ducts will require insulation to prevent condensation. Some of the connections shown outside the tent in Fig. D7/1 can probably be located inside the tent to minimize the amount of insulation required.

If an enclosed panel type truck is used it may be possible to provide a canvas enclosure between the tent and the truck to protect all of the connections.

In any case, care must be taken to make sure that there is no opportunity for the make-up air to be contaminated by the engine exhaust.

III. DATA COLLECTING SHEET....

Name:*
Serial number:
Age:
Sex:
Height: (cm.)
Weight: (lbs.)   (Kg.)

Ethnic group or
nationality:
Occupation:
Stepping height: (ins)   (cm)
Ambient temperature: °C DB   °C WB
Place of exmination:
Date of examination:

Name of Investigator:

Time:	Rectal temp. (°C)	Tympanic temp. (°C)	Heart rate /min.	Body wt. kg.	Av. room temp. DB WB (°C)	immediately after weighing — water drunk ml.	immediately after weighing — Urine passed ml.	O₂ usage ml/min.

WARM-UP

0 min.								
30 min.								

WORK PERIOD I

15 min.								
30 min.								
45 min.								

WORK PERIOD II

60 min.								
75 min.								
90 min.								

WORK PERIOD III

105 min.								
120 min.								
135 min.								

(*continued*)

Table—continued

SKIN TEMPERATURES (°C)

	Cheek	Chest	Back	Forearm	Thigh	Palm
Before						
45 min.						
90 min.						
135 min.						

* Full details of the subject and his population group are to be entered in the **BASIC IDENTIFICATION SHEETS,** as laid down in the Technical Introduction.

D8. A MOBILE HOT-ROOM FOR FIELD USE

Description of the design, construction, and performance of a portable climatic chamber.

INTRODUCTION

Temperature- and humidity-controlled facilities in the form of so-called climatic chambers, form part of the essential basic facilities that are necessary for certain physiological and psychological studies related to the effects of thermal environment on the well-being and productivity of man.

Before describing the portable unit itself, the major requirements with regard to the environmental conditions within the chamber which must be satisfied will briefly be referred to.

RANGE OF ENVIRONMENTAL CONDITIONS

The correct and realistic choice of the environmental conditions with regard to the air temperature, humidity, and velocity levels which are to be maintained within the climatic chamber is an important pre-requisite for the design of the temperature- and humidity-control system. Of particular importance is the accuracy to which these variables are to be controlled.

The design of the portable climatic chamber described below is based on the following range of environmental conditions over which the air temperature, humidity, and velocity levels have to be controlled within the chamber:

Air temperature—40°F to 120°F±1°F (4·4°C to 48·4°C ± 0·5°C).

Humidity—From a minimum dew-point temperature of 40°F (4·4°C) to saturated conditions±5% relative humidity.

Air velocity—From 60 to 200 f.p.m. (ca. 20–60 m./min.).

Apart from adequate thermal insulation in the outside walls of the chamber (which will ensure that the temperature of the inner surface of the walls is reasonably close to that of the air), no provision is considered necessary for controlling the wall temperatures as such.

DESCRIPTION OF THE CLIMATIC CHAMBER

The portable climatic chamber is built in the form of a caravan, 9 ft. 8 in. high by 8 ft. 0 in. wide by 19 ft. 4 in. long (2·95m. × 2·44 m. × 5·90 m.) (including the length of the tow-bar, approximately 5 ft. (1·5 m.) in length) and weighs 2850 lbs. (1290 kg.) net. (See Fig. D8/1.)

The aravan is divided into two sections or compartments by means of a partition of light construction, which is fitted with an interconnecting door.

The one compartment, which is 7 ft. high by 7 ft. wide by 9 ft. 6 ins. long (2·13 m. × 2·13 m. × 2·90 m.), is utilised as the test section, or climatic chamber; the required environmental conditions of air temperature and humidity being obtained by circulating air at a controlled temperature and humidity through the chamber.

The other compartment, adjacent to the climatic chamber, serves as an ' air-lock ', and is fitted with an outside door of the type used in cold storage rooms. The main object of the ' air-lock ' is to prevent outside environmental influences being carried through to the climatic chamber whenever the outside door is opened or closed. In this connection, care should always be taken to ensure the outside door is closed before the connecting door between the climatic chamber and the ' air-lock ' is opened. Air temperatures within the ' air-lock ' are ' controlled ' to some extent, by exhausting a certain percentage of the air supplied to the main test chamber through the ' air-lock '. Thus, suitable openings are provided at a low level in the partition (between the climatic chamber and the ' air-lock ') and an exhaust vent is fitted to the roof.

The outer walls of the caravan, which are thermally insulated with a six-inch layer of fibreglass, are lined with galvanised iron and aluminium sheeting on the inside and outside respectively. Both the galvanised iron and aluminium coverings for the walls of the caravan are properly sealed to prevent the excess migration of moisture into the insulation.

The air temperature and humidity control system

The temperature and humidity control unit (apart from the air distribution ducts, the thermostats, and the hygrostat, which are permanently installed inside the chamber, as well as the electronic controllers which are fixed to the outside of the caravan), is transported as a separate unit and erected on site in the position shown in Fig. D8/1.

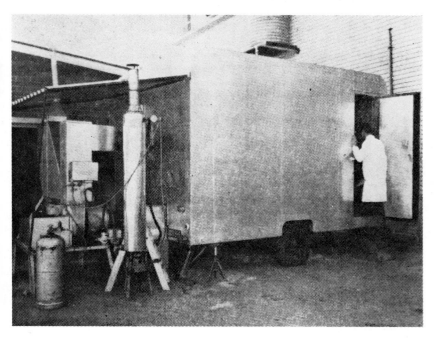

Fig. D8/1 Portable climatic chamber showing the position of the temperature and humidity control unit.

Fig. D8/4 The 'Satchwell' duatronic controllers which are used for controlling temperatures and humidities within the portable climatic chamber.

The diagrammatic layout of the control system is shown in Figs. D8/2 and D8/3.

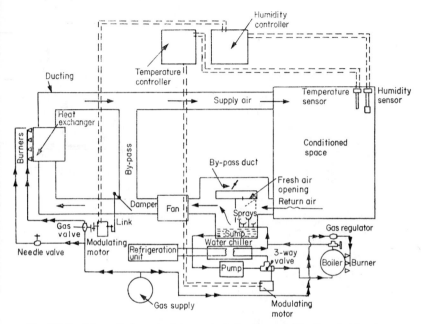

Fig. D8/2   Schematic layout of the controls for the portable climatic chamber.

The air temperature and humidity control system basically consists of a fan, temperature-controlled water sprays, and a low-pressure gas-fired air heater together with the necessary air-distribution and control equipment.

The basic principles of operation of the system are similar to the system used for controlling temperatures in a human calorimeter.

In the case of the portable climatic chamber the air temperature and relative humidity conditions are controlled by means of the water sprays and the finned-tube air heater or re-heater respectively. The following is a brief description of the system:

(i)   Temperature control

The return air from the climatic chamber together with a certain amount of fresh air is passed through a series of temperature-controlled water sprays in order to attain the required temperature condition. (The rate at which fresh air is drawn into the system is controlled manually by means of a damper.)

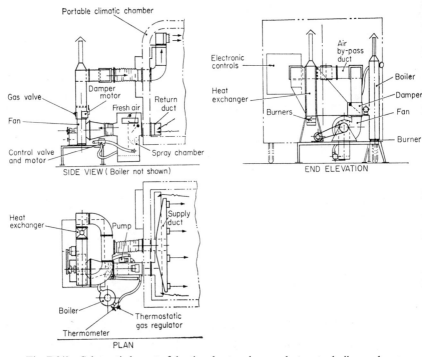

Fig. D8/3   Schematic layout of ducting, heat exchanger, hot-water boiler, and spray chamber, for the portable climatic chamber.

Basically, the temperature control system consists of a temperature sensing element (of the electrical resistance thermometer type), which is installed in the conditioned space, an electronic controller, water-heating and chilling units, a three-way motorised mixing valve, and, of course, the water spray itself.

The three-way valve automatically controls the temperature of the spray water and hence the air temperature condition in the climatic chamber, by regulating the relative rates at which the spray water is circulated through either the gas-fired water-heater and/or the water-chilling unit. (The spray water is continuously circulated between the sump of the spray chamber and the sprayer nozzles.)

On temperature fall within the chamber, the flow rate of water through the heating unit is automatically increased, and that through the water-chilling unit decreased, by means of the three-way mixing valve.

On temperature rise, the reverse action takes place.

The electronic controller which is used is of the two term type, with proportionate and integral control characteristics. The latter characteristic enables the three-way mixing valve to be moved at a speed proportional to the magnitude of the air temperature deviaticn from the desired value. Two term controllers such as the above, whilst having the inherent stability of proportional controllers, provide greater accuracy, since their integral action always eliminates offset. The electronic controllers are shown in Fig. D8/4, facing p. 403.

The water-heating unit is in the form of a vertically-mounted cylindrical tank 10 ins. (25·4 cm.) in diameter by 5 ft. (1·5 m.) high. The tank is fitted with 20 vertical tubes of ¾ in. (19 mm.) diameter which pass through the boiler shell.

Heating is obtained by letting the hot gases from a low-pressure gas-fired ring burner (situated immediately below the tank) pass through the tubes. (The water circulates through the shell, around the tubes.)

The water temperature within the tank is automatically controlled at the required value by means of a gas thermostat and gas regulator installed in the gas supply line to the burner.

The water-chilling unit consists of a cylindrical tank containing the evaporator or cooling coil of a direct expansion refrigeration unit. Control of water temperatures within the tank is by means of a simple 'on-off' system which automatically switches the refrigeration unit on or off, depending on whether the temperature of the water in the tank is above or below the desired value, respectively.

(ii) Humidity control

Relative humidity conditions within the chamber are controlled by reheating the air after it has passed through the water spray unit.

Basically, the relative humidity control system consists of an electrical resistance hygrometer which is installed in the chamber itself, an electronic controller, a finned-tube gas-fired air heater, and a by-pass duct.

On relative humidity fall within the chamber, the heat input to the reheater is automatically reduced, and, at the same time, a certain amount of air is allowed to by-pass the heater through the by-pass duct. (The actual amount of air which is allowed to by-pass the heater is automatically controlled by means of a motorised damper, which, at the same time, also controls a needle valve in the main gas supply line to the reheater.)

On relative humidity rise within the chamber, the by-pass duct is automatically closed, and the heat input to the reheater is increased (by increasing the gas flow rate to the burner).

The reheater consists of 25 $\frac{3}{4}$ in. (19 mm.) diameter tubes, 3 ft. (91·5 cm.) long, fitted with 1$\frac{1}{4}$ in. (32 mm.) diameter 25 SWG annular brass fins spaced $\frac{1}{8}$ in. (3·4 mm.) apart. The tubes are laid out on a 1$\frac{1}{2}$ in. (38 mm.) triangular pitch in 5 banks (each bank having 5 tubes). The heater is installed in a duct having cross-sectional dimensions of 36 ins. by 8 ins. (91·5 × 20·5 cm.).

The required degree of heating is obtained by allowing the hot gases from the burners (which are installed immediately below the reheater) to flow through the tubes in an upward direction, thereby heating the air which flows transversely across the outer surface of the tubes.

(iii) Velocity control

A damper is provided in the delivery duct of the fan for the purpose of varying the air circulation rate and hence the velocity conditions within the chamber.

The air circulation rate with the damper fully open is of the order of 750 cfm (21·2 cu. m./min.) resulting in an average velocity in the chamber itself of the order of 200 fpm. (60 m./min.).

Lower velocities can be obtained by closing the supply damper. However, it is recommended that velocity levels within the chamber itself should not be reduced to values below 60 fpm, (20 m./min.) otherwise excessive spatial temperature gradients will be set up.

CALIBRATION TESTS

For a full description of the response and stability characteristics of the chamber, the spatial temperature distribution within the chamber, and the air velocity distribution, the reader is referred to Hodgson, T., (1966) in 'Human Adaptability and its Methodology,' Ed. H. Yoshimura and J. S. Weiner, Tokyo.

D9 SALT AND WATER STUDIES

I. INTRODUCTION

    (a) General

        (i)   Balance studies

        (ii)   Sweat salt output

        (iii) Water loading and deprivation tests

    (b) Observations to be made

        (i)   Balance studies

        (ii)   Sweat salt output

        (iii) Water loading and deprivation tests

    (c) Sampling

II. TECHNIQUES

    (a) Balance studies

    (b) Sweat salt output in standardised tests

    (c) Water loading and deprivation tests

III. DATA COLLECTING SHEETS

    (a) Balance studies

    (b) Sweat salt output

    (c) Water loading and deprivation tests

I. INTRODUCTION

(a) General:

(i) Balance studies:

In temperate climates the water and salt taken in the food is always more than enough to cover a healthy person's requirements, and the excess is excreted by the kidney. These requirements are not always met in places where it is very hot, for then the water and salt necessarily lost in the sweat may be so great, and yet incompletely appreciated, that a state of salt or water deficiency ensues which is very prejudicial to performance and health.

Requests therefore are frequently made for the salt and water requirements of individuals or groups of people who are going to hot climates, or who have to work in hot environments. No precise answer can ever be given because both vary:—

      (a)   as between one individual and another

      (b)   according to the climatic environment

      (c)   according to the work to be done

      (d)   according to the degree of acclimatisation,

(b), (c) and (d) must therefore be defined in each investigation.

(ii) Sweat salt output:

The output of salt in the sweat is profoundly influenced by two factors: the intake of salt in the diet, and the level of sweating. The latter in turn is dependent upon the environmental conditions, and the state of acclimatisation of the individual, and is subject to large individual variation from causes not well understood. It follows that any intra- or inter-group comparison of sweat salt loss even under standardised climatic conditions will reflect differences in diet and state of acclimatisation as well as personal individual variation. It has been suggested that inherent differences in salt output by sweating exist (Ohara). To demonstrate this would require that all subjects are maintained on a strictly similar and standardised salt intake, and brought to a similar, presumably full, state of acclimatisation. If only the diet is kept stabilised, individual and group differences will simply reflect differences in sweating output, and therefore to a large extent the state of acclimatisation. If subjects are tested in a low state of acclimatisation the salt loss is certain to reflect merely differences in salt intake.

In the absence of agreement on standard levels of salt intake and acclimatisation, it is clear that a casual estimate of salt output either by collection in a Fox suit by 'washing down', (see **D5**) or by extrapolation from capsule collection (Ohara), would be extremely difficult to interpret.

The most that could be inferred from the results of such casual tests is that they reflect roughly the dietary salt intake.

Obviously, if salt intake is assessed from the food consumed, there is little point in an equally obvious estimation based on salt loss in the urine and the sweat.

(iii)   **Water deprivation and water load tests:**

In healthy subjects the kidneys are able to regulate excretion to maintain normal body fluid and electrolyte levels during many different types of activity in a wide range of environments. The amounts excreted also depend upon intake and for this reason there is normally little information provided by measuring 'spot' levels of body fluid and urinary constituents. A better guide to a subject's renal function can be obtained by producing over-hydration and under-hydration and then studying the response.

The response obtained is, however, not dependant only on the magnitude of these two stimuli. The environmental conditions and the degree of the subject's acclimatization are important, since they influence loss of water, electrolytes and urea by sweating and other mechanisms. Similarly, the changes observed during the test will be influenced by the activity allowed during the tests, and by food (and therefore fluid, electrolytes and protein) consumed, and by the time of day in relation to circadian rhythms of excretion. Unless the tests are carried out in such a way as to minimize such influences, it will be difficult to assess ethnic or acclimatization differences.

These tests should ideally be combined with studies of water, electrolyte and urea losses through sweating (see **D5**). The period of equilibration before the water deprivation test is very suitable for a study of the patterns of circadian rhythms of renal excretion.

(b)   Observations to be made:

In all studies, personal details of each subject must be recorded, and details of their activities. Environmental conditions should be defined by measurements of temperature, humidity, and wind-speed at regular intervals (e.g. 6-hourly). (See **H.**)

An estimate of each individual's state of acclimatization should also be given.

(i)   Balance studies:

(1)   The following measurements are required to assess water balance:
   (a)   the intake of water in the food and fluids consumed.
   (b)   the volume of the urine.
   (c)   the changes in body weight.

(2)   The following measurements give the salt requirements:
   (a)   the daily intake in food and drink.
   (b)   the output in the urine.

(ii)   Sweat salt output:

The collection is best carried out by means of a 'Fox Suit' (see **D5**). If the Ohara capsule collection procedure is used with the indirect heating technique, the observations to be made will include continuous recording of body temperature (rectal and/or ear), weight loss, and the skin temperature near each capsule.

(iii)   Water deprivation and water load tests:

(a)   Water deprivation test

(1)   During equilibration period:

activity

diet

weight changes

urine flow and biochemical and other estimations on all urine specimens.

(2) During period of water deprivation:

activity

weight changes

urine flow and biochemical and other estimations on all urine specimens.

Collection of blood and serum at 35 hours and 59 hours for biochemical and other estimations.

Calculation of urea, creatinine and osmolar clearances after 35 hours and 59 hours.

(b) **Water load test**

(1) Volume of fluid drunk.

(2) Hourly urine flow before and after drinking; and biochemical and other estimations on all urine specimens.

(3) Collection of blood and serum at the peak of diuresis for biochemical and other estimations.

(4) Calculation of urea, creatinine and osmolar clearances at the peak of diuresis.

(c) **Sampling:**

As all the above procedures are elaborate, it is only feasible to study groups of about 15–30 subjects drawn from one sex and a narrow age range (young adults in the first instance). Equal numbers of control subjects from other ethnic, occupational or ecological backgrounds should be studied if possible.

II. TECHNIQUES.

(i) Balance studies:

The calculation of salt and water balances entails a detailed analysis of the amount and composition of all fluid and food ingested, as well as the accurate measurement of urinary, faecal, and cutaneous losses. The period of investigation should be a week, but anything over 24 hours will yield valuable information if the subject is in equilibrium with his environment. A 72-hour period is probably the best to aim for. During this period, all food and fluid intake is recorded and sampled.

Methods are as follows (see also **E2** and **E3**):—

Measurement of the food intake, and the analysis of those parts of it whose composition cannot be ascertained from tables. (This can be immensely simplified by preliminary work, and the use of a standard diet for the period of study.)

Measurement of the salt added to the food. This can be done fairly simply in a number of ways, e.g. the continuous use of one container which can be weighed at the beginning and end of the period of measurement, or by the use of small containers calibrated to deliver a known weight from a measured volume.

Measurement of the intake of water from the fluids and food consumed. This is made relatively easy by the use of calibrated drinking vessels.

Carmine 'markers' are given at the beginning and end of the 72-hour periods, in order to relate food intake to faecal loss. Samples are recorded and stored in a separate deep-dreeze.

The urine must be passed into vessels in which it can be measured and kept sterile. The procedure can be made quite simple, and necessarily varies with the sexes. 5 ml. samples of 24-hour urines must be saved for analysis. The containers, which should be made of plastic or glass, depending on the conditions to be faced, should be prepared, numbered, and labelled in advance.

Sweat losses: The first requirement is an accurate record ($\pm$ 10 g.) of body weight, and for this a 'Spido' man-balance is suitable. (See **A1**). Each subject is weighed nude three times a day, e.g. at 10.00, 16.00, and 22.00 hrs., in order to calculate total body weight losses. Sweat solutes are collected by washing the subjects at the time of weighing by means of a distilled water shower. Washings are collected in a large polythene bag, the volume measured, and a sample taken for analysis. Each subject wears washed sets of cotton underclothing (or pyjamas as appropriate) which are changed at each time of showering during the 72 hours, and these are again washed to collect absorbed solutes.

With this information the salt and water requirements can be calculated thus:—

(a) The absolute daily water requirement given a steady body weight is the intake/day from all sources, but a considerable margin of safety must be allowed if the volume of the urine is less than 1,000 ml/day.

(b) The absolute salt requirement/day is the amount ingested from all sources minus the amount excreted in the urine. A surplus over and above this must be allowed if the amount excreted in the urine is less than 2 g NaCl/day.

(ii) Sweat salt output:

(a) Capsule collection:

For field use, sweating is induced by immersing both feet in water at 43°C up to the knees. After 35 min. exposure, successive collections of sweat are made on filter paper kept within the capsule for, say, three periods of ten minutes each, with ten minutes' interval between. This procedure is well combined with that described in **D10.** The details are as follows:—

The experiment takes place in a hot room (DB: 45°C, WB: 25°C, and rel. humidity: 20%). Sweat samples are collected at 20-minute intervals during the 2-hour exposure, from forehead, chest, and forearm, using the sweat capsule and filter paper disc method (Ohara). Each capsule covers a skin area of 14.2 sq.cm. Chloride and total cation concentrations of the sweat samples collected in the filter-paper discs are determined by soaking the discs for 24 hours in distilled water, and analysing with an Amino-Cotlove chloride titrator (American Instrument Company Cat 4–4420A), and a Laboratory Cationic Electrode (Beckman Cat 39047) with an electrometer (Keith Instrument Company model 603), respectively. Rectal temperature is measured with a thermistor electrode. Heart rate is monitored by ECG recording and skin temperature is recorded by copper-constantan thermojunctions on forehead, chest, forearm, back, and thigh. The total sweat volume is measured by weighing the body before and 1 and 2 hours after exposure.

(b) Collection in Fox Suit:

For procedure and Data Collecting Sheet, see **D5.**

(iii) Water deprivation and water load tests:

(a) **Water deprivation test**

General considerations.

The subjects must be accommodated under cover during the tests and there must be adequate facilities for collection and storage of blood and urine specimens and for the extensive biochemical testing, which may involve transport of specimens. (See **B1** and **B2**). The facilities available, and the cost involved, will largely determine the number of subjects who can be tested.

Equilibration period.

There should be a period of equilibration lasting at least 3 days before the test, and longer if the diet of the groups being studied is likely to have been deficient in fluid, salt or protein. The aim in this period is to ensure that no subjects are in a negative balance for the substances noted. The diet, of which a summary must be kept, should be the same for all subjects and should if possible be prepared previously so that salt and protein composition is known. Otherwise it should consist of natural foods for the group being studied. Free fluids should be given, and no strenuous exertion should be allowed. The following measurements should be made:—

body weight: to be measured at 6 a.m. and 6 p.m. on accurate scales

urine flow: 24-hour specimens to be collected, the volume measured, and one aliquot of each kept for testing.

Period of water deprivation.

The subjects should be kept at rest and under cover, and deprived completely of fluids and food, except that glucose sweets may be allowed in small amounts (e.g. up to 2 per hour) as requested. Close supervision is essential, and an observer must be present at all times.

The test should be commenced at 1800 hr and continued for 36 hours at least and for 60 hours if possible, finishing at 0600 hr as this is when urinary concentration is greatest due to circadian rhythm changes. The following measurements and collections should be made:

body weight: To be measured at the commencement of the test and there-after 6-hourly, on accurate scales.

urine flow: Specimens to be collected separately for each 6-hour
                     period, the volume measured, and one aliquot kept for
                     testing.

                     On all aliquots of urine the following should be determined:
                     pH, specific gravity, Na^+, K^+, Cl^-, urea and creatinine
                     concentrations and osmolarity, and qualitative tests for
                     protein and glucose.   Labelling of specimens is of great
                     importance, and containers must be leak-proof.

blood: Should be collected at the commencement of the test and at
                     35 hours and 59 hours, together with urine from 34–36
                     hours and 58–60 hours to allow calculation of clearances.

The estimations required on these blood specimens are haemoglobin
concentration, haematocrit, mean corpuscular haemoglobin concentration,
(MCHC), and concentration of glucose and urea, and serum should be saved
for measurement of electrolyte and creatinine concentrations and osmolarity.

NOTES

1. Tests of physical performance may be carried out at the end of the
    test if indicated (see **C.**)

2. Clearances should be calculated as follows:
    Clearance (ml/min) — $\dfrac{UV}{p}$ where U = urinary conc. (mg/100 ml)

    $\qquad\qquad\qquad\qquad\qquad$ V = urinary flow (ml/min)

    $\qquad\qquad\qquad\qquad\qquad$ p = plasma conc. (mg/100 ml).

    except for urea clearance at urinary flows of less than 2 ml/min when
    standard clearance (s.c.) should be determined:

    $$s.c. = \frac{U\sqrt{V}}{p}$$

(b)   Water load test:

General considerations.

Some general points are discussed under (iii), above. The equilibration period
need not be as long for this test, and one day is considered adequate, unless
the subjects are likely to be dehydrated initially. The main object of the test
is to show what degree of diuresis is possible, this being an index of renal
haemodynamics.

Equilibration period.

During this 24-hour period, the food and fluid intake should be regulated as described in (iii) above, and body weight and urine flow measured similarly, one aliquot of the 24-hour urinary collection being kept for later analysis.

Period of water loading.

Subjects should empty their bladders initially and urine should then be collected for one hour before the water load. In the middle of this hour a resting blood sample should be taken, and resting osmolar, urea and creatinine clearances can later be calculated.

At the beginning of the second hour, all subjects should quickly drink a volume of water (about 1·25 l) equal to 2% of their body weight. Urine should thereafter be collected in hourly periods for 4 hr, and one aliquot of each hourly specimen saved for testing, after the volume has been measured. In the middle of the third hour, i.e. $1\frac{1}{2}$ hr. after ingestion of water, a second blood sample should be collected to enable estimates to be made of haemodilution and of renal clearances at the peak of diuresis. The tests to be carried out on all urine, blood and serum specimens are as indicated in the water deprivation test.

III. DATA COLLECTING SHEETS

(a) Balance studies:

Name:*   Place of study:
Serial number: Date study commenced:
Age: Occupation:
Sex: Ethnic group (or nationality):

Name of investigator:

	DAY	1	2	3
Body weights: (kg.)	1000 hrs.			
	1600 hrs.			
	2200 hrs.			

Sweat output (ml.) (from washings and underclothing):		1	2	3
	1000 hrs.			
	1600 hrs.			
	2200 hrs.			

Total NaCl in sweat (mg.)			

Food intake: (gms.)	Total protein			
	Total carbohydrate			
	Total fat			

Water intake: (ml.)	From food			
	Total fluid drunk			

Salt intake:	First weight of container (to 0·1 gm.)			
	Last weight of container (to 0·1 gm.)			
	Total salt intake (mg.)			

Urine output:	Total urine passed (ml.)			
	Total NaCl in urine (mg.)			

* Full details of the subject and his population group are to be entered in the **BASIC IDENTIFICATION SHEETS,** as laid down in the Technical Introduction.

III. DATA COLLECTING SHEETS (contd.)

(b) Sweat salt output:

Name:*   Place of examination:
Serial number: Date of examination:
Age: Occupation:
Sex: Ethnic group (or nationality):

Name of investigator:
Conditions of hot-room: DB: °C
                           WB: °C
                           Rel. humidity: %

Time (mins.)	0	20	40	60	80	100	120
Body weight (kg.)		—	—		—	—	
Chloride concn.							
Total cation concn.							
Heart rate/min.							
Rectal temp.							
Forehead temp.							
Chest temp.							
Forearm temp.							
Back temp.							
Thigh temp.							

Temperatures to be recorded to 0·1 °C.

* Full details of the subject and his population group are to be entered in the **BASIC IDENTIFICATION SHEETS,** as laid down in the Technical Introduction.

III. DATA COLLECTING SHEETS (continued)

(c) Water loading and deprivation tests

(i) Water deprivation test:

Name:*
Serial no.:
Age:
Sex:
Dates of study:

Place of study:
Occupation:
Ethnic and tribal origin (or nationality):
Name of investigator:

I.

"Day" (24-hour period)	Time	Body wt. (kg)	Urine flow (ml.)	Code for urine specimen	Code for blood specimen	Environ-mental temp. (°C)	R.H. (%)	Wind speed (km/hr)	COMMENTS (including summary of all food and fluid intakes)
1	1800								Subjects to empty bladder
1	0600								
2	1800								
2	0600								
3	1800								
3	0600								

(continued)

Table—continued

		Blood sample taken				Blood sample taken / Urine collection 0400–0600				Blood sample taken / Urine collection 0400–0600

4 (1st day of water deprivation)	1800									
	2400									
	0600									
	1200									
5	1800									
	2400									
	0500									
	0600									
	1200									
6	1800									
	2400									
	0400									
	0500									
	0600									

*Full details of the subject and his population group are to be entered in the **BASIC IDENTIFICATION SHEETS**, as laid down in the Technical Introduction.

CONTINUED ON DATA SHEET II

II. URINE SPECIMENS:

"Day"	Time	Code	Vol. of original specimen (ml)	S.G.	pH	Glucose conc. (0/+/ ++/ +++/ ++++)	Protein conc. (0/+/ ++/ +++/ ++++)	Na$^+$ conc. (mEq/l)	K$^+$ conc. (mEq/l)	Cl$^-$ conc. (mEq/l)	Urea conc. (mg/100ml)	Creatinine conc. (mg/100ml)	Osmolarity (m-osmole /kg H$_2$O)
2	1800												
3	1800												
4	1800												
	2400												
	0600												
	1200												
5	1800												
	2400												
	0600												
	1200												
6	1800												
	2400												
	0400												
	0600												

III. BLOOD SPECIMENS

"Day"	Time	Code	Na$^+$ conc. (mEq/l)	K$^+$ conc. (mEq/l)	Cl$^-$ conc. (mEq/l)	Urea conc. (mg/100ml)	Creatinine conc. (mg/100ml)	Osmolarity (m-osmoles/ kg H$_2$O)
4	1800							
5	0500							
6	0500							

III. DATA COLLECTING SHEETS (continued)

(c) Water loading and deprivation tests
(ii) Water load test:

Name:*
Serial no.:
Age:
Sex:
Dates of study:

Place of study:
Occupation:
Ethnic and tribal origin (or nationality):
Name of Investigator:

"Day" (24-hour period)	Time	Body wt. (kg)	Urine flow (ml)	Code for urine specimen	Code for blood specimen	Environ-mental tempera-ture (°C)	R.H.	Wind speed (km/hr)	COMMENTS (including volume of fluid drunk)
1	0600								Subjects empty bladder
	1800								
2	0600								0600–0700 is period of base-line
	0630								Blood sample taken
	0700								Water drunk (.....ml)
	0800								
	0830								Blood sample taken
	0900								
	1000								

URINE SPECIMENS

"Day"	Time	Code	Vol. of original specimen (ml)	S.G.	pH	Glucose conc. (0/+/++/+++/++++)	Protein conc. (0/+/++/+++/++++)	Na$^+$ conc. (mEq/l)	K$^+$ conc. (mEq/l)	Cl$^-$ conc. (mEq/l)	Urea conc. (mg/100ml)	Creatinine conc. (mg/100ml)	Osmolarity (m-osmole/kg H$_2$O)
1	0600												
	0700												
	0800												
2	0900												
	1000												
	1100												

BLOOD SPECIMENS

"Day"	Time	Code	Na$^+$ conc. (mEq/l)	K$^+$ conc. (mEq/l)	Cl$^-$ conc. (mEq/l)	Urea conc. (mg/100ml)	Creatinine conc. (mg/100ml)	Osmolarity (m-osmole/kg H$_2$O)
2	0630							
	0830							

*Full details of the subject and his population group are to be entered in the **BASIC IDENTIFICATION SHEETS,** as laid down in the Technical Introduction.

D10. SWEAT-GLAND COUNTS OVER THE WHOLE BODY

I. INTRODUCTION
    (a) General
    (b) Observations to be made
    (c) Sample size

II. TECHNIQUES
    (a) Equipment
    (b) Procedure

III. DATA COLLECTING SHEET

I. INTRODUCTION

(a) General:

The basis of this counting method is the plastic impression technique introduced by Thompson and Sutarman. (**Trans. Roy. Soc. Trop. Med. Hyg., 47.**
(5): 412-417, 1953). The plastic solution, dissolved in a volatile solvent is painted
over the skin surface, allowed to dry and then removed by means of Sellotape.
The tape is mounted on a glass slide and the print can be projected enlarged
on to a screen. When the sweat glands are active the plastic film is interrupted
by holes corresponding to individual sweat glands, and these are counted
over, say, 1 sq. cm. of body surface. The need to sample the whole body in
the manner described below has been established by Weiner (**J. Anat., 95,**
451, 1961).

Sweating is induced by immersion of one leg and one arm in hot water at
43/44°C in a warm draught-free enclosure.

The method enables the density of sweat glands in different areas to be
counted, for gradients to be elucidated and for a total count to be obtained.
The method can be used only where a power supply is available for heating
and stirring the tanks.

(b) Observations to be made:

1. Prints to be taken on 16 sites (twice on each) as follows:

Forehead	Back, lumbar
Cheek	Buttock
Upper arm, lat.	Thigh, lat/post.
Forearm, ant.	Thigh, ant.

Hand, dorsal	Thigh, med/post.
Chest, above nipples	Leg, lat.
Abdomen, at level of umbilicus	Leg, med.
Back, over scapula	Foot, dorsal.

2. From the body measurements (see below) the following 7 regional surface areas (and the total surface area) will be obtained:

Head	Thighs
Arms	Legs
Hands	Feet
Trunk	

(c) Sample size:

During the period of growth the density of sweat glands remains high but falls in different areas of the skin as the skin surface itself increases. Thus the changes in sweat gland density during growth should strictly be investigated on a longitudinal basis. Alternatively, fairly large samples (e.g. 25 individuals at least) would be needed at each narrow age range. For adults a useful number would be 50 individuals of each sex. Taking into account the inter- and intra-subject variation in the total sweat gland count the sample sizes needed to detect with 95% certainty a 12% difference in the means between two populations (at the $p = 0.05$ level) would be at least 30 subjects from each.

II. TECHNIQUES.

(a) Equipment required

Plastic solution   Polyvinyl formal (powder), a 5% solution in ethylene dichloride with 1 ml. dibutyl phthalate.

Transparent Adhesive Tape   1 in. (2·5 cm.) and 0·75 in. (2 cm.) " Sellotape ". 72 yard packs are convenient. It must be clear and free from bubbles. A frame (section below) is required for holding 7 cm. strips of Sellotape.

Electric hair clippers and razor. Hand clippers and ordinary razor can be used but electric ones preferred.

Towelling bathrobe, towels and briefs
Kleenex   or similar paper tissues.
Brush   0·5 in. (1·3 cm.) flat sable.
Plastic ruler
Microscope slides   1 in. (2.5 cm.) with sticky labels
Ball point pens
Flexible steel tape   Chesterman No. 30.

A tank of sufficient size to take a man's leg. One having a length of 26 ins. (66 cm.) and breadth of 16 in. (25 cm.) with depth of 18 in. (46 cm.) is adequate.   Installation of a 3 Kw. kettle element to be manually controlled by a voltage regulator gives satisfactory service.   A portable electric stirrer, properly screened, is used to circulate the water.   Care must be taken that earthing arrangements are in order.   A thermostatically controlled tank having a built-in circulating pump is ideal.

A smaller tank of metal or heavy plastic to submerge one arm about 12 ins. × 12 ins. × 14 ins. (30 cm. × 30 cm. × 36 cm.).

Water-bath temperature controlling device such as a " Tempunit " to heat the smaller tank.

(b)   Procedure

Preparation of the subject

Record height, weight, age, sex, and any other relevant particulars.

Take body measurements (du Bois) in cms. as follows (see Fig. D10/1):—

HEAD: AB 0·308
   A — Around vertex and point of chin.
   B — Coronal circumference around occiput and forehead, just above eyebrows.

ARMS: F (G+H+1) 0·611*
   F — Tip of acromial process to lower border of radius, measured with forearm extended.
   G — Circumference at level of upper border of axilla.
   H — Largest circumference of forearm (just below elbow).
   I — Smallest circumference of forearm (just above head of ulna).

*Factor 0·558 if F is measured over olecranon with forearm flexed.

HANDS: JK 2·22
    J — Lower posterior border of radius to tip of second finger.
    K — Circumference of open hand at the meta-carpo-phalangeal joints.

TRUNK: (including neck and external genitals in the male, breasts in female)
    L (M+N) 0·703
    L — Suprasternal notch to upper border of pubes.
    M — Circumference of abdomen at level of umbilicus.
    N — Circumference of thorax at level of nipples in the male and just above breasts in the female.

THIGHS: 0 (P+Q) 0·508
    O — Superior border of greater trochanter to the lower border of the patella.
    P — Circumference of thigh just below the level of perineum.
    Q — Circumference of hips and buttocks at the level of the great trochanters.

LEGS: RS 1·40
    R — From sole of foot to lower border of patella.
    S — Circumference at level of lower border of patella.

FEET: T (U+V) 1·04.
    T — Length of foot including great toe.
    U — Circumference of foot at base of little toe.
    V — Smallest circumference of ankle (just above malleoli).

NOTE: The constants for arms, thighs, etc., when multiplied by the measurements of one side give the surface area for both sides. To find total surface area add the seven parts.

Mark an area of about 3 ins. × 2 ins. (7 × 5 cm.) on each of the 16 sites on one side of the body thus: (see Fig. D10/2),

Forehead

Cheek

Upper arm, lat.

Forearm, ant.

Hand, dorsal

Chest, above nipples

Abdomen, at level of umbilicus

Back, over scapula.

Back, lumbar

Buttocks

Thigh, lat/post.

Thigh, ant.

Thigh, med/post.

Leg, lat.

Leg, med.

Foot, dorsal.

The dotted lines, which need not be drawn on the subject, indicate the relative positions of the prints.

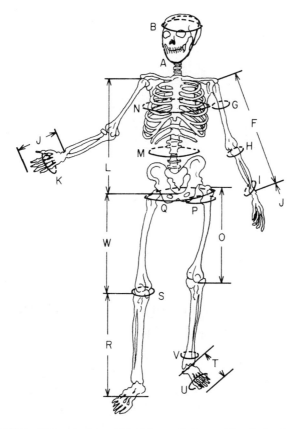

Fig. D10/1   Measurements required for surface area (description in text).

Clip, where necessary, and shave each site. It is necessary to shave all sites including those on the back, abdomen and forehead which may appear to be devoid of hair. The electric shaver is much preferred for this purpose.

To remove skin debris use 1 in. (2·5 cm.) Sellotape to take strips off the marked sites (without the plastic solution). Continue until the tape comes off the skin relatively clear. Two to three strips only should be used on the cheek and forehead but more will be required for the other sites, particularly those on the buttocks and lower limb.

Re-mark the sites.

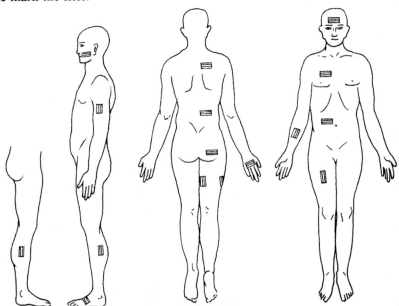

Fig. D10/2   Sites for taking sweat-gland counts (see text).

Warming up the subject and print-taking

Prepare the plastic solution a day in advance. Cut and mount 7 cm. length of ¾ in. Sellotape for taking the prints. Label sufficient 3 in. × 1 in. micro scope slides and mark each one with the subject's initials or serial number, th date, site and print number. Arrange in order.

With the subject fully prepared, the experimental procedure can be started

The subject should immerse as much of one leg (the unmarked side) as possible in the water-bath at 43/44°C. The arm on the same side should also be immersed in water at the same temperature. A room temperature of not more than 30°C should be provided. Air movement must be minimal and the subject should be clear of draughts. The subject should have a towelling robe draped over him, which is removed a few minutes before taking the first series of prints.

The first series of prints, which takes about 15 mins. to complete, is taken on the sites previously prepared after 40 mins. of heating. The second series should start at 60 mins., and if it is necessary to take a third series this should be at 80 mins. A third set of prints would not normally be taken unless one of the earlier series contained imperfect prints or there were indications that a high sweat rate had not been reached during the first series.

Thoroughly dry the area with Kleenex just before taking the print and ensure that no sweat runs down on to the plastic, which should be applied in one sweep thinly and evenly to cover about $2\frac{1}{2}$ in. (6 cm.) As the solvent vapour is harmful, the subject must keep his eyes closed and should hold his breath when the plastic is applied, and while it is drying, on the forehead, cheek and chest.

Some transitory discomfort may be felt, particularly on the forehead.

When the plastic has dried, about 15 secs. after application, it is removed with Sellotape. The strips are gently pressed onto the skin and removed in the direction of the natural lie of the hairs (if any).

The subject's pulse and body temperature should be monitored during the experiment.

If a small tank is not available to heat the arm both legs should be immersed. The leg and foot counts then obtained might be unreliable. If, however, the leg to be observed was removed after 40 mins. of immersion and subsequently wrapped with towelling or blanket to reduce the heat loss, instead of replacing the leg in the tank, better results might be expected.

On completion the subject is removed from the bath. Any plastic remaining is removed and he is then dried down and re-weighed to obtain the sweat loss. Some " itchiness " may be experienced in the leg at this stage but it does not persist and after a drink and a rest in a cooler room, followed if possible by a shower, the subject is completely recovered.

Care must be taken when disposing of any waste plastic solution.

Counting the active glands

The slides are projected at a magnification of not less than × 30. It is convenient to have an entire sq. cm. in view. If 3 sq. cms. are counted on two prints from each site the total number of counts for the whole body surface would be 96.

III. DATA COLLECTING SHEET

Total body count of active sweat glands.

Place of examination:	Subject's serial no:
Date: Age:	Ethnic group (or
Name:	nationality):
Sex:	Time in bath:
Height: cm.	Time out of bath:
Weight: kg.	Time of prints: 1 2 3
Occupation:	Mouth Temp. °C: 1 2 3
	Pulse: 1 2 3

Surface area (sq. cm.)

	Measurements (cm.)	Area (sq. cm.)			Measurements (cm.)	Area (sq. cm.)
Head	A		Thighs	O		
	B			P		
Arms	F			Q		
	G		Legs	R		
	H			S		
	I		Feet	T		
Hands	J			U		
	K			V		
Trunk	L					
	M		Total surface area:			
	N					

(*Continued*)

III. DATA COLLECTING SHEET (Continued)

Sweat gland counts (per sq. cm.)

	1st print		2nd print		3rd print if req.		Mean of 4 or 6 counts	Mean of region
	1	2	3	4	5	6		
Forehead								
Cheek								
Up. arm								
Forearm								
Hand								
Chest								
Abdomen								
Up. back								
Mid. back								
Buttock								
Thigh l/p.								
Thigh ant.								
Thigh m/p.								
Leg lat.								
Leg med.								
Foot								

(Continued)

III.   DATA COLLECTING SHEET (Continued)

Region	Area (sq. cms)	Mean count	No. of sweat glands
Head			
Arms			
Hands			
Trunk			
Thighs			
Legs			
Feet			
Total			

Name of Investigator: . . . .

D11. THERMAL COMFORT ASSESSMENT

I. INTRODUCTION
  (a) General
  (b) Sampling

II. TECHNIQUES

III. DATA COLLECTING SHEET

I. INTRODUCTION

(a) General:

Thermal comfort data are scarce for the warmer climates, and even quite simple observations, carefully made on a sound basis, can be of value. The investigation of thermal discomfort can lead to improvements in building design, and in the use of existing buildings. Two levels of observation could be considered for field survey work: (a) subjective observations, with a minimum of physical measurement (level A): and (b) subjective observations accompanied by physical measurement (level B).

In the first place it is useful to establish that a thermal problem exists, to locate it in time and place, and to assess its magnitude. This can be done without making any measurements of environmental conditions, by systematically questioning the people concerned in the way described below (A).

If in addition at least some measurements of environmental conditions can be made, then it should be possible to describe what the thermal environment is like at times when the people concerned consider conditions to be most pleasant, and again when they consider them to be most extreme, by the method (B) given below. The descriptions may be more, or less, complete depending on the measurements it is found possible to make.

A detailed and extensive investigation into a particular thermal problem could yield an environmental formula summating the effects on people of temperature, air movement, humidity, and heat radiation; a description of thermal behaviour of different types of building; and an estimate of the incidence of discomfort for individuals and groups of people. This is a more serious undertaking, but worth-while where a thermal problem is severe, and the experimental resources are available.

(b) **Sampling:**

The irreducible minimum would be 4 subjects each with 10 hourly observations reasonably well spread over day and night. A more realistic sample would be 6 subjects with 50 observations. A desirable sample would be 20 subjects with 150 observations evenly spread over the 24 hours. Data for a single project should be concentrated within a short period—say a month—and not spread over the year.

II. TECHNIQUES

Level A:

To locate and assess a thermal problem a representative sample of the resident population should be selected. A sample of 6 or more, up to 20, people is required. They should each record at regular intervals of 1 hour their personal subjective assessment of warmth or coolness according to the Bedford scale, which runs;

much too cool,	abbreviated	as	MTC	can be	recorded	as 1
too cool,	,,	,,	TC	,, ,,	,,	,, 2
comfortably cool,	,,	,,	CC	,, ,,	,,	,, 3
comfortable and neither cool nor warm,	abbreviated	,,	NCNW	,, ,,	,,	,, 4
comfortably warm,	,,	,,	CW	,, ,,	,,	,, 5
too warm,	,,	,,	TW	,, ,,	,,	,, 6
much too warm,	,,	,,	MTW	,, ,,	,,	,, 7

by placing a mark in the appropriate column in the pro-forma which follows, writing against it the time. Time should be measured from midnight, or an explanatory note added, where there might be doubt; e.g. in parts of Asia time is sometimes measured from sunset.

The record should be made continually for a reasonable spell, e.g. 6 to 8 hours, at a time; and successive spells arranged so that the whole 24 hours is reasonably evenly covered by observations. The subject should meanwhile carry on with his or her ordinary daily routine, apart from staying awake late, on some nights, or waking early, to ensure even coverage.

In the course of 2 to 3 weeks each subject might be expected to accumulate some 100 or so observations of subjective warmth. The project should then terminate, although it could be repeated at another time of year. Separate samples of men, women, and older children might also be used, and this would be worthwhile if, as is commonly the case, thermal experience differs markedly between these groups.

A plot of the percentage of each Bedford assessment, in the total number of assessments, hour by hour, should show at once at what times of day people are most comfortable thermally, and at what times they are coolest, and at what times warmest. Inspection would show in which types of building discomfort is most likely to occur; and the overall percentage of assessments of discomfort (MTC, TC, TW, MTW) is a measure of the severity of the local problem, assuming even coverage of the 24-hour period.

It may be useful if very brief comments are added in the ' Remarks ' column regarding the amount of clothing being worn from time to time, the level of physical activity, and the type of building in which the subject is.

Level B:

The heat balance of the human body and the sensation of warmth are affected by the environmental conditions, and if possible these conditions should be measured both when most comfortable and when most extreme, in a particular local case. There is no single physical measurement which will completely describe the thermal environment in all circumstances, and if only one type of measurement can be made a careful choice is necessary.

The globe temperature is the easiest and the most informative of measurements in most cases. This is the reading of an ordinary thermometer whose bulb is at the centre of a 6-inch blackened copper globe. The reading changes only slowly; and is affected by the air temperature, the air velocity, and the amount of heat radiation falling on the globe. In humid environments however the wet-bulb temperature is to be preferred. This is the reading of a very well-ventilated thermometer whose bulb is covered with a very clean wick moistened with distilled water; ventilation is best secured by swinging the thermometer, as in the whirling hygrometer, the thermometer being read immediately after the whirling stops. If both globe and wet-bulb readings can be made the environment can be considered to be fairly well described.

A still more complete set of environmental measurements can be made by adding to the above the ordinary dry-bulb temperature and the air velocity, the latter being measured with a kata thermometer. Provision is made in the pro-forma for all four measurements to be recorded, in this order of preference.

The thermal environment is apt to follow a diurnal pattern, and to economise effort measurements need only be made at certain cardinal periods, i.e. when conditions are (a) most nearly ideal and (b) most extreme. Commonly this means taking observations at dawn (extreme of coolness), at about an hour after sunrise (change from coolness to warmth), in the early afternoon (extreme of warmth), and at midnight (change from warmth to coolness); but in particular cases the pattern may be different from this, e.g. in kitchens the warmest period is likely to be just before the main meal is ready, at whatever time of day, and the periods of observation should be adjusted accordingly.

III. DATA COLLECTING SHEET

Name:*   Ethnic group or nationality:
Subject no.:   Height (cm.):
Age: Weight (kg.):
Sex:
Occupation:
Address:
Dates of this study:
Season of year:
(For Level B: Kata type: (see notes (a) and (b) below)
               Kata factor:)

Levels A and B

(Tick in appropriate column)

Date	Time	MTC (1)	TC (2)	CC (3)	NCNW (4)	CW (5)	TW (6)	MTW (7)	Clothing	Activity	Type of build-ing

Remarks:

For Level B, add the following:

Globe	WB	DB	air velocity (c)	kata time

(a)   The high temperature type of kata thermometer (silvered), cooling from 130° to 125° F is usually to be preferred.

(b)   The factor varies somewhat from one kata to another. It is marked on the back of the stem by the maker.

(c)   Whether or not a kata measurement is made, it is useful to remark on the amount of air movement, and if possible to make an estimate by watching the movement of, e.g. cigarette smoke.

* Full details of the subject and his population group are to be entered in the **BASIC IDENTIFICATION SHEETS,** as laid down in the Technical Introduction.

D12. MORPHOLOGICAL MEASUREMENTS IN RELATION TO CLIMATIC STUDIES

I. INTRODUCTION

    (a) General

    (b) Observations to be made

    (c) Sampling

II. DATA COLLECTING SHEETS

I. INTRODUCTION

(a) General:

It is recommended that in all studies of climatic adaptation the basic battery of anthropometric measurements as laid down in **A1** (' short list ' or ' full list '), should be carried out. It is, however, extremely important to recognise that particular morphological observations are of significance in relation to heat, cold, and high altitude studies respectively.

(b) Observations to be made: (For all techniques, reference should be made to the Sections cited below)
Of particular interest are the following:

1. Height and weight, for the DuBois surface area (See **A1**).

2. Regional circumferential and longitudinal measurements for assessing regional surface areas. These are of interest also in relation to regional differences in skin temperature (See **A1**).

3. Body composition, particularly fat and muscle, are relevant to studies of heat tolerance. For recommendations on technique see **A5**.

4. Body shape is relevant to climatic adaptation. This can be specified by anthropometry (see **A1**) and by somatotype (see **A3**).

5. Body hair distribution (see **B15**).
    Of particular interest in relation to high altitude studies are those measurements related to pulmonary function (see **C5**), and some anthroposcopic observations (see **B15**), e.g. hair distribution.
    Of particular interest in relation to ultra-violet light intensity is the

measurement of skin colour (see **B11**), and hair and eye colour (see **B15**).

II. DATA COLLECTING SHEETS

For the data sheets relevant to the above observations, reference should be made to the appropriate Sections in the Handbook.

E. NUTRITIONAL STUDIES

E1. ASSESSMENT OF HUMAN NUTRITIONAL STATUS

I. INTRODUCTION
   (a) General
   (b) Observations to be made

II. TECHNIQUES

III. DATA COLLECTING SHEETS

I. INTRODUCTION

(a) General:

The need for carrying out an evaluation of nutritional status as an essential item of background information has been emphasised, specifically in relation to population surveys of growth and physique, or working capacity, in studies of thermal and altitude tolerance, in genetic studies, and in all multi-disciplinary investigations. A background medical examination would naturally also be carried out on the same subjects. (See **F1**.)

Procedures will be described below for:

A.   A rapid or minimal nutritional assessment, for use in restricted or pilot field studies.

B.   A comprehensive nutritional assessment for use in intensive investigations, and certainly in all multi-disciplinary studies where requisite personnel and resources would be available.

(b) Observations to be made:

A.   The minimal nutritional assessment should comprise:—

1. Age ascertainment.
2. Limited anthropometry.
3. Physical examination. (Simple schedule.)
4. Estimation of blood haemoglobin.
5. Filling up of a questionnaire (appropriate to the particular community) to provide some information on the kinds and frequencies of foods eaten.

B. The comprehensive nutritional assessment should comprise:—

1. Age ascertainment, and photograph if possible.

2. A more extended list ('short list') of anthropometric measurements.

3. Physical examination in accordance with Group 1 list of WHO.

4. Collection of blood for biochemical tests of nutritional significance. (WHO list with cholesterol and lipids added.)

5. If possible, biophysical examination, (radiography, dark adaptation, etc.)

Note:

In many multi-disciplinary investigations, it will be essential to assess two further items of nutritional significance on each subject.

These are:

(i)   The activity pattern (see **C6**), and

(ii) Food intake (see **E2** and **E3**)

II. TECHNIQUE

a. Minimum nutritional assessment:

1. Age ascertainment—for techniques see Technical Introduction.

2. Limited anthropometry (height, weight, skin-folds (triceps and subscapular), arm circumference, biilio-cristal diameter)—for techniques see **A1**.

3. Physical examination.

The following **simple schedule** is taken from Jelliffe, D. B., (1966): 'The Assessment of the Nutritional Status of the Community', WHO Monograph Series No 53 (hereinafter referred to as WHO Monograph 53), p. 49.

(A detailed description of these signs is given in WHO Monograph 53, or the pages referred to in brackets in the following list.)

HAIR

Dyspigmentation.	(p. 18)
Easy pluckability.	(p. 19)
Sparseness.	(p. 16)

FACE

Moon-face   (p. 19)

EYES

Bitot's spots.   (p. 21)
Conjunctival xerosis.   (p. 21)
Pale conjunctiva.   (p. 21)

MOUTH

Angular stomatitis.   (p. 25)
Cheilosis.   (p. 25)
Glossitis.   (p. 27)
Swollen, bleeding gums.   (p. 30)

THYROID GLAND

Goitre   (pp. 30–32)

SKIN

Oedema (bilateral).   (p. 36)
Follicular hyperkeratosis (type 1).   (p. 33)
Pellagrous dermatosis.   (p. 33)

SKELETON

Epiphyseal enlargement (wrist).   (p. 37)
Rickety rosary.   (p. 37)
Persistently open anterior fontanelle.   (p. 37)
Harrison's sulcus.   (p. 37)
Bossing of skull.   (p. 37)
Knock-knees.   (p. 37)
Bow-legs.   (p. 37)

4.   Estimation of blood haemoglobin—for technique see **F4**.

5.   Questionnaire on kinds and frequencies of foods eaten—see **E4**. Experience has shown that these questionnaires can be extremely useful.

It is agreed that all these items should be regarded only as pointers to the nutritional condition, and require careful interpretation.

b.   **Comprehensive nutritional assessment:**

1.   Age ascertainment—for techniques see Technical Introduction.

2.   ' Basic list ' anthropometry—see **A1**.

3.   Physical examination.

The following signs indicate with considerable probability deficiency of one or more nutrients in the tissues at present or in the recent past. For a detailed description of these signs, and illustrations of the conditions, see WHO Monograph 53, pp. 16–41.

HAIR
     Lack of lustre
     Thinness and sparseness
     Dyspigmentation of proximal part of hair
     Flag sign
     Easy pluckability

FACE
     Diffuse depigmentation
     Naso-labial dyssebacea
     Moon-face
     Pallor

EYES
     Xerosis conjunctivae
     Xerophthalmia (including keratomalacia)
     Bitot's spots
     Angular palpebritis
     Pallor of mucous membranes

LIPS
     Angular stomatitis
     Angular scars
     Cheilosis
     Pallor of mucous membranes

TONGUE
Oedema
Scarlet and raw tongue (glossitis)
Magenta tongue
Atrophic papillae

TEETH
Mottled enamel

GUMS
Spongy, bleeding gums

GLANDS
Thyroid enlargement
Parotid enlargement

SKIN
Xerosis
Follicular hyperkeratosis, types 1 and 2
Petechiae
Ecchymoses
Pellagrous dermatosis
Flaky paint dermatosis
Scrotal and vulval dermatosis

NAILS
Koilonychia

SUBCUTANEOUS TISSUE
Oedema
Reduced amount of fat

MUSCULAR AND SKELETAL SYSTEMS
Intramuscular or subperiosteal haematomas
Craniotabes
Frontal and parietal bossing
Epiphyseal enlargement (tender or painless)
Beading of ribs
Knock-knees or bow-legs
Diffuse or local skeletal deformities

INTERNAL SYSTEMS

    Gastro-intestinal:
      Hepatomegaly
      Ascites
    Nervous:
      Psychomotor change
      Mental confusion
      Sensory loss
      Motor weakness
      Loss of position sense
      Loss of vibratory sense
      Loss of ankle and knee jerks
      Calf tenderness
    Cardio-vascular:
      Cardiac and peripheral vascular dysfunction
      Reduced pulse rate

Interpretation of signs in relation to nutrient deficiencies.

Jelliffe (1966), comments as follows: (WHO Monograph 53)

" The interpretation of clinical signs can best be made by using a ' grouping of signs ' which have been commonly found to form a pattern associated with the deficiency of a particular nutrient.

" However, the clinical patterns on which these ' groupings of signs ' are based differ, in detail or in the most prevalent combinations of signs, in various parts of the world, depending upon the quality, degree, duration, and speed of onset of the malnutrition. Other factors may include the balance of other foods in the prevailing diet, genetic influences, the age and activity of the person, and the environment in which he lives, as regards both environmental hygiene and climate, and exposure to infection and parasitism.

" Age plays a particularly important part in the clinical signs produced by nutrient deficiency. The different pictures produced in young children and in adults as a result of ascorbic acid lack or protein-calorie malnutrition are clear-cut instances. Furthermore, age plays a significant, though not fully understood, part in determining the incidence and nature of the eye manifestations of Vitamin A deficiency. In particular, the signs in early childhood appear to differ from those seen in school-children.

" Patterns of clinical signs associated with specific nutrient deficiency cannot be standardised precisely for all areas of the world, although there is always substantial agreement on the major features encountered. For example, the clinical picture of kwashiorkor, while varying in detail from one region to another, retains a core of signs found universally.

" In some instances, a clinical appraisal of certain signs may be all that is required for a rapid screening survey, as in the use of the ' niacin deficiency ' group of signs to ascertain the prevalence of overt pellagra. More often, however, survey work based on clinical signs, even with the groupings suggested, is best supported and confirmed by (a) appropriate anthropometric measurements, (b) selected biochemical tests, and (c) investigation of the local diet, preferably by food-consumption surveys, considered in relation to local ecological circumstances. Each of these methods is imperfect and incomplete; used together, in carefully planned and locally relevant combinations, they can give the fullest information."

4.   Blood collection for biochemical tests—see **B1**, **B2** and **F4**.

The following list of biochemical studies applicable to nutrition surveys was proposed by the WHO Expert Committee on Medical Assessment of Nutritional Status (Technical Report Series No. 258, 1963) who distinguished two categories, viz:—

First category: Tests included in the first category are those which have been most extensively applied in nutrition surveys, and have had their usefulness demonstrated. They are relatively simple and their use is feasible in general nutrition surveys. The urine studies included are those which require only a single urine specimen; samples of blood and urine should preferably be collected from subjects in the fasting state. Since this is not always possible, the investigator may have to resort to random specimens. It is recognised that the previous meal may influence the levels of some of the constituents in blood and urine. However, under ordinary circumstances in nutrition surveys this would not seriously bias the results.

The haemoglobin concentration affords useful, albeit non-specific, information on the state of health. Hence it is desirable that it should be determined in all general nutrition surveys. If anaemia is encountered, other supporting investigations are required to determine its cause.

Second category: Application of the methods in the second category usually involves relatively more complicated procedures than those of methods in the first category. These methods are designed in most instances to gain more accurate and specific knowledge of particular nutritional inadequacies suggested by the application of methods in the first category, as well as by the other survey data. For example, high total serum protein concentrations accompanied by either low or normal albumin levels may be found to be prevalent. In this case electrophoretic studies of serum protein fractions may be considered necessary to confirm the albumin values by a different technique and to investigate contributions of globulin fractions to the abnormal total protein levels.

Nutritional Deficiency	First category *	Second category
Protein	Total serum protein Serum albumin Urinary urea (F) * *	Serum protein fractions by electrophoresis. Urinary creatinine per unit of time. (T) * *
Vitamin A	Serum vitamin A Serum carotene	
Vitamin D	Serum alkaline phosphates in young children	Serum inorganic phosphorus
Ascorbic acid	Serum ascorbic acid	White blood cell count Ascorbic acid Urinary ascorbic acid Load test
Thiamine	Urinary thiamine (F) * *	Load test Blood pyruvate Blood lactate RBC haemolysate trans-ketolase
Riboflavin	Urinary riboflavin (F) * *	RBC riboflavin Load test
Niacin	Urinary N-methyl-nicotinamide (F) * *	Load test Urinary pyridine (N-methyl-2-pyridone-5-carbonamide)
Iron	Haemoglobin ⎱ thin blood Haematocrit ⎰ smear	Serum iron % saturation of transferrin
Iodine		Urinary iodine (F) * * Tests for thyroid function (see **F4**)
	Serum cholesterol Serum lipids.	

Notes:

* Urinary creatinine used as reference for expressing other urine measurements in First category.
* * Expressed per gram of creatinine.
(F) In a single urine specimen, preferably fasting.
(T) In timed urine specimens.

Serum cholesterol levels vary widely in population groups with different dietary habits. This determination may often be included in nutrition surveys because of the reported association of serum cholesterol levels with atherosclerosis.

5.   Biophysical Tests:—

If possible, radiography should be included in the comprehensive nutritional assessment (see **A4**). In addition to this, dark-adaptation is the most widely-used test of physical function.

(i) Radiography: (From WHO Monograph 53 pp. 94–5)

While routine radiographic studies of population groups are rarely possible, or indeed required, it is sometimes valuable to carry out these investigations on a sample of a population if the physical signs and other circumstances suggest that rickets, osteomalacia, fluorosis or beri-beri may be present. This type of survey may also sometimes be of value in the retrospective assessment of malnutrition, as with rickets and possibly protein-calorie malnutrition in early childhood. In such circumstances, the following are the principal signs sought:—

Rickets:

    (a) Active—Widened concave (cupped), rarefied, frayed distal ends of long bones, usually radius and ulna;

    (b) Healed—Concave line of increased density at distal ends of the long bones, usually radius and ulna.

Osteomalacia:

    Deformity and loss of density of bones, especially the pelvis.

Infantile scurvy:

    (a) Loss of density, ground-glass appearance of long bones;

(b) Line of increased density, sometimes with lateral spur formation due to increased calcification of metaphysis, with underlying zone of rarefaction, usually best seen at the knee.

Beri-beri: Increased cardiac size.

Advanced fluorosis: Increased density of bones, with coarse trabeculation and thickening of the cortex; calcification of ligaments; osteophytic outgrowths at tendinous insertions, and marginal lipping of vertebrae. Changes most marked in the spine. (Grech and Latham, **Trans. Roy. Soc. Trop. Med. Hyg., 58,** 566, 1964.)

(ii) **Dark-adaptation:** (From WHO Monograph 53. p. 95)

Although this measurement can be valuable in the objective evaluation of the complaint of night-blindness, one of the causes of which is vitamin A deficiency it has several limitations (Kinney and Fellis, **Fed. Proc. 17**, 103, 1958), The main drawbacks are; (a) tests of dark-adaptation are not a specific measure of vitamin A deficiency and other factors responsible for its impairment are difficult to eliminate; (b) it is not easy to conduct them in certain age and population groups; and (c) responses to the tests are not entirely free from subjectivity. In spite of all these difficulties, dark-adaptation measurement are of value in special circumstances—for example in epidemics of night blindness where the authenticity of the complaint itself needs to be established

In addition to the above, the following should form part of the comprehensive nutritional assessment:—

(1) Questionnaire on food availability and patterns of food intake. (See **E4**).

(2) Food intake by weighing. (See **E2**).

(3) Habitual activity by diary and pulse-counting methods. (See **C6**).

III.   DATA COLLECTING SHEETS

(a)   *For minimum nutritional assessment:*

Occupation:

Name:*
Subject no.:
Age:
Sex:
How age assessed?:
Height:
Weight:
Biilio-cristal diameter

Occupation:
Birth-place:
Date of examination:
Place of examination:
Address of subject:
Ethnic and tribal origin (or nationality):
Triceps skin-fold:
Subscapular skin-fold:
Arm circumference:

Physical examination
Place a tick against signs observed

Dyspigmentation
Easy pluckability
Sparseness
Moon-face
Bitot's spots
Conjunctival xerosis
Pale conjunctiva
Angular stomatitis
Cheilosis
Glossitis
Swollen, bleeding gums
Haemoglobin %:
Stool—comments:

Goitre
Bilateral oedema
Follicular hyperkeratosis (type 1)
Pellagrous dermatosis
Epiphyseal enlargement (wrist)
Rickety rosary
Persistently open anterior fontanelle
Harrison's sulcus
Bossing of skull
Knock-knees
Bow-legs

The questionnaire on the kinds and frequencies of foods eaten is to be filled in for both the minimal and the comprehensive nutritional assessments.

* Full details of the subject and his population group are to be entered in the **BASIC IDENTIFICATION SHEETS,** as laid down in the Technical Introduction.

Name of Investigator................................

(b)   *For comprehensive nutritional assessment*

Name :*	Birth-place :
Subject no. :	Present address :
Age :	Date of examination :
How age assessed ? :	Place of examination :
Sex :	Ethnic and tribal origin (or nationality) :
	Occupation :

The Data Collecting Sheet for the ' basic list ' of anthropometric measurements is given in **A1.**

Physical examination

Place a tick against the signs observed

Lack of lustre of hair
Thinness and sparseness of hair
Dyspigmentation of proximal part of hair
Flag sign
Easy pluckability of hair
Diffuse depigmentation of face
Naso-labial dyssebacea
Moon-face
Facial pallor
Xerosis conjunctivae
Xerophthalmia (including keratomalacia)
Bitot's spots
Angular palpebritis
Pallor of mucous membranes of eyes
Angular stomatitis
Angular scars
Cheilosis
Pallor of mucous membranes of lips
Oedema of tongue
Scarlet and raw tongue (glossitis)
Magenta tongue
Atrophic lingual papillae
Mottled dental enamel
Spongy, bleeding gums
Thyroid enlargement
Parotid enlargement
Xerosis (skin)
Follicular hyperkeratosis (type 1)
Follicular hyperkeratosis (type 2)
Petechiae

Ecchymoses
Pellagrous dermatosis
Flaky paint dermatosis
Scrotal and vulval dermatosis
Koilonychia
Oedema of subcutaneous tissue
Amount of fat excessive in subcutaneous
   tissue
Intramuscular or subperiosteal
   haematomas
Craniotabes
Frontal and parietal bossing
Epiphyseal enlargement (tender or
   painless)
Beading of ribs
Knock-knees
Bow-legs
Diffuse or local skeletal deformities

Hepatomegaly
Ascites
Psychomotor change
Mental confusion
Sensory loss
Motor weakness
Loss of position sense
Loss of vibratory sense
Loss of ankle and knee jerks
Calf tenderness
Cardiac and peripheral vascular
   dysfunction

(Continued)

Other (specify):

Pulse rate: Photograph attached?: yes/no
Stool—comments: Clinical impression:
Haemoglobin %:   marasmus—yes/no
                                                                 pre-kwashiorkor—yes/no
                                                                 kwashiorkor—yes/no

Biochemical tests (First category only)

Total serum protein:
Serum albumin:
Urinary urea (single fasting urine specimen):   /gm. of creatinine
Serum Vitamin A:
Serum carotene:
Serum alkaline phosphates (young children):
Serum ascorbic acid:
Urinary thiamine   (single fasting urine specimen):   /gm. of creatinine
Urinary riboflavin   „   „   „   „   /gm. of creatinine
Urinary N-methyl nicotinamide   „   „   /gm. of creatinine
Haemoglobin:
Haematocrit:
Serum cholesterol:
Serum lipids:
Radiographic measurements to be recorded on data sheet given under **A4.**
Radiographic measurements carried out?: yes/no.
Tick if observed: Rickets   Beri-beri
                            Osteomalacia   Advanced fluorosis
                            Infantile scurvy

Results of measurement of dark-adaptation, if carried out:

The questionnaire on the kinds and frequencies of foods eaten is given in **E4.** This is to be filled in for both the minimal and the comprehensive nutritional assessments

* Full details of the subject and his population group are to be entered in the **BASIC IDENTIFICATION SHEETS,** as laid down in the Technical Introduction.

E2. HOUSEHOLD FOOD INTAKE SURVEY

I. INTRODUCTION
   (a) General
   (b) Observations to be made
   (c) Sampling

II. TECHNIQUES
   (a) Weighed Food Survey
   (b) Larder Method
   (c) Equipment

III. DATA COLLECTING SHEETS
   (a) Dietary Survey Family Record
   (b) Weighed Food Survey
   (c) Larder Method
      1. Larder Stock Record
      2. Meals in and outside home
   (d) Average daily household dietary intake

I. INTRODUCTION

(a) General:

For the assessment of food intake on a family basis, two methods are available for field use. These are:

(a) The 'Weighed Food Survey'. This involves the weighing and/or measuring of each food before it is eaten, and recording the quantities of food wasted or otherwise not consumed by the family during the survey period.

(b) The 'Larder Method'. This involves the weighing and/or measuring of each food in the larder at the beginning and at the end of the survey period, combined with recording the quantities of all food purchased during the period, and of food wasted or otherwise not consumed.

Either of these methods can be carried out by the housewife if literate, after careful instruction. In many cases, however, the responsible investigator will need to train a team of lay helpers; each of these could observe up to 9 families over a 10-day period. (See II TECHNIQUES, below).

A 7-day period of observation should be aimed for, but otherwise the observations should cover at least a 3-day period.

(b) Observations to be made:

1. Carry out preliminary census and select a sample.

2. Explain in detail to the housewife in each family which it is proposed to study, what information is to be collected.

3. Fill out a preliminary questionnaire to ascertain the range and types of foodstuffs in current use, and code these. Also establish the routine of the ' week ', or other comparable short-term eating cycle. A recall questionnaire on the kinds and frequencies of foods eaten is given in **E4**.

4. (a) In the Weighed Food Survey, every item as prepared for consumption at mealtime by the family must be weighed; food not consumed (including waste) must be weighed after the meal. Each item is weighed before subdivision into individual helpings.

    (b) In the Larder Method, in addition to the observations already mentioned, it is desirable (though not essential) to record qualitatively the food eaten by the members of the family and any visitors present. This can be done by recall (see below).

5. The Dietary Survey Family Record (see III below) is to be filled out for each family studied.

6. The aim of this type of study is to establish the average intake over the period of observation, and the consumption for each household, of the following:

total calories	calcium	riboflavin
total protein	phosphorus	niacin
animal protein	iron	vitamin C
fat	Vitamin A	vitamin D
carbohydrate	thiamine	

If facilities are available, an aliquot sample of any food whose composition is not known may be kept in a plastic bag or bottle, preserved in a deep-freeze, and subsequently analysed in a bomb calorimeter.

Ancillary information which is required is as follows:

(1) Information on the ' food year '.

(2) Nutritional assessment of the individuals in the families studied. (see **E1**).

(3) Assessment of the habitual activity of the individuals in the families studied. (see **C6**).

(4) Medical examination of the individuals in the families studied. (see **F1**).

(5) Environmental description. (see **H**)

(c)   Sampling: *

The existence or absence of lists of families in the community to be studied should be ascertained during the initial visit. Official census rolls, if not more than two years old, are useful for sampling. Local census information is likely to be located in provincial or national capitals, and can be consulted there. Occasionally, communities have lists of families that are kept up-to-date. In recent years, health personnel in centres in remote areas have made censuses in order to plan the services required. In campaigns against malaria, typhus, and other diseases, houses may have been 'mapped' and records made of the families living in them. In some countries, rural school-teachers make censuses of the population to determine the number of children of school age in the community. Religious leaders also maintain lists of families. Nevertheless, lists of these various kinds, which are reasonably complete, are not found as often as one might wish.

Partial lists of other kinds are more frequently available. These may include lists of families with children at school, owners of land, holders of water rights, owners of livestock, or individuals qualified to vote. Such lists, although valueless for sampling purposes because they do not represent the entire community, may provide important information about the community and also about the individual families which will be studied in the survey sample.

If the group to be surveyed is fairly large, it would be advisable to carry out a pilot survey on a sub-sample immediately before starting the extensive survey, in order to select the most suitable day or days of the week for the final survey. When the sample is being selected, individuals who are affected with a pathological condition causing them to be unable to carry out their normal daily occupations, should be excluded.

For further notes on random sampling (systematic and unrestricted, stratified sampling, sample size, etc.) see FAO Manual, pp 24–37.

II.   TECHNIQUES

The investigator should fill out the Dietary Survey Family Record (see III, below), for each family studied.

---

* (From Reh, E., (1962), FAO Nutritional Studies, No. 18: 'Manual on Household Food Consumption Surveys', referred to above as 'FAO Manual'.)

The approach to the family is important. Workers should be as friendly as possible, and if necessary must accept hospitality where to refuse would offend. It is important that the introduction to the families should be through people who are already respected in the area.

On the first visit to the family it should be made clear (as it already should also be to the local authorities):—

(1) Who the worker is and whom he/she represents;
(2) The purpose of the visit and of the survey;
(3) Why this household has been chosen (e.g. by lottery);
(4) That the results will be reported without names;
(5) What is required from the family;
(6) The relationship of the survey to health and welfare, its scientific importance, and what the results will be used for;
(7) The responsibility and contribution of the family in representing others.

The greatest care must be taken to avoid modifying the dietary habits of the family.

The relationship between the survey leaders and workers and the morale of the teams will greatly influence the success of the study.

It is necessary to remember that survey work is tiring and that the workers should be allowed sufficient time and opportunity for recreation.

From the food intake, the consumption of each of the nutrients is calculated. For this purpose, computer programmes are now available, or can be written for the purpose, using the nutrient content of each food item, either determined by special chemical analysis, or calculated from available food tables. The analysis should provide data on the average daily intake per person of the following:

calories	calcium	thiamine
total protein	phosphorus	riboflavin
fat	iron	niacin
carbohydrate	vitamin A	vitamin C

(a) The Weighed Food Survey:

The actual weighing of foods is the technique most likely to give accurate quantitative data in most situations. It has the dangers that people change their habits when under observation, or are unwilling to cooperate for a whole survey period. It may be advisable to take a longer period than that fixed for the survey for a test number of families, to see whether results change as families become accustomed to the study.

The ' weighed ' survey technique is time-consuming where the survey worker has to keep all the records as she (or he) has to be present at most family meals and cannot survey more than a few families simultaneously. The number will depend on the distances between households, and on patterns of eating. Where the housewife herself weighs the food and can do much of the recording, the survey worker can teach the housewife what to do, and can make the inventory (if included—see Larder Method, below) at the beginning, and thereafter only pay short, daily, supervisory visits until she calls to make the final inventory. This enables one worker to study about 8–10 households during approximately the same period, provided that the dwellings are not too scattered. It is advisable, however, to ' stagger ' the starting interviews and inventories over the first few days (e.g. Day 1: 4 inventories and 7 short visits; Day 2: 3 inventories and 4 short visits; Day 3: 2 inventories and 7 short visits) as the inventories take a long time. By the fourth day short visits would be made to nine families, and by the eighth day the final inventories would have begun. All nine would be completed in ten days.

Records can start at any time of day. After breakfast the weights of foods already eaten at breakfast that day may either be estimated by recall or the survey can be continued until after breakfast on the final day. If the record is started later on in the day, it may be more convenient to adopt the second alternative, i.e. to continue the cycle to the same hour on an extra final day, e.g. before supper on Monday to before supper on the following Monday.

Each container or cooking vessel from which food is to be served is to be weighed with its contents immediately before the food is distributed, and then again after the dish is completed, together with any food not distributed. After the food has been consumed, the portions remaining uneaten should be collected together and pooled so far as possible to correspond with the dishes as originally served.

Note that food eaten outside the home must be recorded by recall.

Items used continually (e.g. sugar, butter, salt) must be recorded.

Interviews should inconvenience households as little as possible.

' Leading ' questions (i.e. questions suggesting that a particular answer is desired) should never be asked.

(b)   The Larder Method

The basic aim here is to make an accurate and continuous check on the larder stock. On the first visit, every commodity that enters into the diet (see **E4**) in the larder is weighed or its quantity measured. The housewife is instructed to keep separate (e.g. in a separate box) all additional purchases, and only to put these in the larder or to use them after they have been weighed by the investigator. Similarly, she is instructed to keep separate all food wasted or to be thrown out, which can only be disposed of after weighing and recording by the investigator. On the final call (e.g. at the end of the 7th day), the stocks in the larder are all reweighed.

This information is entered into the Larder Stock Record (see III below). In addition it is desirable daily to record descriptively the food served at each meal, and the members of the household (and visitors) partaking of each item. This may need to be done by recall after the meal has been eaten. Information on meals taken outside the home by members of the family must also be recorded (see III below).   These data will enable some weighting to be made of the food items in relation to individual intake.

(c)   Equipment

Measuring cylinders or graduated beakers are required for measuring liquids.

Apparatus for measuring heights and weights (see **A1**) will be required if no assessment of nutritional status (see **E1**) is being carried out on the sample.

A random numbers table is useful for sampling purposes.

Scales for weighing the food should be easy to carry and sufficiently sturdy to withstand hard use. A lightweight type of spring scale with a platform top, on which articles of any shape may be placed, is the most practical. A suitable instrument meeting this specification is the Salter No. 50D dietary scale, weighing to 500 gm. by 2 gm., and incorporating a sliding scale for ease of subtraction of the weights of the containers. This model, however, is currently out of production, and an alternative instrument is the Salter 33 D model. (See Fig. E2/1).

This scale is available from (in the U.K.):

> George Salter & Co. Ltd.,
> Weighing Machine Division,
> 31–33 High Holborn,
> London W.C.1.

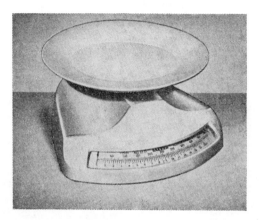

Fig. E2/1   Salter 33 D dietary balance. (16 oz. × ⅛ oz. and 500 × 5 gms.)

No. 33D.   DIETARY BALANCE

Features

Wide base and low height give great stability. Dial slopes at the right angle for easy reading and has a dust-excluding transparent cover.

Zero adjust screw.

Specification
Resilient plastic case, and saucer.
White dial with black markings.

Graduated	Saucer Diam.	Net Weight	Height Overall
16 oz. × ⅛ oz. and	7″	1 lb. 8 oz.	4″
500 × 5 g	17·8 cm	·64 kg	15 cm

Guaranteed by Salter Quality Control to an accuracy of better than one part in 85.

Fig. E2/1   Price: Approx. £3   2   6

Scales with balancing levers and hanging pans, which will swing in the breeze or may slip out of notches, although theoretically more accurate, are troublesome in the field. Special packing is needed for transportation over long distances or over rough roads. Suitable scales are often difficult to find, even in large cities, and plans to obtain them should be made long in advance of the survey period. Two types of food scales will normally be required, one for weighing small items under a kilogram (see Fig. E2/1), and one for bulkier items weighing up to 5–10 kg.

III. DATA COLLECTING SHEETS..

(a) *Dietary Survey Family Record*

Family name: Number in household (total):
Family serial number: Religion of family:
Address: (if various, specify)
Length of time at present address:
No. of days of observation:
Dates of observation: Season of year:
Give details of pattern of meals over
   day and week:

Names of members of family, with age, sex, and occupation:

Names of other occupants of household, with age, sex, and occupation (including
   lodgers, permanent visitors over survey period, etc.):

Type of dwelling:
No. of rooms in house:
Separate kitchen room: yes/no   indoor/outside   own/shared
Has **E4** (recall questionnaire on kinds and
   frequencies of foods eaten) been filled in?: yes/no
Water supply: tap in dwelling/tap in village/surface tank/well/spring/sluggish
               river/running river/lake or pond/other.
Household animals (specify):

Other general remarks:

Signature of Investigator: ....

III. DATA COLLECTING SHEETS (continued)

(b) Weighed food survey

Family name:

Family serial number:

Address:

Ethnic group or
nationality:

Composition of family:

Code for use in table below:

	Code	Age
Household head	H	
Wife	W	
Eldest son	S_1	
Second son (etc.)	S_2	
Eldest daughter	D_1	
Second daughter (etc.)	D_2	

CODE DAY:

Date of this record:

Day of week:

Scale number:

Name of observer:

	Code	Age	Sex
Visitors	V_1		
	V_2		
	V_3		
	V_4		
	(etc.)		

(continued)

Table—continued

Time	Name of meal	Record all consuming *each food* using code above	Description of food and method of cooking USE A NEW LINE FOR EACH FOOD	Weight of container	Weight of container + food	Weight of container + waste	Eaten by members of family + visitors	Wt. of food eaten	Food code	Sent to lab. for analysis yes/no

			LAB. USE ONLY		

MEALS OUTSIDE HOME. Give estimates of quantities of each food eaten and description and method of cooking.

(Continued)

Table—continued

FOODS REQUIRED DAILY

	Weight of container	Before breakfast first weight (food + container)	IF REFILLING NECESSARY Weight of food (if any) + container before refilling	Weight of food + container after refilling	At night last weight (food + container)	LAB. USE ONLY Weight of food consumed in day	Food code
Butter							
Margarine							
Jam (type)							
Marmalade							
Sugar							
Milk							
Salt							
Others (specify)							

(c) Larder Method
(1) Larder Stock Record

Name of Housewife : Address :

Family/Household number :

Ethnic group or nationality : First call : date :

NAME OF INVESTIGATOR : time :

Final call : date :

time :

COMMODITY (full description)	Quantity at first call (gms./oz) *	Additional purchases (gms./oz.) * each day							Total purchased + larder stock (gm/oz) *	Final call (gm/oz) *	LABORATORY USE ONLY			
		1	2	3	4	5	6	7			Total used	Food code	Sent for analysis yes/no	Quantity sent for analysis

•Draw a circle around the units in which your quantities are measured.

III. DATA COLLECTING SHEETS (continued)

(d) *Average Daily Household Dietary Intake:*

Family name:

Family number:

Address:

Details of composition of family:

Period of observation—no. of days:

dates:

Number in family:

Ethnic group or nationality:

Name of Investigator. . . . .

Notes on basis for weighting:

	Average daily intake for family	Average daily intake per capita (by simple division)	Weighted daily average intake
Carbohydrate (gm)			
Fat (gm)			
Protein (gm)			
Animal protein (gm)			
Total calories (kcal)			
Carbohydrate as % of total Cals.			
Fat as % of total Cals.			
Protein as % of total Cals.			
NDp Cals. %			
Mineral salts: Ca (mg)			
P (mg)			
Fe (mg)			
Na (gm)			
K (gm)			

(continued)

Table—continued

Vitamins: A and carotene(i.u.)			
B—thiamin (mg)			
riboflavin (mg)			
niacin (mg)			
C (mg)			
D (i.u.)			
Water intake: Drinking water and beverages (ml)			
Water in food (added and metabolic) (ml)			

E3. INDIVIDUAL FOOD INTAKE BY WEIGHING

I. INTRODUCTION

(a) General:

Individual food intake by weighing can only be carried out efficiently where the subjects are literate, can use the scales, and are fully cooperative. Otherwise observers will be needed to carry out the individual weighing and recording operations, and as this is likely to interfere greatly with the meal it is probably not normally possible. It is therefore preferable in these cases to carry out a household survey (see **E2**).

The food intake over at least a 3-day, and preferably a 7-day period will have to be followed.

In many countries it is difficult to carry out individual 'weighed' surveys of several family members at one time, especially when there is much variety in the diet or where family members help themselves from central dishes continuously throughout the meal. In some cultures, however (for example in Western Nigeria), where a complete meal is served at one time to each individual and where the family does not eat simultaneously, it is possible to weigh the food of each person without too much trouble.

(b) Observations to be made:

(1) Carry out preliminary census and select a sample.

(2) Explain in detail to the individuals concerned what information is to be collected, and the methods to be used, in accordance with 'Techniques', below.

(3) Fill out a preliminary questionnaire to ascertain the range and types of foodstuffs in current use, and code these. Also establish the routine of

the ' week ', or comparable short-term eating-cycle. A questionnaire on the kinds and frequencies of foods eaten is given in **E4**.

(4)   The Dietary Survey Personal Record must be filled out.

(5)   Every food item + container is to be weighed as served up for consumption.

(6)   The food remaining uneaten is to be weighed on every occasion.

(7)   The aim of this type of study is to establish the average intake over the period of observation, and the consumption for each individual of the following:

total calories	calcium	riboflavin
total protein	phosphorus	niacin
animal protein	iron	vitamin C
fat	vitamin A	vitamin D
carbohydrate	thiamine	

If facilities are available, an aliquot sample of any food whose composition is not known may be kept in a plastic bag or bottle, preserved in a deep-freeze, and subsequently analysed in a bomb calorimeter.

Ancillary information which is required is as follows:

(1)   Information on the " food year ".

(2)   Nutritional assessment of the individuals in the sample (see **E1**)

(3)   Assessment of the habitual activity of the subjects in the sample (see **C6**)

(4)   Medical examination of the individuals in the sample (see **F1**)

(5)   Environmental description (see **H**)

II.   TECHNIQUES

To the investigator: (i)   Fill out the Dietary Survey Personal Record for each subject.

(ii)   Explain to each subject the following instructions.

(iii)   For details of the types of scales, see **E2**.

INDIVIDUAL DIETARY SURVEY INSTRUCTIONS

For the survey period you are provided with:

1. A **flat plastic plate** to weigh most solid foods on, e.g. bread, roast meat. You need not eat off this plate.

2. **A small plastic fruit bowl** to weigh " sloppy " foods in, e.g. rice pudding, custard, apple pie. You need not eat from this plate. (Alternatively, a single large shallow plastic bowl suitable for weighing both solid and liquid foods could be used.)

3. A **plastic pint measure** for milk.

4. **A plastic heat-resistant pint measure** for **HOT** liquids.

5. **Small plastic pots** to contain your personal needs of sugar, butter, jam, margarine.

6. **Scales.** The scales provided weigh up to 16 oz. (or 500 gm.) Each section of the scale represents $\frac{1}{8}$ oz. (or 2 gm.) Please read the weights to the nearest $\frac{1}{8}$ oz. (or 2 gm.). It is greatly preferable that all weights throughout the survey be recorded in grams and not in oz.

PLEASE WEIGH AND ENTER IN YOUR RECORD BOOK ALL FOODS THAT YOU EAT

Foods such as butter, sugar, jam and milk, which would be a nuisance to weigh frequently will be set aside in dishes to be used **by you alone.** They should not be used in cooking.

METHOD OF RECORDING

1. **INDIVIDUAL FOODS:** All foods should be weighed separately and their weights recorded. **They should be weighed when cooked, on the specially-provided plate or bowl,** and the container should be re-weighed in the same way after the meal, together with the food waste, if any.

Please remember to give the following details:

a. **Method of cooking,** e.g. roast, stewed, fried, boiled, steamed, etc.

b. **Type of food,** e.g. white bread, marie biscuits, fruit cake, currant pudding, canned pineapple.

c. **Method of weighing,** e.g. fish with or without bone.

2. **MEALS:** Please give the time and the name of the meal in the columns provided, e.g. 8 a.m. breakfast.

   Soup: Weigh soup in the plastic jug and please state the type of soup. (If home-made, give record of ingredients.) This is similarly important for any unusual food.

   Main course: Remember to weigh and record each item separately.
   Food not eaten during meal: Please weigh and record any food left over.

Example

Time	Meal	Description of food (Method of cooking and weighing, i.e. with or without container.) *Use a new line for each food*	Wt. of food + container	Wt. of container + waste	Wt. of food eaten	Code (LAB ONLY)
12 noon	Lunch	Boiled salt beef + plate	385 gm.	275 gm.	110 gm.	SB
		Boiled potatoes + plate	450 gm.	250 gm.	200 gm.	BP
7 p.m.	Supper	Fried hen's egg + plate	125 gm.	105 gm.	20 gm.	HE
		Chip potatoes fried in fat + plate	400 gm.	250 gm.	150 gm.	CP
		Currant bun	35 gm.	nil	35 gm.	CB

MEALS EATEN OUTSIDE YOUR HOME

If possible, please take your scales with you. If not, please describe the meal, for example:

Afternoon tea with my sister—4.0 p.m.

    2 cups of tea with milk
    4 teaspoons sugar
    1 currant bun
    1 marie biscuit

FOODS REQUIRED DAILY

1. *Butter, sugar, jam:* Small pots with lids are provided for you to put your own supplies of these foods in. Please re-fill the pots each morning before breakfast and weigh them (= First weight). Weigh the pots again at night, when you have finished eating for the day (= Last weight). *Always weigh dishes with the lids on.*

2. *Milk:* Re-fill the milk jug each morning and weigh (= First weight). Re-weigh the jug + any remaining milk at night (= Last weight).

MISCELLANEOUS

a. *Chocolates and sweets:* Please weigh these if possible. Otherwise record how much you have eaten and state what it was, e.g. ½ bar of milk chocolate, 3 boiled sweets. It would also be helpful to record the brand names of these items.

b. *Alcohol, soft drinks, tea, coffee:* Record the amount consumed in your record sheet, e.g. 3 cups tea, 1 bottle fizzy lemonade, 1 glass brandy.

IF YOU ARE WORRIED ABOUT ANYTHING, PLEASE ASK THE OBSERVER

(b) **DIETARY SURVEY PERSONAL RECORD**
(To be filled in by investigator.)

Name:*

Subject number:

Age:

Sex:

Season of year:

Obvious physical disabilities:

Brief medical history:

Date this study commenced:

Address:

Religion:

Height (mm):   Weight (kg.):

Weather conditions:

Ethnic and tribal origin (or nationality):

Name of Investigator ....

(For medical assessment see **F1**.)

Rough description of body build:

Birth rank: Birth weight:

Marital status: single/married/living as married/widowed/divorced.

No. of offspring: ... (male)   ... (female)

Smoking status: ... cigarettes per day

             ... cigars per day

             pipe: yes/no

             other:...................

Alcohol: Light drinker/moderate/heavy/teetotal

Sugar in tea:†   Sugar in coffee:†   Sugar in cocoa:†

Milk in tea: yes/no   Milk in coffee: yes/no   Milk in cocoa: yes/no

Give details of pattern of meals over day and week:

‡ Frequency of consumption (with weights) of sweets, chocolates, etc:

No. of occupants of household (excluding lodgers):...... persons

Type of dwelling:

No. of rooms in house:

Separate kitchen room: yes/no   indoor/outside

Bathroom: yes/no   own/shared   indoor/outside

Toilet: yes/no   own/shared   indoor/outside

Occupation:

Occupation of spouse:

Occupation of father: of mother:

Place of work:

Hours of work: Hours of overtime:

Days off per week:

Outside leisure activities (type, frequency, and duration):

Indoor pastimes (type, frequency, and duration):

Other general remarks:

† State number of lumps/spoonfuls; if none, enter 0.

‡ See Note a, p. 493.

III. SAMPLE PAGE OF RECORD BOOK

CODE DAY:

Name:*   Ethnic group or
Serial number: nationality: Date of this record:
Place: Day of week:
Occupation: Scale number:
Containers: *Type*   *Ref. no.**   *Name of investigator:*
         Flat plastic plate   1   *Weight (gm./oz.)*
         Small plastic bowl   2
         Large shallow plastic bowl   3

*For use in Table below.

Time	Name of meal	Description of food and method of cooking USE A NEW LINE FOR EACH FOOD	Container ref. no.	Weight of container + food	Weight of container + waste	LAB. USE ONLY		
						Weight of food eaten	Food code	Sent to lab. for analysis yes/no

FOODS REQUIRED DAILY

Foods	Weight of container	Before breakfast: first weight (food + container)	IF REFILLING NECESSARY Weight of food (if any) + container before refilling	IF REFILLING NECESSARY Weight of food + container after refilling	At night last weight (food + container)	Weight of food con-sumed in day	Food code
Butter							
Margarine							
Jam (type)							
Marmalade							
Sugar							
Milk							
Salt							

*Full details of the subject and his population group are to be entered in the **INDIVIDUAL IDENTITY SHEETS** as laid down in the Technical Introduction.

III.   (2)   DIETARY INTAKE (daily average)

Name :*   Ethnic and tribal origin (or nationality) :
Serial number: Occupation:
Address: Scale number:
Number of days of observation: Dates of observation:
Name of observer:
Carbohydrate   gms.
Fat   gms.
Protein   gms.
Animal protein   gms.
Total calories: (kcal)
Carbohydrate as % of total cals: %
Fat % of total cals: %
Protein % of total cals: %
NDpCal%:

Mineral salts:—   Calcium   mg.
                         Phosphorus   mg.
                         Iron   mg.
                         Sodium   gm.
                         Potassium   gm.

Vitamins:—   Vitamin A (and carotene)   i.u.
                         Vitamin B—thiamin   mg.
                                     riboflavin   mg.
                                     niacin   mg.
                         Vitamin C   mg.
                         Vitamin D   i.u.

Water intake:—   Drinking water and beverages (e.g. tea, coffee, beer)   ml.
                         Water in food (added and metabolic)   ml.

---

* Full details of the subject and his population group are to be entered in the **BASIC IDENTIFICATION SHEETS,** as laid down in the Technical Introduction.

E4. RECALL QUESTIONNAIRE ON KINDS AND FREQUENCIES OF FOODS EATEN (NON-QUANTITATIVE)

QUESTIONNAIRE ON KINDS AND FREQUENCIES OF FOODS EATEN

Name of investigator:

Serial no.: Age: Sex: Place: Date: Occupation:
Name: Ethnic group or nationality:

Please indicate by the numbers given if you have had anything to eat in the categories below at the times indicated. Otherwise leave space blank.

	CEREALS	STARCHY ROOTS AND FRUITS	STARCH FLOURS	PULSES AND OIL-SEEDS
	1. Rice 2. Wheat 3. Maize 4. Millet 5. Other (specify)	1. Cassava 2. Potatoes 3. Yams 4. Plantains 5. Breadfruit 6. Taro 7. Other (specify)	1. Sago 2. Cornflour 3. Arrowroot 4. Other (specify)	1. Peas 2. Beans 3. Dhal 4. Grain 5. Ground-nuts 6. Soya beans 7. Other beans 8. Other (specify)
Early morning				
Breakfast				
Mid-morning				
Midday meal				
Afternoon				
Evening meal				
Supper				
Bedtime				

Table—continued

	ANIMAL PRODUCTS (NOT FATS) 1. Meat 2. Fish 3. Eggs 4. Milk 5. Cheese 6. Other (specify)	OTHER FRUIT AND VEGETABLES 1. Green leaves 2. Roots and stems 3. Vegetable fruits 4. Citrus fruits 5. Mangos 6. Other (specify)	SUGARS 1. Refined sugar 2. Molasses 3. Syrups and jams 4. Confectionery 5. Other (specify)	FATS AND OILS 1. Vegetable oils 2. Lard 3. Butter 4. Ghee 5. Margarine 6. Other (specify)
Early morning				
Breakfast				
Mid-morning				
Midday meal				
Afternoon				
Evening meal				
Supper				
Bedtime				

QUESTIONNAIRE ON KINDS AND FREQUENCIES OF FOODS EATEN—continued

	CONDIMENTS AND SPICES 1. Curry 2. Soya sauce 3. Pepper 4. Other (specify)	MINERAL SALTS 1. Common salt 2. Lime (CaOH) 3. Other (specify)	BEVERAGES 1. Tea 2. Coffee 3. Cocoa 4. Kaffir beer 5. Other beer 6. Palm wine 7. Other wines 8. Spirits 9. Other (specify)
Early morning			
Breakfast			
Mid-morning			
Midday meal			
Afternoon			
Evening meal			
Supper			
Bedtime			

F. MEDICAL AND METABOLIC STUDIES

F1. GENERAL MEDICAL EXAMINATION

I. INTRODUCTION

   (a) General
   (b) Sampling

II. DATA COLLECTING SHEETS

   (a) Health status—1. Personal examination

                              2. Laboratory examination

   (b) Socio-medical data

I. INTRODUCTION

(a) General;

In all multi-disciplinary investigations an essential first step is to obtain a background knowledge of the medical status of the community. This is of importance in its own right, but for the further specialised tests to be carried out, e.g. on working capacity, climatic tolerance, etc., healthy individuals will need to be selected, and it is also necessary to know how far these are representative of the community as a whole.

In nearly all ' simple ' communities there is inadequate knowledge of what diseases are prevalent, quite apart from a knowledge of what are the particularly interesting problems for study. What is needed first is a general disease survey. It is not intended in this Handbook to deal with the specialised and formidable task of designing specialised epidemiological surveys. Of such surveys, those dealing with cardiovascular studies are of major interest, and have relevance to the IBP. The conduct of such studies is described in considerable detail in Rose, G.A., and H. Blackburn, (1966)*, " Cardiovascular Population Studies: Methods ", WHO, Geneva. Other important epidemiological surveys associated with IBP projects concern congenital defects (see **F6**) and thyroid disease (see **F5**). These and similar studies figure in the national programmes of various countries.

Furthermore, an interest in all diseases in a population, or in the ' level of disease ' or the 'disease load ', is a legitimate one. The symptoms and the interference with full function are perhaps the most real aspects of disease to the sick, but they have been inadequately studied, probably because of the difficulty of measuring them.

* To be republished as WHO Monograph: 1968.

The aims of a medical survey in a ' simple ' community should be:

(a)   A description of the disease pattern and disease load in a country where existing information is rudimentary.

(b)   The understanding, as far as possible, of the factors responsible for producing the situation which is found.

(c)   Provision of medical help to the subjects of the survey.

The demographic observations which might also usefully be made are dealt with fully in Section **G**.

Data Sheets are provided to record the results of the General Medical Examination under:

(a)   Health status—1.   Personal examination
                        2.   Laboratory examina-
                             tion

(b)   Socio-medical data

In addition, a form is available for recording a **Personal and Family Medical History**. This may be obtained from the HA Office, 21, Bedford Sq., LONDON W.C.1.

(b)   **Sampling;**

The General Medical Examination is an essential and high-priority feature in all population studies, both those where the population as a whole will be examined (e.g. for genetic analysis), or where the population will need to be sampled for a subsequent intensive study (e.g. work capacity or climatic tolerance). It is highly desirable in ' primitive ' groups to make as intensive a medical study as possible, that is, as a morbidity survey. (See also **F2**).

The disease load of a large population can only be studied directly by observing a sample of the population including all ages and both sexes.

Anything like a random sample of individuals in the population over a wide area is quite impracticable for many reasons. If a random sample is taken, information lies buried which might help in the understanding of certain characteristics where interactions between individuals play some causative role. Obvious examples of such characteristics are those due to genes, which pass from parents to offspring, those due to domestic environmental characteristics and those due to invasions by pathogens which spread from person to person.

These groups include most diseases. The minimum sampling unit for study should therefore be the household or family group. Many features of the environment are fairly constant over the whole of a human settlement, in primitive situations almost always a village, and so they only need to be described once. Hence concentration on a few settlements will greatly simplify the description of the environment. If all members of a geographically circumscribed population are studied, definite statements can be made about the observations on a definable population, subject of course to limitations inherent in the investigations. For these and other reasons, attempts should be made to study complete populations.

The choice of populations becomes an important matter. It is likely to be a compromise between what was first thought to be ideal and what was later found to be practical. In an exploratory study it may be desirable to choose ' typical ' populations representative of important kinds of population. In comparative studies of adaptation it may be desirable to choose populations who differ as widely as possible from each other with regard to the characteristics to be studied, while in prospective studies of adaptation it may be desirable to make studies before and after some significant change. The factors determining choice are likely to be highly characteristic for each investigation so it is hardly profitable to discuss them here, except to state that the reasons for choosing the particular population should be clearly stated, even when they are not respectable ' scientific ' ones.

As many observations are made on each individual, only a small number of people can be studied, coming from a small number of inhabited places. The number of people studied is important in determining the choice of what is to be investigated in a prevalence survey. Only those characteristics which are sufficiently common to be found several times can profitably be studied.

It is characteristic of unsophisticated tropical communities that a small number of clinical conditions is responsible for most of the morbidity and these conditions may occur in a very high percentage of the population. Hence clinical observations on small numbers can be expected to yield more information on the disease pattern than in more sophisticated communities, where numerous clinical entities each contribute a small part to the total disease load.

III. DATA COLLECTING SHEET

(a. Health status: 1 : Personal Examination)

* For full details, see Individual

Identity Sheet (01)

IBP/HA Project ref. no.	1 ☐☐☐☐
Study number	5 ☐☐

Subject's name: *

Serial number	7 ☐☐☐
Sex (M = 1 ; F non-parous = 2 ; parous 1 = 3 ;parous 2 = 4 ; parous 3 or more = 5)	10 ☐

Place of examination:

Age (years) *	11 ☐☐
Examination date (year + 3 decimals — see table in Technical Introduction)	13 ☐☐☐☐☐
Procedure category	18 ☐☐

CODE FOR "NOT APPLICABLE" = X; CODE FOR "DATA NOT RECORDED" = Y

For full demographic information,
*see G*1.

Height (mm)	20 ☐☐☐☐
Weight (kg)	24 ☐☐☐☐
Demeanour (alert = 1 ; dull = 2)	28 ☐
Development—muscle mass (good = 1 ; poor = 2)	29 ☐
Development—sucbutaneous fat (excessive = 1 ; adequate = 2 ; deficient = 3)	30 ☐
Anaemia (absent = 0 ; present = 1)	31 ☐

(continued)

(Personal examination—contd.

Vaccinated
(scar = 1 ; not vacc-
inated = 2 ; vaccinated, no
scar = 3)   32 ☐

If diseased, specify :

Skin
(supple = 1 ; dry = 2 ;
diseased (specify) = 3)   33 ☐

Yaws
(no history = 0 ; disease
present = 1)   34 ☐

Hair
(NAD = 1 ; sparse = 2 ;
other (e.g. lack of colour,
easy pluckability) (specify)=3) 35 ☐

If other, specify :
(see also **E1**)

Lips
(NAD = 1 ; cheilosis = 2 ;
angular stomatitis = 3 ;
other (specify) = 4   36 ☐

If other, specify :
(see also **E1**)

Tongue
(NAD = 1 ; raw (sore) = 2 ;
fissured = 3 ; atrophied
papillae = 4 ; hypertrophied
papillae = 5 ; other (specify)
= 6)   37 ☐

If other, specify :

Teeth
(NAD = 1 ; carious = 2 ;
other (specify) = 3)   38 ☐

Total number of teeth
decayed, missing, or filled   39 ☐

If other, specify :

Gums
(NAD = 1 ; inflamed = 2 ;
retracted = 3 ; scurvy = 4 ;
other (specify) = 5)   41 ☐

If other, specify :

Throat
(NAD = 1 ; enlarged/
inflamed tonsils = 2 ; other
(specify = 3)   42 ☐

(continued)

(Personal examination—contd.)

Code for condition of eye	
NAD	1
Conjunctival scarring	2
„ inflammation	3
Pannus	4
Corneal ulcer or corneal opacity	5
Cataract	6
Other or combination (specify)	7

Eye (left)
(use code at left)   43 ☐

Eye (right)
(use code at left)   44 ☐

Sight
(Normal = 1 ; partially
blind = 2 ; totally
blind = 3 ; wears
glasses = 4)   45 ☐

Thyroid gland
(normal = 1 ; enlarged = 2)   46 ☐

Lymphatic glands
(normal = 1 ; enlarged
(specify which group, add
'S' if suppurating) = 2)   47 ☐

For fuller details, see **F5**.

If enlarged, give details :

Ear (left)
(use code at left)   48 ☐

If other, specify :

Code for condition of ear	
NAD	1
Dry perforation	2
Discharging	3
Partially deaf	4
Totally deaf	5
Other (specify)	6

Ear (right)
(use code at left)   49 ☐

If other, specify :

Duration of cough
(NAD = 1 ; periodic from
childhood = 2 ; continuous
from childhood = 3)   50 ☐

If other, specify :

Chest illness history
(none = 0 ; bronchitis = 1 ;
TB = 2 ; cancer = 3 ;
other (specify) = 4)   51 ☐

If other, specify :

Lung (left)
(NAD = 1 ; emphysematous
= 2 ; bronchitis = 3 ;
pleural effusion = 4 ;
pneumonia = 5 ; other
(specify) = 6)   52 ☐

(continued)

Personal examination—contd.

If other, specify:

Lung (right)
(NAD = 1; emphysematous
= 2; bronchitis = 3;
pleural effusion = 4;
pneumonia = 5; other
(specify) = 6)   53 ☐

Present cough
(occasional = 1; frequent
= 2; haemoptysis = 3)   54 ☐

Apex beat
(absent = 1; mid-costal
line $\pm \frac{1}{4}'' = 2$; under 1″
out = 3; over 1″ out = 4)   55 ☐

Murmurs
(none = 0; mitral incom-
petence = 1; mitral stenosis
= 2; aortic incompetence
= 3; aortic stenosis

If other, specify:

= 4; other (specify) = 5)   56 ☐

Heart
(normal = 1; enlarged = 2)   57 ☐

Liver
(NAD = 0; finger-breadth
below right costal margin
= 1; 2 fb. = 2; 3 fb. or
more = 3)   58 ☐

Spleen
(Schiffner 0; 1; 2; 3; 4;
below umbilicus = 5)   59 ☐

Specify any other abnormality of
abdominal viscera:

Penis
(NAD = 1; sores = 2;
scars = 3; discharge = 4;
stricture = 5; other or
combination (specify) = 6)   60 ☐

If other, specify:

Scrotum
(NAD = 1; hydrocoele = 2;
ulcer = 3; other (specify)
= 4)   61 ☐

(*continued*)

514   F   *Medical and Metabolic Studies*

Personal examination—contd.

If other, specify :	Bladder (NAD = 1 ; other (specify) = 2)	62 ☐
If other, specify :	Vagina (NAD = 1 ; sores = 2 ; scars = 3 ; discharge = 4 ; other (specify) = 5)	63 ☐
	Knee-jerks (active = 1 ; inactive = 2)	64 ☐
	Ankle-jerks (active = 1 ; inactive = 2)	65 ☐
If abnormal, specify ;	Pupil (left) (normal = 1 ; abnormal (specify) = 2)	66 ☐
If abnormal, specify :	Pupil (right) (normal = 1 ; abnormal (specify) = 2)	67 ☐
If abnormal, specify :	Legs (bones normal = 1 ; abnormal (e.g. genu valgum)—(specify) = 2)	68 ☐
	Tropical ulcers present = 1 ; absent = 0)	69 ☐
Other changes of legs, (e.g. osteomyelitis, chronic tibia right) :	Oedema (present = 1 ; absent = 0)	70 ☐
	Mantoux test (not done = 0 ; positive = 1 ; negative = 2)	71 ☐
	Pulse rate/min.	72 ☐
If not oral, specify :	Oral temperature (°C)	73 ☐☐☐

Signature of Investigator . . . .

(continued)

Personal examination—contd.

For full information on :—Colour-blindness, testing, see **B9** and **B10**.

Anthropometric measurements and techniques, see **A1**.

Thyroid studies and measurements, see **F5**.

G6PDD testing in the field, see **B3**.

Haematological, immunological, and other serological tests see **F4**.

Dermatoglyphics, see **B12**.

Radiographic measurements, see **A4**.

Nutritional assessment, see **E1**.

Demographic studies, see **G1**.

Environmental description, see **H**.

See also : **PERSONAL EXAMINATION—FINDINGS**
HEALTH STATUS—LABORATORY TESTS

(Personal Examination—FINDINGS)

* For full details, see Individual Identity Sheet (01)

IBP/HA Project ref. no.	1 ☐☐☐☐
Study number	5 ☐☐☐

Subject's name:*

Serial number	7 ☐☐☐
Sex (M = 1 ; F = 2)	10 ☐

Place of examination:

Age (years)*	11 ☐☐
Examination date (year + 3 decimals—see table in Technical Introduction)	13 ☐☐☐☐☐
Procedure category	18 ☐☐

CODE FOR "NOT APPLICABLE" = X; CODE FOR "DATA NOT RECORDED" = Y

FINDINGS

Code 0 for condition absent; code 1 for condition present

Malaria	20 ☐	Injuries (specify)	34 ☐
Filariasis	21 ☐	. . . .
Gonococcal infection	22 ☐	. . . .
Syphilis	23 ☐	Heart disease (specify)	35 ☐
Yaws	24 ☐	. . . .
Leprosy	25 ☐	. . . .
Scabies	26 ☐	Polio	36 ☐
Schistosomiasis	27 ☐	Signs of malnutrition	37 ☐
Trypanosomiasis	28 ☐	Anaemia	38 ☐
Onchocerciasis	29 ☐	Whooping cough	39 ☐
Bronchitis	30 ☐	Measles	40 ☐
T.B.	31 ☐	Inguinal hernia	41 ☐
Relapsing fever	32 ☐	Umbilical hernia	42 ☐
Congenital deformities	33 ☐	Helminths	43 ☐
(specify)		Ulcers (specify) . . . . .44 ☐

. . . .　　　　　　　　　　　. . . . .

Other conditions found—give details:

Signature of Investigator:. . . . .

(a. Health status—2. Laboratory investigation)

* For full details, see Individual	IBP/HA Project ref. no.	1 ☐☐☐☐
Identity Sheet (01)	Study number	5 ☐☐
*Subject's name:**	Serial number	7 ☐☐☐
	Sex (M = 1 ; F = 2)	10 ☐
Place of examination (field):	Age (years)	11 ☐☐
Name and address of laboratory:	Examination date (year + 3 decimals—see table in Technical Introduction)	13 ☐☐☐☐☐
	Procedure category	18 ☐☐

CODE FOR "NOT APPLICABLE" = X; CODE FOR "DATA NOT RECORDED" = Y

Where specimens have not been collected, code Y

Height (mm) 20 ☐☐☐☐

Weight (kg) 24 ☐☐☐☐

Stools
Diarrhoea (yes = 1 ; no = 0) 28 ☐

Sputum
Give details :

Haemmorrhage (yes = 1 ; no = 0) 29 ☐

Ascaris O. (present = 1 ; absent = 0) 30 ☐

Hookworm (present = 1 ; absent = 0) 31 ☐

Swabs—give details of findings
Nose:

Taenia (present = 1 ; absent = 0) 32 ☐

Throat:

Entamoeba histolytica (present = 1 ; absent = 0) 33 ☐

Skin:

Other:

Other microorganisms (yes = 1 ; no = 0) 34 ☐

Specify other microorganisms :

(continued)

(a. Health status—2. Laboratory investigation—contd.

Blood

See also **F4.**

Hb gm/100 ml.	35	□□□
M.C.H.C. %	38	□□□
P.C.V.	41	□□□
Red cell count (x 10^{-6})	44	□·□□
Malaria parasites (present = 1; absent = 0)	47	□
Microfilariae (present = 1; absent = 0)	48	□

Details of anaemia:

Anaemia (none = 0; yes (specify) = 1)	49	□
Kahn +ve = 1; Kahn −ve = 2; WR +ve = 3; WR −ve = 4; no test = 5	50	□

Urine

Albumin mg /100 ml.	51	□□□
Sugar mg/100 ml.	54	□□□
Blood (absent = 0; present = 1)	57	□

Microorganisms—give details:

Microorganisms (absent = 0; present = 1 (give details))	58	□

Culture –give details:

Signature of Investigator.......................

II. DATA COLLECTING SHEETS
(b) Socio-medical data:

Name of Investigator:

Name of subject: *
Serial number:
Age:

Date of examination:
Place of examination:
Sex: M/F
Ethnic and tribal origin (or nationality):

WHERE A CHOICE IS INDICATED, PLACE A CIRCLE AROUND THE APPROPRIATE WORD

Marital status: single/married/living as married/divorced/widowed

**Name of village of residence:

**Latitude of village: **Altitude of village:

Occupation: infant/school/at home/domestic/cultivator/labourer/light industry/heavy industry/clerical-office/military service/other

Hours of work—average per week:

Outdoor leisure activities (type, frequency and duration):

Indoor pastimes (type, frequency and duration):

Type of dwelling: hut/long-house/shack or lean-to/European type (detached)/European type (semi-detached or terraced)/apartment block/other

Construction of dwelling: mud or clay or wattle/adobe/thatch/wood/corrugated iron (metal)/brick/concrete/other

Number of rooms in dwelling:

No. of household occupants (excluding lodgers, etc.): . . . . (adults)
. . . . (children)

No. of lodgers, permanent visitors, servants, etc. in household: . . . . (adults)
. . . . (children)

Separate kitchen-room: yes/no indoor/outside own/shared
Separate bathroom: yes/no indoor/outside own/shared
Separate toilet: yes/no indoor/outside own/shared

Type of toilet: none/pit/privy/flush

***Number of meals per day:

***Staple foods:

Water supply: tap in dwelling/tap in village/surface tank/well/spring/sluggish river running river/lake or pond/other

Animals in village or commonly contacted: dogs/cats/poultry/pigs/goats/cattle/sheep/horses/other

Vectors: anopheles/aedes/tse-tse/flies/ticks/bugs/lice/snails

Health services: professional/native/none

* Full details of the subject and his population group are to be entered in the **BASIC IDENTIFICATION SHEETS,** as laid down in the Technical Introduction.
** See also **H,**
*** See also **E.**

F2. CONTINUED MORBIDITY SURVEY

I. INTRODUCTION

II. NOTE ON THE RECORDING OF MORBIDITY;
The Diagnostic Index (E-Book).

I. INTRODUCTION

CONTINUED RECORDING OF MORBIDITY DATA

Whenever possible, consideration should be given to the institution on a local basis of a continuing system of recording of morbidity data. The first medical survey as described in **F1** would form the basis of such a longitudinal study, which would of course have to be continued by enlisting the support of a local hospital, clinic, or general practitioner. For the recording of the data there is available the well-tested system of the Royal College of General Practitioners of Great Britain. Their ledger system and classification of morbidity is already in use in many countries. An abbreviated classification has also been prepared. For information concerning the ledger, types of recording sheets, and their coded classification, contact should be made with:

> The Records and Statistics Unit,
> The Royal College of General Practitioners,
> 14, Princes' Gate, Hyde Park,
> LONDON, S.W.7.

The Records and Statistics Unit of the Royal College of General Practitioners has for some years concerned itself with the design of methods of measurement of illness seen by doctors in the first instance, and ways in which these measurements may be recorded in a form which makes subsequent statistical analysis easy.

The College is aware that modern developments in science and technology have led medical research ever further from the beginnings of disease and that in many countries almost the whole research potential is concentrated in hospitals and institutions where the later stages of disease are observed. Study of man's failure to adapt to his environment and the early stages of morbidity that represent the first discernible evidence of that failure, has by comparison been grossly neglected.

It seemed likely that the need for field studies of the distribution of illness in populations would be recognised in many countries and that it would be desirable to establish comparability of definitions and terminology, so far as practicable, at as early a stage as possible in the investigation of a comparatively new research field. Thus priority was given to a classification of morbidity relatable to the International Classification of Disease, but practical and applicable under the circumstances of general practice. A classification was introduced in 1963 which has been found workable, but which will be reconsidered and revised if necessary at five-yearly intervals.

The classification of diseases was designed for use in British practice but the section on tropical diseases will be revised when sufficient experience has been gained by observers in tropical countries. Meanwhile the Records and Statistics Unit is anxious that its methods should be given wide trial.

II. RECORDING OF MORBIDITY; THE DIAGNOSTIC INDEX (E–BOOK).

This ledger method uses the College Classification of morbidity and enables records of diagnoses made within it to be made in relation to the date of occurrence, identity of the patient, as well as other predetermined characteristics. Various forms of ledger sheet can be used, depending on the degree of sophistication required of the records. Simple recording sheets are used where hand-sorting is undertaken while data which will be mechanically sorted after direct transfer to punch-cards is recorded on more elaborate sheets in columns numerically related to those on the punch-cards themselves.

Evidence from various countries suggests that the Diagnostic Index may be widely applicable. Its use as a research tool by those responsible for scientific expeditions has, on theroretical grounds at least, much to commend it. The system is self-contained, robust, compact and portable, the Twinlock ledger and spare record sheets weighing about 5 lb. (2–3 kilograms). Cards carrying the complete classification on front and reverse, for desk or table reference, are encased in plastic and will stand up to rough handling.

It is understood that expeditions to a given territory are normally undertaken in two stages, a first visit with a subsequent follow-up two years or so later.

On each visit an assessment is made of the morbidity pattern displayed by the population examined. The Diagnostic Index could be introduced during the first phase of the study and the medical observer could use it for recording his observations. Some disease-groups might require to be expanded. Use would no doubt be made of the facility within the classification for recording of incompleted diagnoses.

Under ideal circumstances the medical observer to the expedition should take the opportunity to instruct the local medical people in the territory concerned in the use of the Diagnostic Index. The Index ledger may be left behind with the service doctor, or at the hospital serving the area under study. Record sheets completed during the first phase of the study will be removed and placed in a transfer ledger to accompany the returning doctor. A fresh set of ledger sheets, with spares, should be inserted for the remaining doctor who would be asked to continue recording until the second visit paid by the expedition.

In this way recording initiated by the expedition might be maintained after its departure and further data become available to it immediately on its return to the area. Furthermore the exercise might itself constitute a contribution to the improvement of the health care services of the locality, and as such commend itself to those responsible for the provision of medical services.

It is likely that different versions of the medical record sheet would be used, depending on whether the remaining observer was a medical assistant field worker or a medically qualified worker at a district or mission hospital. There is no reason why the method should not be applied by partially trained observers where information at a sophisticated level cannot be obtained.

Where the ledger is used at a hospital serving a wide area record can be made of a number of characteristics of the individual, not necessarily those selected for application in Britain. Codes can be devised for locality of origin, tribal or ethnic group, cultural or religious characteristics and dietary habits. Further recordable characteristics will suggest themselves to those with experience of expedition work. The maintaining of records of this kind at hospitals and centres which do not normally contribute to organized research might provide their staff with a new interest in field epidemiology.

Abnormalities in the distribution of disease, departures from the established pattern for the district or territory, have already been observed. The distribution of Burkitt's Lymphoma and alimentary cancer is already being studied in Africa. Use of methods such as those suggested above might lead to the discovery of other conditions meriting closer study in their own right. Evidence can be gathered at the same time concerning the characteristics of the environment* in which the abnormality of morbidity presentation is found. If need be details of environment and disease may be conveyed to the same punch-card. Association, positive and negative, between environmental factors and morbidity, speculative at first, might become sufficiently established by these means to suggest possible cause and effect relationships.

If illness represents failure on the part of an organism to adapt to its environment, measurements at the point at which the failure is first observed are clearly essential. It is hoped that the methods proposed by the College will receive critical scrutiny and that they may be found capable of development to secure international comparability in a new and vitally important research field.

* See Section **H**.

F3. BLOOD PRESSURE DETERMINATIONS

I. INTRODUCTION

(a) General

(b) Sampling

II. TECHNIQUE

(a) Procedure

(b) Recording

(c) Note on training

(d) Equipment

III. DATA COLLECTING SHEET

I. INTRODUCTION

(a) General:

Indirect auscultatory arterial blood pressure is measured with a cuff, sphygmo-manometer, and stethoscope.

The measurement of indirect blood pressure is made in cardiovascular population studies for a number of reasons;

(1) Blood pressure is one of the few quantitative measures of a basic cardiovascular characteristic, i.e. pressure in the system.

(2) It is associated, probably causally, with several forms of cardiovascular disease.

(3) It is highly related to the risk of future cardiovascular disease mortality and morbidity.

(4) It is inter-related with other variables which may need to be sub-classified according to blood pressure level; for example if two populations differ in their overall rates for ECG S–T and T findings, it is helpful to know whether the differences persist within individual blood pressure groups.

Indirect pressure is simply, rapidly, painlessly, and inexpensively measured. However, there are many problems in characterising the indirect blood pressure of an individual which still require attention. Studies leading to standardised methods are greatly hindered by difficulties in controlling all variables save the one under examination. The validity of the indirect method has not been precisely established due to problems in simultaneous measurement of intra-arterial pressure, in the same extremity, under " normal " conditions of the artery, etc. Biological variability in blood pressure is great, with moment-to-moment variation due to multiple stimuli, as well as longer cyclic variations.

Variation in blood pressure measurement is also important. There is an unconscious, easily demonstrable, observer preference for certain terminal digits, usually 0 or 5, and bias for and against certain blood pressure levels (e.g. 140/90 as ' limits ' on insurance forms.) Reading back to the point of visual oscillations from that of the auscultatory end-points occurs, with over-compensation, and is a common source of systematic error. Simply forgetting the pressure values between the moment of reading and the tabulation may happen. Variable cuff inflation and deflation speeds may cause variations in recorded pressures. The true blood pressure may itself be affected by the examiner's behaviour and the circumstances surrounding the measurement.

These and other sources of error can cause serious problems in dealing with values in population studies where variability and small systematic differences between observers may significantly affect conclusions made from the data. Recent studies, including development of mechanically operated instruments, indicate promising approaches to standard methods. The instruments reduce some of the systematic and random errors, and completely eliminate the bias from digit preference and the dependence of subsequent readings on previous ones, which occur in the conventional audio-visual recording of blood-pressure. Automated pressure-recording and read-out devices developed for special monitoring problems in space and in exercise physiology should soon be ready for application in large field studies.

Indirect measurement of brachial artery pressure during exercise can be performed using standard clinical procedure (i.e. sphygmomanometer). Although systolic pressure can be accurately recorded in this way, the measurement of diastolic pressure is more difficult. Since diastolic pressure is relatively unaffected by muscular exercise, the resting diastolic presssure may be used in the calculation of **mean** arterial systemic pressure, etc.

The measurement of blood pressure is of course a part of the general medical survey (see **F1**), and in relation to age and physique can yield useful data of a survey kind, especially where the community is relatively remote from medical services. Blood pressure estimation is of course a key component in intensive cardiovascular population studies, but this requires a specialised team and equipment, and observations of a comprehensive kind

Such cardiovascular studies are not within the scope of many field expeditions, though there may be situations where such studies (which are best promoted and coordinated through WHO) can be utilised for many aspects of human adaptability studies. A detailed guide to cardiovascular population studies, including sample proformae, is available from WHO: Rose and Blackburn (1966 and 1968). A physical examination form particularly appropriate to cardiovascular studies is given under Appendix 8 in the above-mentioned publication.

(b) Sampling;

Since blood pressure measurements are an integral part of the medical examination, the sample size will depend on the overall purpose of the multi-disciplinary study. If the nutrition and health of the community are prime objects of the study, groups of families or whole villages will need to be investigated. Otherwise, samples will be drawn from the general population for specific purposes, e.g. growth measurements, climatic tolerance, physical fitness, etc. (See Eilertsen and Humerfelt, **Acta Med. Scand.**, **183,** 293–305, 1968). Reference should be made to those Sections in this Handbook dealing with these topics for more detailed guidance.

In inter-population studies values among adults have mostly fallen in the range of 110–160 (systolic) and 70–100 (diastolic). In intra-population studies, the following approximate standard deviations (in mm.) have been found ·

	Systolic	Diastolic
Within-subject, same occasion	9	8
Within-subject, between occasions	9	7
Between-subject (excluding component due to within-subject variation)	14	7

II. TECHNIQUES

(a) Procedure:

Suggested standard conditions for indirect blood pressure recording are as follows :

(1) Comfortable temperature of the examination room.

(2) Arm not constricted by clothing.

(3)   Avoidance of exertion, exposure to cold, eating or smoking for half-an-hour prior to recording.

(4)   No postural change for five minutes prior to recording.

The standard procedure for recording is as follows:

(1)   A pressure cuff with bladder at least 12 × 22 cm. is snugly applied to either arm, its lower border 2–3 cm. above the ante-cubital space; apply cuff early and leave in place during interview and physical examination. The cuff size should be recorded, and the same site used on all subjects throughout the study. Several manufacturers supply a type of nylon hooklet-locking cuff. These are recommended for their considerable convenience.

(2)   The sitting position is suggested only because of its facility; each arm is supported comfortably at the vertical level of the 4th intercostal space at the sternum ('heart level') within a range of 0°–45° angle from the trunk.

(3)   If the supine position is employed, each arm is supported on the bed at 0°–45° angle from the trunk.

(4)   In the visual method the cuff is rapidly inflated to a level above the radial palpatory pressure. Detailed instructions appropriate to the instrument actually used should be consulted.

(5)   Promptly start run-down of the mercury column at a 2 mm. per second rate of fall.

(6)   Systolic pressure level is determined by the first perception of sound.

(7)   Diastolic 4th phase level is determined when the sounds cease to be tapping in quality, and are fully muffled. Changes in loudness are discounted. The lower of the two points of change is recorded.

(8)   Diastolic 5th phase level is determined by the perception of disappearance of sound.

(9)   Cuff is deflated to zero pressure.

(10)   Readings are tabulated, in the visual method, to the nearest 2 mm. Hg. (See DATA COLLECTING SHEET.)

(11)   The process is repeated as desired by the investigator.

(b) Recording:

The blood pressure values recorded should be carefully described. The first recording made at examination is the one usually employed, but averages may be given in addition. Tabulations are made of both the 4th and 5th phase diastolic levels. Total distributions by age and sex should be provided in any report of the study. Examples of distributions of blood pressure by individual examiners should also be given.

(c) Note on training:

Training in blood pressure registration is necessary, whatever method is used, as systematic differences between observers may be larger than the true differences under investigation between populations. Training films are available which demonstrate observer variation and allow calibration to an average for the group tested. A convenient training procedure is available using audio tape recordings. Realistic play-back of tape-recorded Korotkoff sounds through a stethoscope earpiece is used first to train and then to test the observer, who activates stop-watches at the start of a run-down, and arrests them at systolic and diastolic end-points. 'Standard values' from readings taken by experienced observers are compared against the trainee's average for 12 subjects, and the training continues until the systematic differences from the standard are at a minimum. As a calibration procedure, the tape recording can be used to check for trends, for example, between the start and end of a survey.

With or without tape or film material, training on actual subjects is required for the field staff. This is best done by assigning a group of 10 or 12 subjects to each of the several observers for replicate readings and analysis of the variations. It is essential that significant systematic variations be eliminated between observers by repeated training. During the field study, a random allocation of a sample of the subjects is made for replicate readings by each observer, to assess the quality of the presssure recording and detect systematic observer differences. It is preferable, when more than one examiner is involved, that they operate simultaneously, examining alternate subjects. Though any systematic observer differences would seriously affect the distributions, such a routine would largely preserve the validity of blood pressure relationships studied within the population.

(d) **Equipment:**

(i) Automated equipment is now available, but no one type of apparatus appears to be entirely satisfactory, and this equipment is not recommended.

(ii) For continuous measurement of blood-pressure on groups of subjects, a technique employing a modified aneroid sphygmomanometer has been described by Davies, T. W., and H. E. Lewis, **J. Physiol. 188,** p. 7–8, 1967.

III. DATA COLLECTING SHEET

Name*:   Ethnic and tribal origin (or nationality) :

Age :   Occupation :

Subject no. :   Height (mm) :   ▢▢▢▢

Sex :   Weight (kg) :   ▢▢▢▢▢

                                          Suprailiac skin-fold (mm) :   ▢▢▢

Place :   Subscapular skin-fold (mm) :   ▢▢▢

Date :   Triceps skin-fold (mm) :   ▢▢▢

                                          Chest skin-fold
                                             (juxta-nipple) :   ▢▢▢

                                          Upper arm circumference (mm) : ▢▢▢

Observer :   Chest circumference (mm) :   ▢▢▢
Chest pain or discomfrot :   yes/no   Abdomen circumference

                                             (umbilical level) :   ▢▢▢

Angina : Grade I/Grade II/none   Thigh circumference (mm) :   ▢▢▢

Possible infarction :   yes/no

Intermittent claudication :   Grade I/Grade II/none

Systolic blood pressure :

Diastolic Phase 4 :

Diastolic Phase 5 :

Smoking status (ring one) :   non-smoker
                              ex-smoker
                              cigarettes only (filter)
                              cigarettes only (non-filter)
                              pipe or cigars only
                              mixed

* Full details of the subject and his population group are to be entered in the **BASIC IDENTIFICATION SHEETS,** as laid down in the Technical Introduction.

F4. HAEMATOLOGICAL, IMMUNOLOGICAL, AND OTHER SERO-LOGICAL TESTS

I. INTRODUCTION

- (a) General
- (b) Observations to be made
- (c) Sampling

II. TECHNIQUES

- (1) Haemoglobin estimation
- (2) Haematocrit
- (3) Red cell count
- (4) Serum antibodies
- (5) Equipment

I. INTRODUCTION

(a) General;

The collection of blood in the field is important not only for genetic studies (see **B1**), but also for evaluating the nutritional (see **E1**) and medical (see **F1**) status of the subject. Determination of the haemoglobin content, the red cell volume, and the red cell count are of obvious importance for detecting anaemia, the effects of high altitude, etc.

Human adaptability studies provide a particularly effective situation for obtaining information on immunological status on a world basis. This is because blood will be collected (with associated demographic data) on many populations, particularly in connection with genetic studies. Part of the sera so obtained should be made available for immunological tests as a contribution towards mapping the world-wide distribution of various infectious agents. Collections of sera can serve various purposes, and these are fully described in WHO Technical Report Series No. 181.

(b) Observations to be made;

The following tests should be carried out wherever possible; they are described in greater detail under TECHNIQUES, below:

1. Percent haemoglobin.

2. Haematocrit.

3. Red cell count.

4. Estimation of serum antibodies.

(c) **Sampling;**

For general survey purposes, a usual minimum sample size of 100, adult males, adult females and children in each of the groups, should be aimed for. The exact number and composition of the sample will naturally depend on the purposes of the investigation. Adults over the age of 65 years would be an interesting subdivision. Thus, in a comprehensive nutritional and medical study, for example, it may be possible to obtain blood samples from all the inhabitants of a village.

II. TECHNIQUES

(1) Haemoglobin estimation;

(a) **Sample taken in the field and sent to a laboratory.**
Capillary or venous blood may be collected in any solid anticoagulant (see **B1**), and sent to a suitable laboratory (see **B2**), where the standard cyanmethaemo-globin method is applied. The test can be carried out on blood which has been stored at 4°C for several days, provided it has not become seriously infected. The laboratory technique for the estimation of haemoglobin percentage is described in Broadsheet 56 of the Association of Clinical Pathologists, (January, 1967).

(b) **Samples determined in the field.**

Whereas in the laboratory the haemoglobin content of blood is usually measured by photoelectric colorimetry, investigators in the field are not likely to have facilities for this method. The alternative is a visual method. In general, visual methods which depend upon the matching of the colour of the blood (diluted or undiluted) with that of a coloured solution or glass standard are unreliable. It is preferable, in a visual method, to match light-intensity. The need for an appropriate instrument which is realistically portable, is reasonably priced, and which meets the requirements for haemoglobinometry of the International Committee for Standardisation in Haematology (1965), has led to a modification of the original M.R.C. grey-wedge photometer.

This instrument, named the Haemoscope, (see also (5) below) measures $16 \times 6 \times 6$ cm.; the illumination is by two flashlight batteries. The Haemoscope is provided with two independent scales for use with blood diluted 1 in 200 as oxyhaemoglobin or cyanmethaemoglobin. To avoid confusion, only one of these scales is visible at any one time, the other being covered by a removable plate. The scales are precalibrated to conform to the cyanmethaemoglobin reference standard of the I.C.S.H., and the individual user is able to ensure that the scale calibrations are correctly aligned for him by the reading he obtains on the oxyhaemoglobin or cyanmethaemoglobin scale with a neutral glass standard or a cyanmethaemoglobin standard solution, respectively. Results are read directly as haemoglobin content in g/100 ml. (The International Committee for Standardisation in Haematology (Sec: Dr. S. M. Lewis, Postgraduate Medical School, London W.12) is prepared to help with checking by means of an international cyanmethaemoglobin standard.)

In the field, haemoglobin determinations are carried out by a single observer. The diluent used is 0·04% ammoniated water.

The Haemoscope appears to serve its purpose admirably, and is consistently reliable, even in the hands of inexperienced users. (For further details, see: **Brit. Med. J.**, **2**, 1167–8, 13th November 1965.)

(2) Haematocrit;

In the field, the ' Micro-centrifuge ', introduced by B. Holmstedt* (Stockholm), is more easily portable, cheaper, and more efficient than conventional hand centrifuges. (See (5) below.) Details of the construction of this instrument and instructions for its use are given in Holmstedt, B., **Science, 149**, No. 3687; 977–978, 27th August, 1965.

(3) Red cell count:

A simple substitute for the micropipette for drawing up capillary blood specimens (usually 0·02 ml.) for blood counts, is a capillary tube cut to size so as to contain the exact volume of blood when completely filled.** A capillary tube is easy to manipulate, and obviates the need for cleaning of pipettes, and is therefore recommended for field use. After filling the capillary, it is then dropped into a test-tube containing an appropriate volume of diluent solution. This convenient method of blood collection and dilution is particularly suitable as a field technique, but hitherto has been of limited value owing to

---

* Address: Dept. of Toxicology, Swedish Medical Research Council, Karolinska Institutet, Stockholm 60, Sweden.

** Lewis S. M., and H. Benjamin, **J. Clin. Path. 18**: 689, 1965.

the difficulty in preparing capillaries of exact volume. A further disadvantage was the presence of contaminant blood dried onto the outside of the capillary where it had been in contact with the flow, while attempts to wipe off this excess might result in a loss of a portion of the blood contained within the capillary.

By a continuous-drawing process, capillary tubing can now be manufactured economically with uniform bore, and free from measurable taper. Accordingly, as the volume is constantly proportional to the length, tubes of the required capacity can be obtained, and it is possible to ensure an accuracy within narrow limits of tolerance. By providing a length of tubing greater than that necessary for the required volume and an accurately-determined break-off point, it is possible to avoid contamination of the exterior of the portion of the tube which will be placed in the diluent.

Length AB (See Fig. F4/1) provides a tube with a capacity of 0·02 ml., and BC is a length greater than that of AB. To facilitate subsequent break-off, B is scored, and the site of the score is indicated by a mark painted on the non-calibrated portion of the tube just beyond that point. End C is brought into contact with the source of blood. When sufficient blood has been drawn up, by capillary attraction, to reach B, the tube is inverted so that the blood flows down and completely fills AB. The tube is snapped at B, and the portion AB is dropped into a test-tube containing a measured volume of the appropriate diluent solution. This is shaken vigorously to ensure that all the blood escapes into the diluent.

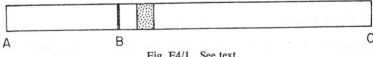

A   B   C

Fig. F4/1   See text.

This procedure provides a method for blood dilution with an accuracy in routine practice at least equal to that obtained by the use of BSS verified micropipettes.

(4)   Estimation of serum antibodies:

The collection and separation of sera for immunological testing is describe in **B1**. In general, the following antibodies of medical significance would b identified: respiratory viruses, some arboviruses, poliomyelitis and othe enteroviruses, measles, etc.

The serum (or plasma) collected in IBP surveys will also be used for estimating the various plasma protein fractions as well as plasma lipids.

For a full discussion on the range of tests on sera, see WHO Report 181. Details of sampling are found on pp .xxii–xxvii of this publication; information on collection, subdivision, and transport of blood samples is given in **B1** and **B2**.

(5)   Equipment:

(a)   The Haemoscope:

> This instrument is manufactured by;
> Keeler Optical Industries,
> Clewer Hill Road,
> WINDSOR,
> Berkshire,
> England.

who also manufacture the ' M.R.C. ' grey-wedge photometer for the estimation of haemoglobin. The latter instrument is more accurate than the Haemoscope, but is more expensive. It may be run off a 12-volt battery, whereas the Haemoscope is entirely self-contained.

(b)   The ' Micro-centrifuge '

> This instrument is available from:
> Ingenjörsfirman Instrumenttjänst,
> Box 57,
> SUNDBYBERG 1,
> Sweden.

The accessories required are the following: suction device, lead-in rod, spare string, length of heparinised polyethylene tube. A descriptive leaflet is also provided.

The inclusive price, per instrument with accessories, is about US $10.00.

" Among other uses, the centrifuge serves to obtain plasma for immunoelectrophoresis and flocculation and agglutination tests, and for determination of plasma cholinesterase and total solids (refractometrically). Haematocrit values may be obtained and blood parasites concentrated." (Holmstedt, 1965).

F5. THYROID AND RELATED STUDIES

I. INTRODUCTION

    (a) General

    (b) Observations to be made

    (c) Sampling

II. TECHNIQUES

III. DATA COLLECTING SHEETS

I. INTRODUCTION

(a) General:

The thyroid gland plays a regulatory role in adaptation to many ecological stresses, such as cold, heat, and particularly iodine shortage. In some populations at high altitudes, a combination of cold and iodine shortage occurs.

There is, at the present, no accepted method for studying the effect of cold exposure or cold adaptation on the thyroid function in man. The provisional procedure described below is based on proposals put forward by O. Wilson.

Useful information from a clinical examination of the thyroid can be obtained in the field by an experienced observer. Blood can also be collected and sent to a laboratory for estimation of protein-bound iodine (PBI). The basal metabolic rate can also be measured in the field, using relatively simple equipment. Techniques involving the measurement of the turnover of radio-iodine by the thyroid gland may only be carried out successfully by using monitoring and counting equipment suitable for field work.

(b) Observations to be made:

Both direct and indirect methods of evaluating thyroid activity are available. They include the following:

1. Clinical examination of the thyroid (see **F1**).
2. Handling of radio-iodine by the gland.
3. Estimation of PBI in the blood.
4. Measurement of the basal metabolic rate.

Procedures 2–4 are described below under TECHNIQUES.

(a) **Sampling:**

The sample should be as large as possible since certain conditions of interest are rare, and their incidence can only be determined reliably if the sample is very large. The minimal sample size, of a few hundred, should include all age groups and both sexes.

II. TECHNIQUES

1. **Clinical examination of the trial** (see **F1**).

2. **Examination of uptake of radio-active iodine by the thyroid gland:**

This procedure will only be possible for well-equipped and well-trained personnel. It can, however, be successfully carried out in the field, given suitable facilities (O. Wilson, personal communication). A suggested technique is the following:

A single oral dose of 20 microcuries radio-iodide (I^{131}) is administered. The thyroid radio-iodine uptake is measured by a collimated scintillation counter at 1, 2, 6, 24 and 48 hours.

Three blood samples may be conveniently taken by needle and syringe, or ' Vacutainer ' (see **B1**) at 4 and 24 hours after administration of the oral dose, for the determination of the PBI^{131} conversion factor, for which either trichloroacetic acid precipitates or ion-exchange resin eluates are used. If this is not possible, a single blood sample may be taken at 48 hours.

24-hour urine samples are obtained for the determination of I^{131} excretion. The radio-iodine level in urine and plasma samples is measured with a well-type crystal detector.

3. **Estimation of protein-bound iodine in the blood.**

It has been shown that there is a significant correlation in healthy people between protein-bound iodine level and taste sensitivity to PTC (see also **B6**). This makes it most desirable, at least in goitrous areas, to carry out tests for both PTC taste sensitivity and for PBI in the blood. Full details of techniques etc., are to be found in Widstrom, G., and A. Henschen., **Scand. J. Lab. Clin. Invest. Suppl.**, 257, 1963.

To estimate protein-bound iodine satisfactorily, 5 ml of serum or plasma are required, collected under conditions, and into containers scrupulously free of iodine. This implies, for example, that iodine cannot be used as a skin disinfectant, for it must neither be handled by the field operator, nor applied to the individual subject. Again, any anti coagulant used must be completely free of iodine impurities, etc. In order to guard against the introduction into the survey of results artificially modified by drugs and/or iodine-containing compounds administered to the subject, and further to guard against contamination of the laboratory system with iodine, it will be necessary to screen subjects for this investigation very carefully. A note should be made on the Data Collecting Sheet of the clinical diagnosis of the thyroid condition of the subject, the family history of goitre, any previous treatment of a thyroid condition during the previous two months, and the reproductive history of all female subjects.

4.   Measurement of the basal metablic rate.

Climate exerts considerable influence on basal metabolism; observations in the Antarctic and in Japan have given considerable evidence of a significant increase in metabolism with decreased environmental temperature, whether continuous or seasonal. BMR may also be related to such factors as diet and activity, and is therefore a valuable measurement to make in a population study incorporating habitat contrasts, which is the type of study particularly appropriate to the aims of the IBP.

Although the technique for measuring the oxygen usage is well established, it is not easy to achieve strict basal conditions. A suitable procedure would be to measure the metabolic rate in a subject immediately after waking on three successive days, and to record the third reading. This in most cases will be the lowest.

III. DATA COLLECTING SHEET

Name*:   Ethnic and tribal origin
                                                 (or nationality):

Subject no.:

Age: Sex: M/F   Occupation:

Puberty: Pre-/post-

Place (village and district):

Date:

Observer:

---

(1) **Measurement of uptake of radioactive iodine by the thyroid gland:**

Thyroid radio-iodine uptake measured by neck-mounted scintillation counter at:

        1 hr.:

        2 hrs.:

        6 hrs.:

        24 hrs.:

        48 hrs.:

I 131 in urine (24 hr. sample):

I 131 level in plasma at: 4 hrs.:

                        24 hrs.:   or 1 sample at 24 hrs.:

                        48 hrs.:

(2) **Level of PBI in the blood:**

Clinical diagnosis: Euthyroid/hypothyroid/hyperthyroid.

Details of family history of goitre:

Details of any previous (within 2 months) or present treatment:

Reproductive history:

(3) **Other measurements:**

Basal metabolic rate:

PTC taster status (see **B6**):

---

* Full details of the subject and his population group are to be entered in the **BASIC
IDENTIFICATION SHEETS,** as laid down in the Technical Introduction.

F6. LIST OF CONGENITAL DEFECTS

I. INTRODUCTION

II. LIST OF CONGENITAL DEFECTS

I. INTRODUCTION

The few surveys so far made of congenital defects suggest that human populations may differ appreciably in their characteristic spectra of frequencies of different types of defect and it is possible that their total loads of defect also differ. In any multidisciplinary type of field investigation in a primitive population it would be of interest to obtain some indication of the numbers and type of defect that occur. It would not be possible, initially at any rate, to undertake a survey of all births over a period among these peoples as is at present being done under the auspices of the WHO among samples of more advanced populations. Moreover, many of the defects that cause only slight reduction in survival probability in Western populations may indeed be lethal in the more rigorous conditions under which primitive populations live. Whatever is seen, then, may give a minimal estimate of the true frequency of occurrence. Nonetheless, it is felt that observations of the more easily identifiable conditions in the field would be of interest, partly in order to obtain a preliminary estimate of their frequencies, and partly to draw attention to those populations in need of more intensive investigation.

There is set out below a suggested list of gross conditions which a qualified observer should be able to identify in the field without too protracted an examination of the subject. Careful history taking will distinguish these from similar acquired conditions. This list is based on that which has previously been used under field conditions without complicated apparatus or sophisticated clinical facilities. Those investigators wishing to utilise a more comprehensive list of congenital defects are referred to the forthcoming revised international classification of congenital defects. However, it must be stressed that remote and isolated populations may well manifest genetic or congenital conditions that are very rare or unknown elsewhere, or atypical forms of known aberrations, and it will therefore also be valuable to make careful descriptions of such deviations from normality.

II. LIST OF CONGENITAL DEFECTS

1. Posture and General.

*   Dwarfs
    Hereditary and congenital ataxias
    Kypho-scoliosis
    Mental defectives
*   Mongolism
*   Osteochondrodystrophy (Achondroplasia)

2 Head, Neck and Face.

*   Anencephaly
      Craniosynostosis
      Crouzon's anomaly
B15 Eyebrows continous across mid-line
      Klippel-Feil syndrome
      Mandibulo-facial dysostosis
*   Microcephaly
      Micrognathia
*   Neck cysts, e.g. Cystic hygroma, Thyroglossal cyst
      Platybasia
      Sclera—blue in colour
      Skull shape aberrations—Acrocephaly, Oxycephaly, Plagiocephaly,
                        Scaphocephaly, Trigonocephaly
      Webbed neck
B15 White forelock

3. Eyes.

      Aberrant eyeball size, e.g. Buphthalmus, Cryptophthalmus,
                   Megalophthalmus, Microphthalmus
      Absence of cilia
      Absence of fold of eyelid
      Accessory eyelid
      Aniridia
*   Anophthalmus
      Coloboma iridis
*   Congenital nystagmus
      Congenital strabismus and extraocular muscle defects
      Dislocation of lens
*   Hypertelorism
B15 Melanosis bulbi or sclera
      Pterygium
*   Ptosis

4. Ears.

      Absence of auditory canal
*   Absence of auricle
*   Absence of earlobe
*   Accessory auricle or prearicular sinus

(continued)

II. LIST OF CONGENITAL DEFECTS—continued

Atresia or stenosis of auditory canal
Auricular appendage
Congenital deafness
B15 Darwin's tubercle
*   General aberrant shape of external ear
B15 Hairy pinnae
Low-set ears
Macrotia
Microtia
Pointed ear
Polyotia

5. **Nose.**

*   Absence or atresia of nose
Bifid or cleft nose
Congenital closure or stenosis of nose
Notching in tip of nose

6. **Mouth.**

Bifid tongue
*   Cleft lip (hare-lip) with cleft palate
*   Cleft lip (hare-lip) without cleft palate
*   Cleft palate without cleft lip
Gothic palate
*   Macroglossia
Microglossia
B14 Supernumerary teeth

7. **Trunk.**

Congenital scoliosis
*   Inguinal hernia
*   Multiple neurofibromatosis
*   Umbilical fistula
Umbilical hernia

8. **Sex organs.**

Absence of prepuce
Bifid penis
Double penis
*   Epispadias or hypospadias
Gynocomastia
Hermaphrodism
Undescended testicle

9. **Limbs.**

*   Absence of extremities (Congenital amputation)
Bow legs
*   Congenital dislocation of hip

(*continued*)

II. LIST OF CONGENITAL DEFECTS—continued

Genu valgum
* Multiple exostoses

10. Extremities.

* Brachydactyly
Clawfoot or split foot
* Clubfoot
* Congenital arthrogryposis
Ectrodactyly
* Equinovarus or talipes
Genu recurvatum
Marfan's syndrome
Metatarsus abductus
Nail-patella syndrome
* Polydactyly
Short metatarsals or metacarpals of phalanges
* Syndactyly
Webbed fingers or toes

11. Skin, hair, and nails.

Accessory nipples
Absent nipples
* Albinism
Congenital alopecia
Cutis hyperelastica
Epidermolysis bullosa
Haemangioma
* Ichthyosis congenita
Multiple melanomata
Papilloma of skin
Pigmented nevus
Van Kippel-Lindau syndrome
Xeroderma pigmentosum

* Conditions marked thus can be regarded as major congenital defects according to recent Japanese surveys.

In Sections **B14** and **B15** of the Handbook, further reference is made to certain of these conditions, as noted in the above list.

G. DEMOGRAPHIC ASSESSMENT AND RELATED SOCIO-CULTURAL FACTORS

General Comments

G1. Socio-demographic studies in relation to genetic constitution

G2. Socio-demographic studies in relation to female reproductive performance

G. DEMOGRAPHIC ASSESSMENT AND RELATED SOCIO-CULTURAL FACTORS

General Comments

Demographic data have hitherto not been as widely utilised as they deserve in studies of the biology of non-Western human populations. This stems partly from the fact that demography has tended to be regarded as a social science, partly that biologists have not been fully aware of the wealth of the quantitative information that may be available for a human population, or how useful this can be in problems of human ecology, nutrition, genetics, epidemiology, health and female reproductive performance. In the postwar period however, a number of studies have demonstrated that such data of adequate reliability can be collected. In genetics, for example, such studies have shown how they can be used to trace the action of natural selection and at what ages it is effective, to partition selection into components due to differential fertility and mortality, to show how changes in isolate size are being brought about and at what rates, what their biological effects are, and more generally to test assumptions about genetical models.

There are three rather distinct purposes for which the collection of socio-demographic data has to serve. It has to give guidance on and the appropriate data sheets for (1) the collection of family data to make possible the construction of genealogies from the point of view of the genetic implications (inbreeding, gene flow by lineage); (2) the collection of marriage " performance " data leading to the assessment of fertility in terms of family size in relation to age of mother, etc.; (3) the collection of data from females to establish their " reproductive efficiency " in terms of (a) pregnancy history, (b) labour history, (c) post-mortem history, (d) during lactation.

The two Sections **G1** and **G2** indicate the type of information that it would be profitable to include in field studies, particularly where an expedition can only stay in the field for a relatively short time. It should be emphasised, however, that demographic studies will certainly be more fruitful the longer the period available for obtaining a close relationship with the local population.

The fact is that demographic data cannot be obtained with any degree of accuracy from a primitive people by any short intensive system of interviewing. Instead the long-period indirect method of the field anthropologist is required, one moreover highly trained both in the art of non-directive interviewing and in the concepts of theoretical anthropology and psychology. Ideally such an individual would precede the biological investigation team into a population and indeed probably largely complete his demographic investigations before their arrival; and during this period he or she would become acquainted with the social system of the population, and with the finer linguistic points, identify individuals in a genealogical matrix and by residence and social position map the villages relevant to the investigation, and obtain detailed knowledge of those cultural variants that may lead to inaccuracy or falsification of the information specifically sought in the programme.

During this period he or she should learn what matters have to be handled with extreme tact, for many of the questions requiring answers are indeed likely to lead to potentially explosive situations either as regards the stability of relationships within the population studied or as regards the safety of the investigators themselves. It may well be that some of the questions cannot be answered by any one subject or in a given social situation, because he is unable, unwilling, or forbidden to divulge the information; but if none of these restrictions apply then there is little reason why the required information should not be obtained by a properly trained and competent investigator. Success will depend on the methods he uses; if an interpreter's services are used, the investigator will probably find it profitable to use a male interpreter when dealing with male subjects, and a female when talking to female subjects. The whole data should be collected by interviews with one subject at a time, not with a group, and the Data Sheets have been designed with this object in view; checking comes from comparison with the personal observations of the investigator, and from comparison with the information given by other individuals; when discrepancies are obvious, then re-interview should on no account suggest that additonal information has come from some other source. The apparent repetition in parts of the Data Sheets is deliberate, designed to allow further clarification on the part of the interviewer.

G1. SOCIO-DEMOGRAPHIC STUDIES IN RELATION TO GENETIC CONSTITUTION

I. INTRODUCTION

    (a) General

    (b) Observations to be made

    (c) Sample size

II. TECHNIQUES

    (i) Questionnaire on parental and sib relationships

    (ii) Questionnaire on marriage and offspring

III. DATA COLLECTING SHEETS

I. INTRODUCTION

(a) General:

The aim of the enquiry set forth in the Data Sheet below is the construction of biological genealogies. The questions are limited to the grandparental generation, since in general this is as far as accurate knowledge is likely to go. It is possible that in some communities genealogies may be traced further back where registers and parish records are available. For the use of routine records for the construction of genealogies the reader is referred to Sutter, J., **Population, No. 1,** pp. 76–98, 1966. (Revue bimestrielle de l'Institut National d'Etudes Demographiques, 23, avenue Franklin D. Roosevelt, Paris, 8e). Some of the information asked for in part (i) and part (ii) of the Data Sheet will make possible an estimate of differential fertility and mortality as between different unions; these are of course of importance in relation to the distribution and perpetuation of particular genetic characters. Some of the data are of importance in relation to inbreeding and consanguinity, and the rate and direction of gene flow may also be indicated from a knowledge of the terrestrial distribution of parents and grandparents.

(b) Observations to be made:

(i) For all informants obtain information on parental and sib relationships (Data Sheet, part (i)).

(ii) For all informants obtain information on marriage and offspring (Data Sheet, part (ii)).

(iii) Ancillary:
1. Medical examination (see **F1.**)
2. Nutritional assessment (minimum if time limited) (see **E1.**)

(c)   Sample size:

The number of informants should as a minimum conform to and not be less than those subjects from whom blood is taken for genetic studies (see **B1**) or on whom anthropometric (**A**), and anthroposcopic (**B15**) observations are made. These samples will themselves have been selected on a stratified basis from a community which is fairly large. In many instances it will be possible to conduct both genetic surveys and demographic questioning on a complete village or tribal band.

II.   TECHNIQUES

The importance of intensive and tactful questioning of members of the community has been stressed in the ' General Comments ' above.

(i)   Parental and sib relationships.

Part (i) of the Data Sheet is devoted to identification of the subject and of family relations, and ideally should be completed for every individual in a community and certainly for all those on whom detailed biological studies will subsequently be made.   Apart from its value for identification purposes and for establishing genealogies, from it will also emerge useful information on geographic dispersal of individuals and hence of gametes; on fertility and mortality; and the utilisation of the female reproductive span. The fertility data in this part relates to the reproductive performance of the informant's parents. His (or her) own performance (i.e. the second generation) is assessed in part (ii).

Notes:

1.4   A subject may go under a variety of names, and it is important to note all, and who uses them.

1.6 & 1.7   Villages of residence and of birth should be identified on a map.

1.8, 1.9, 1.10   For some individuals in some communities it may be possible to obtain a record of age, whereas in most it will only be possible to obtain an assessment of age, (see also Technical Introduction). Each observer should note carefully the criteria that he uses for age assessment, and assessment should be applied even for those individuals whose true ages are known in order to give some indication of the accuracy of the assessment system. Some communities are divided formally into age grades or sets and these should also be noted and equated with chronological age.

1.12, 1.13, 1.14, 1.15, 1.16 For some peoples this nomenclature of social subdivision may not be possible and the appropriate alternative system should be noted.

2.1, 3.1, 4.5, 4.6 This repetition is intentional, as an individual regarded as a full sib by a subject may in fact have a different mother or father.

2.19 indicates relationship of father's father to father's mother.

3.19   ,,   ,,   of mother's father to mother's mother.

3.20   ,,   ,,   of father to mother.

1.7.1, 2.1.1, 2.7.1, 2.13.1, 3.1.1, 3.7.1, 3.13.1, 4.1.1, 5.1.1, 6.1.1 All these entries relate to 'date of birth' and in many cases will not be obtainable with great accuracy. The alternative entry is 'estimated age', which should be noted.

Columns 2 to 6, 3.18, 4.4, 5.4 & 6.4 should be noted in as much detail as possible; people in many primitive groups are so interested in death that there is keen observation of the process and the preceding symptoms to which a rapid and abbreviated translation of the vernacular does not do justice.

6.1–6.6 Will allow an estimate of the rate of replacement of biological relationship by social; posterity remembers the latter.

(ii) **Marriage and offspring**

This part should be completed for all individuals. From it should emerge some idea of the importance of marriage as the threshold to reproduction in the community, the distribution of ages at which reproduction commences. This section is of primary importance in any subsequent study of fertility.

Notes:

8.1 Note whether these are concurrent or consecutive, and dates if possible.

8.3 Is of primary importance in ascertaining inbreeding in the community; it should be traced as comprehensively as possible.

8.4 & 8.5 Should be established as accurately as posssible.

8.6 & 8.7 Establish the rate and direction of gene flow per generation.

9.5   Helps to indicate the changes in sex ratio with age in the community.

9.6 & 9.7   Should indicate extramarital and premarital unions, and show their importance in the fertility of the community.

8.2.1 & 9.2.1   These entries relate to ' date of birth ' and in many cases will not be obtainable with great accuracy. The alternative entry is ' estimated age ', which should be noted.

III. DATA COLLECTING SHEETS

(i) **Parent and sib relationships (QUESTIONNAIRE FOR ALL SUBJECTS)**

IBP/HA Project ref. no.: ☐☐☐☐   Study no.: ☐☐

Name of Investigator.....................

(1) Subject

1.1 Date: 1.2 Place:
1.3 Subject's serial number: ☐☐☐
1.4 **Subject's NAME:**   1.5 Sex: M/F
1.6 Place of residence: 1.6.1 Distance of place of residence from
1.7 Place of birth: place of birth:
    1.7.1 Date of birth:
1.8 Age recorded: 1.9 Age assessed:
1.10 Age grade or set:
1.11 Religion: 1.12 Totem:
1.13 Tribe: 1.14 Section:
1.15 Clan: 1.16 Lineage:

(2) Subject's father

2.1 NAME: 2.1.1 Date of birth:
2.2 Place of birth:
2.3 Place of residence:
    2.3.1 Distance of place of residence from place of birth:
2.4 Clan:
2.5 Alive/dead: 2.5.1 Age now/at death: 2.6 Cause of death:

Subject's father's father

2.7 NAME: 2.7.1 Date of birth:
2.8 Place of birth:
2.9 Place of residence:
    2.9.1 Distance of place of residence from place of birth:
2.10 Clan:
2.11 Alive/dead: 2.11.1 Age now/at death: 2.12 Cause of death:

Subject's father's mother

2.13 NAME: 2.13.1 Date of birth:
2.14 Place of birth:

(continued)

III. (i)—continued

2.15   Place of residence:
       2.15.1   Distance of place of residence from place of birth:
2.16   Clan:
2.17   Alive/dead: 2.17.1   Age now/at death: 2.18   Cause of death:
2.19   Relationship of father's father to father's mother:

(3)   Subject's mother

3.1   NAME: 3.1.1   Date of birth:
3.2   Place of birth:
3.3   Place of residence:
       3.3.1   Distance of place of residence from place of birth:
3.4   Clan:
3.5   Alive/dead: 3.5.1   Age now/at death: 3.6   Cause of death:

Subject's mother's father

3.7   NAME: 3.7.1   Date of birth:
3.8   Place of birth:
3.9   Place of residence:
       3.9.1   Distance of place of residence from place of birth:
3.10   Clan:
3.11   Alive/dead: 3.11.1   Age now/at death: 3.12   Cause of death:

Subject's mother's mother

3.13   NAME: 3.13.1   Date of birth:
3.14   Place of birth:
3.15   Place of residence:
       3.15.1   Distance of place of residence from place of birth:
3.16   Clan:
3.17   Alive/dead: 3.17.1   Age now/at death: 3.18   Cause of death:
3.19   Relationship of mother's father to mother's mother:
3.20   RELATIONSHIP OF SUBJECT'S MOTHER TO SUBJECT'S FATHER:

(*continued*)

III. (i)—continued

(4) Full sibs.

	4.1 Name	4.1.1 Date of Birth	4.2 Alive/ Dead	4.3 Age now/ At Death	4.4 Cause of Death	4.5 Mother's Name	4.6 Father's Name
1.							
2.							
3.							
4.							
5.							
6.							
7.							
8.							

(5) Half sibs.

	5.1	5.1.1	5.2	5.3	5.4	5.5	5.6
1.							
2.							
3.							

(6) Adopted sibs.

	6.1	6.1.1	6.2	6.3	6.4	6.5	6.6
1.							
2.							
3.							

III. DATA COLLECTING SHEETS

(ii) **Marriage and offspring (QUESTIONNAIRE FOR ALL SUBJECTS)**

IBP/HA Project ref. no.: ☐☐☐☐   Study no.: ☐☐

SUBJECT'S NAME: Sex: M/F   Serial Number: ☐☐☐

Name of Investigator:...................

7.1 Single/married/separated/divorced/widowed

7.2 Age at first marriage: 7.3 Number of wives now:

                                       7.4 Number of wives ever:

	8.1 Name	8.2 Identification no.	8.2.1 Date of birth	8.3 Biological relationship to subject	8.4 Spouse's age at marriage	8.4.1 Subject's age at marriage
1st. spouse						
2nd. spouse						
3rd. spouse						

	8.5 Duration of marriage	8.6 Village of residence	8.7 Village of birth	8.7.1 Distance between 8.6 & 8.7	8.8 Alive/ dead	8.8.1 Age now /at death	8.9 Cause of death
1st. spouse							
2nd. spouse							
3rd. spouse							

(continued)

III. (ii)—continued

CHILDREN

	9.1 Name	9.2 Clan name	9.2.1 Date of birth	9.3 Alive/ dead	9.4 Age now /at death	9.5 Sex	9.6 Biological father's name	9.7 Biological mother's name
1.								
2.								
3.								
4.								
5.								
6.								
7.								
8.								

	9.8 Cause of death	9.9 Marital status at death	9.10 Date of marriage	9.11 Age at marriage	9.12 Name of spouse	9.13 Serial no. of spouse
1.						
2.						
3.						
4.						
5.						
6.						
7.						
8.						

G2. SOCIO-DEMOGRAPHIC STUDIES IN RELATION TO FEMALE REPRODUCTIVE PERFORMANCE

I. INTRODUCTION

    (a) General

    (b) Observations to be made

II. TECHNIQUES

III. DATA SHEETS

I. INTRODUCTION

(a) General:

The role of environmental factors in influencing human reproduction and particularly the efficiency of child-bearing is a neglected area of investigation. Comparative studies of communities living in different habitats would throw light on the operation of such factors as socio-economic status, high altitude, hot climates, malaria, ethnic origin, etc.

The assessment of reproductive efficiency requires attention to the following:

(1) **A Social and Fertility Record** to be obtained, ideally, from both males and females. This provides a cross-sectional record of such factors as age at marriage, types of mating, relationship between partners, migration distances, physique of the mother, etc., on family size, fertility, stillbirths, etc.

This type of investigation is within the capacity of teams carrying out community studies over a relatively short period of time, given the necessary services of local interpreters and interviewers, and after establishing a good relationship with the group.

(2) **Studies of the pregnant woman.** This requires essentially a longitudinal approach, and ideally would comprise:

    (i)   the ante-natal history;
    (ii)   the performance during labour;
    (iii) the post-natal history.

(3) **Studies of the lactating woman and the progress of the infant.** This also requires a longitudinal approach.

These longitudinal studies ((2) and (3) above) obviously require continued observation of the sample of women (who will be in different stages of pregnancy at any one time). This would require not only long-term residence in the community, but would have to be based on a hospital or clinic. Within the IBP it may be possible to institute investigations of this kind where such facilities exist, or where a clinic can be set up for the duration of the Programme.

For guidance on these longitudinal studies, reference should be made to the WHO publication (in preparation) and to document HA 25/1 by Dr. D. F. Roberts.

(b) **Observations to be made:**

(i)   Family and marriage relationships (all subjects):—use **G1** Data Sheet.

(ii)   Social and fertility record, (females of reproductive age):—use **G2** Data Sheet

(iii)   Ancillary:—   1.   Medical examination (see **F1**)
2.   ' Basic list ' anthropometry (see **A1**)
3.   Nutritional assessment (minimum if time limited) (see **E1**)
4.   Assessment of habitual physical activity of women (see **C6**).
5.   Description of the enviroment (see **H**)

II.   TECHNIQUES

It is essential that Data Sheet **G1** should be filled in, as this is necessary for many of the entries on sheet **G2**, from which the female reproductive performance is to be assessed.

Explanation of the Social and Fertility Record (Data Sheet **G2** (i)).
For the sake of simplicity, a single Social and Fertility Record has been prepared for use with either male or female subjects, the irrelevant parts being ignored where appropriate.

This Record is intended to identify individuals and ideally should be completed for each individual in a community, but if this is not feasible then it must be available for all those on whom detailed studies will be made, e.g.

pregnant women, and, if possible, the baby's father (who should be interviewed independently).

(1) Subject identification:

In the upper panel of the questionnaire, the standard form of identification as used in all (tabulated) field data sheets in this Handbook is given. In addition, it is essential that the Individual Identity Sheet (01) should also be filled in. Guidance on this form is given in the Technical Introduction.

(2) Height and weight must be entered in this Record, even if the basic list of anthropometric measurements (see **A1**) is to be carried out.

(3) In the case of female subjects information should be recorded as follows: whether pregnant or lactating, or date of last menstrual period; also whether post-menopausal or not.

(4) Obvious physical characteristics:

This would identify not only the blind, deformed lepers, the mentally deranged, simpletons, etc., but also those showing evidence of physical peculiarities, e.g. cleft palate, polydactyly, or tribal markings.

(5) Migration history:

The basic information to be entered here consists of the place of birth, place of present residence and its distance from the place of birth, and the length of time in the present residence. Other relevant details of the migration history, (e.g. reasons for migration and age at each move) may also be recorded.

(6) Date of birth (or present age):

Guidance on age ascertainment is given in the Technical Introduction.

(7) Ethnic origin:

This should be ascertained in some way (e.g. by tribal markings) and should not be assumed. It is important for genetic purposes and should be clearly defined by sub-tribe, etc., where appropriate. If political or other reasons prohibit the question being asked, then this should be noted. In long-term studies as a result of long acquaintance, observation, and discreet questioning, the details required can usually be obtained eventually.

(8) Religion:

It should be fairly easy to code the major religious affiliations in any society. Information on active or passive membership might be important in some societies.

(9) Education:

Possibly the simplest information to collect would be the number of years in full-time formal education. An alternative would be to define ' literate ', ' semi-literate ', and ' illiterate ' for a community. In some preliterate societies, however, religious instruction alone may be of considerable actual or potential social or economic importance. This also applies to training in crafts which may lead to greater opportunities for mobility, seasonal employment and increased income. Details of any vocational instruction should therefore be noted.

(10) Occupation:

This usually provides the major source of income. In some areas seasonal occupations or a multiplicity of jobs are the rule. The chief source of income should be listed first followed by any subsidiary occupations. For women, activities other than normal domestic duties, whether pursued on a regular or seasonal basis in the interests of gain or of survival, e.g. trading or rice farming, should be given in order of importance.

(11) Position held:

Various hereditary, religious, administrative or political positions may carry financial advantages, (e.g. the local tax-collector may receive a commission), or allow certain privileges e.g. a headman may be permitted more wives or be expected to marry ritually every virgin.

(12) Family history:

In many ' primitive ' societies the dead ' are forgotten ' and it may be better to ask about surviving siblings only, rather than incur hostility and resentment by too detailed probing about those deceased, in view of the fact that a full reproductive history is required. In some societies adoption or fostering are common, and it may be impossible to get information on natural parents and their siblings.

In any event, every effort should be made to obtain information on the tribal and ethnic origin of both parents, because of its genetic importance. Detailed studies of kinship and family patterns are dealt with in **G1**.

(13)   Marital summary:

There are enormous variations between different societies or peoples in the range of recognised marital unions and in the number of concurrent unions allowed. Details of marital patterns will indicate the importance of different types of unions and the significance of the timing and continuity of marriage in the fertility of a community. Some knowledge of marriage customs is necessary before a suitable classification can be arrived at for any society. The one given below would probably be suitable for many polygamous societies, particularly in Africa. 'Betrothal' may be taken to indicate 'marriage unconsummated'. 'Living apart' would include desertion or separation for a specific reason, e.g. medical treatment or employment, the nature of which would be indicated by the duration of separation. 'Other states' would include for example, 'nominal marriage', a category of ritual marriage for old women found in some African societies. 'Never married' is the only exclusive category.

(14)   Living standard:

The measure of occupancy is simple and can be used to give various measures of overcrowding. In some areas, seasonal movement to live on farms or to be near water supplies occurs, and it will be appropriate to ask about this, relevant to the current or previous farming season. A detailed questionnaire for socio-medical information is given in **F1**. Housing types are simple in most rural areas, and can easily be coded.

(15)   Marriage and fertility history:

Each spouse or partner should be numbered in chronological order and identified by name and whereabouts; current betrothals should not be numbered, but may be noted separately.

Since in many societies infertility is blamed on the woman and is a matter of shame, women are less likely than men to report childless marriages. Thus comparison of marital histories given independently by men and women ensures greater accuracy of information.

Details of origin will give some idea of exogamy, and ethnic or tribal origin is of genetic importance.

The type of union could be classified as either customary, church, civil, concubinage, casual, or other (specified).

Reason for ending a union would include divorce or desertion, death or annulment. Dates (indicating whether these are actual or assessed) when unions were contracted or ended should be given if possible. Notes should include details of kinship between the partners, and any other relevant information. For men, a note on the previous marital history of the partner, e.g. virgin, widowed twice, etc., would be useful.

Information should be given for each pregnancy on the Reproductive Record (ii). Multiple births should be noted (in the ' birth rank ' column). If dates of birth are not available, birth intervals cannot be calculated. In some agricultural areas, however, the annual sequence of events is so clearly defined that recent birth dates may be assessed with reference to these with a high degree of accuracy.

Contraceptive(s) used would refer to the interval since the last pregnancy and should include details (on a separate sheet if necessary) of any native practices reported. In some societies it might be possible to ask whether a pregnancy was ' intended ', i.e. the couple were trying for conception when it occurred.

When the date of death is not known, it may be possible at least to indicate the age at which it occurred.

Other information could include information on whether abortions were spontaneous or procured.

Other data:

Lactating women are usually easy to identify.

Women may not admit to pregnancy until it is obvious, for a variety of magical or other reasons. If the date of the last menstrual period is recorded (where possible) this would help to identify not only pregnant women but also never pregnant women who had passed the menarche, and also post-menopausal women. In addition it would provide information about post-partum amenorrhoea in lactating women.

(16) Data on fertility from two generations:

The data obtained in **G1**, part (ii), and summarised in **G2**, give fertility information (that is, details of offspring) of the mating unions entered into by the informant. The data which are provided in **G1** part (i) will give information on the reproductive performance of the informant's own parents.

* For full details, see Individual Identity Sheet (01)

	IBP/HA Project ref. no.	1 ☐☐☐☐
Subject's name*:	Study number	5 ☐☐
	Serial number	7 ☐☐☐
	Age (years) *	10 ☐☐
Place of examination:	Date of examination (year) + 3 decimals—see Table in Technical Introduction)	12 ☐☐☐☐☐
	Procedure category	17 ☐☐

CODE FOR "NOT APPLICABLE" = X; CODE FOR "DATA NOT RECORDED" = Y

III. DATA COLLECTING SHEETS
(i) Social and Fertility Record (FOR FEMALE SUBJECTS ONLY)

Address of subject:	Height (mm)	19 ☐☐☐☐
	Weight (kg)	23 ☐☐☐☐
Obvious physical peculiarities:	Birth-date (year + 3 decimals—see Table in Technical Introduction)	27 ☐☐☐☐☐
Birth-place:	Number of years in full-time formal education	32 ☐☐
Present residence:	Housing type (use own code)	34 ☐
	Number of rooms	35 ☐☐
Distance from present residence to birth-place:	Marital status (never married = 0; married one spouse = 1; married more than one spouse = 2; separated = 3; divorced = 4; widowed = 5; other (specify) = 6)	37 ☐
Other details of migration history:		
(If marital status 'other', specify here):	Total number of children living	38 ☐☐
	Total number of children dead	40 ☐☐
Ethnic and tribal origin (or nationality):	If pregnant, no. of months	42 ☐
	Lactating (no = 0; yes = 1)	43 ☐
Position held (if any):	Menopause (pre- = 1; post- = 2)	44 ☐
	L.M.P. date (year + 3 decimals)	45 ☐☐☐☐☐

Occupation:

Religion:

Other details (e.g. of education):

Signature of Investigator . . . .

MARRIAGE AND FERTILITY

(i) History

Name: Serial number: ☐☐☐

Age: Occupation:

Sex: Ethnic and tribal origin (or Study number: ☐ IBP/HA Project ref. no.: ☐☐☐☐

Place: nationality):

Date: Name of investigator:

Marriage no.	Name of partner	Serial no. of partner	Birth-place	Ethnic/ tribal origin or nation-ality	Distance of birth-place from place of residence	Type of union	Date union com-menced	Date union ended	Reason for ending	Notes on kin relationship and previous marital history of partners
1										
2										
3										
4										

(continued)

Table—continued

CHILDREN

Children of marriage no.	Total no.	Living	Dead	Stillborn	No. of abortions	Multiple pregnancies
1						
2						
3						
4						

MARRIAGE AND FERTILITY

(ii) **Reproductive Record:**

(a) **Distribution of births:**

Name (of mother) :
Serial no. :
Age:
Ethnic group (or nationality) :
Place:
Date:
Name of investigator:.................

Age-category (of mother)	Period covered (years)	No. of births
15–19		
20–24		
25–29		
30–34		
35–39		
40–44		
45–49		

Years of marriage	Period covered	No. of births
0–4		
5–9		
10–14		
15–19		
20–24		
25–29		
30–34		

Total boys:
Total girls:
Total children :

(*continued*)

Table—continued

(b)   **Serial analysis of births**

Birth rank (note any multiple births)	Mother's age at each birth	Year of marriage at each birth	Birth interval since last birth	Contraceptives used (if any)— give details

H. ENVIRONMENTAL DESCRIPTION

H1. Habitat in general

H1. HABITAT IN GENERAL

I. INTRODUCTION

II. OBSERVATIONS

    (a)   Main features (topographical, physical, and biotic), and check-lits.

    (b)   Climatological description

I. INTRODUCTION

No investigation of the human biology of a group will be complete without a reasonably detailed specification of the physical and biological environment. The scope of such a description will depend on the personnel and facilities available, and should be carried out in conjunction with geographers, climatologists, botanists, and zoologists.

Within the HA programme, there will undoubtedly be areas whose topography, local climate, vegetation, fauna, etc., are not well known. For the description of the habitat, other Sections of the IBP could be approached; thus the CT Section has laid down survey methods for specifying vegetational types, climate, land topography, etc.

Clearly the extent to which the habitat is investigated must depend not only on the available facilities but also on the particular aims of the study concerned. Thus in some nutritional investigations it may be essential to carry out some form of ethnobotanical survey, to include cultivated and gathered foods, medicinal plants, vegetable body paints, etc. In such studies, accurate species identification of the relevant plants is important.

It may indeed be necessary in some cases to attempt some analysis of soil and water, for example where a team has a special interest in the local availability of such minerals as iron or fluorine, or has been asked to collect samples in connection with some of the surveys under the auspices of the W.H.O. on the distribution of the heavy metals (e.g. lead, arsenic, cobalt, copper, etc.)*

Where the nature of the study involves a knowledge of the local zoonoses, the help of medical ecologists may be essential to obtain an understanding of the local vectors and hosts.

* The international reference centre of the W.H.O. for such work is at the school of Public Health and Administrative Medicine, Columbia University, New York, N.Y. 10032, U.S.A.

It is therefore difficult to lay down in advance a detailed schedule of those items in the physical and biotic environment which would be relevant to human adaptation studies in general. It may however be helpful to set out a list of observations of a geographical and climatological character which would provide at least a basic description of the environment.

II.   OBSERVATIONS:

(a)   Main features (topographical, physical, and biotic) and check-list:*

The check-list prepared for the CT Section (IBP Handbook No. 4) provides a thorough description of the environment; for the purposes of HA surveys, a reduced version of this is presented below:

---

* Much of the material for this section was taken from 'Guide to the check-sheet for IBP Areas ', IBP Handbook No. 4., G. F. Peterken, Blackwell, Oxford, 1967.

CHECK-LIST FOR ENVIRONMENTAL DESCRIPTION IN HA STUDIES

1.1   Name of Investigator:
1.2   Address of Investigator:

2.1   Name of HA area:
2.2   Name of HA subdivision:
2.3   Map of HA area showing boundaries, attached?: yes/no
2.4   Sketch-map of HA area:

3.1   Latitude: deg.   min.   N/S   Longitude: deg.   min.   E/W
3.2   Country:
3.3   State or province:
3.4   County:
3.5   Altitude:
4   Nearest climatological station—

4.1   Name:
4.2   Climatological station on HA area?: yes/no
4.3   If (4.2) not, distance from edge of HA area (state units):
4.4   Direction from HA area:
4.5   Additional data sheet of own climatological observations attached: yes/no

5   **Vegetation:**
      Principal vegetation types (by code)*

Primary structural group	Class	Notes

* See code for vegetation types below

Code for vegetation types (Number = primary structural group; Letter = class)

1—   Closed vegetation (Crowns or peripheries of plants touching or overlapping):—
1A   Forest (closed woody vegetation 5 m. or more tall)
1B   Scrub (closed woody vegetation 5 m. or less tall)
1C   Dwarf scrub (closed predominantly woody vegetation less than 0·5 m. tall)

(continued)

CHECK-LIST FOR ENVIRONMENTAL DESCRIPTION—continued

Code for vegetation types —continued

1D Open forest with closed lower layers (trees with crowns not touching, crowns mostly not separated by more than their diameters)
1E Closed scrub with scattered trees
1F Dwarf scrub with scattered trees
1G Open scrub with closed ground cover
1H Open dwarf scrub with closed ground cover
1I Tall savanna (closed grass or other herbaceous vegetation 1 m. tall or more, with scattered trees)
1J Low savanna (herbaceous vegetation less than 1 m. tall, with scattered trees)
1K Shrub savanna (closed grass or other herbaceous vegetation with scattered shrubs)
1L Tall grass (closed herbaceous vegetation exceeding 1 m. in height, predominantly graminoid)
1M Short grass (closed herbaceous vegetation, less than 1 m. tall, predominantly graminoid)
1N Broad-leafed herb vegetation (closed vegetation, predominantly of broad-leafed herbaceous plants)
1O Closed bryoid vegetation
1P Submerged meadows (vegetation of rooted aquatic herbs, adapted for permanent complete submersion, except in some cases for floating leaves)
1Q Floating meadows (closed vegetation of aquatic herbs, adapted to floating conditions, not rooted in bottom)

2— Open vegetation (plants or tufts of plants not touching but crowns not separated by more than their diameters; plants, not substratum, dominating landscape) :—
2A Steppe forest (often called 'Woodland', or 'Woodland-Savanna') (tree layer and lower layers open, lower layers may be open or sparse)
2B Steppe scrub (like steppe forest, but with shrubs (over 0·5 m. tall) instead of trees)
2C Dwarf steppe scrub (open predominantly woody vegetation less than 0·5 m. tall)
2D Steppe savanna (steppe with scattered trees)
2E Shrub steppe savanna
2F Dwarf shrub steppe savanna
2G Steppe (open herbaceous vegetation, tufts or plants discrete, yet close enough to dominate the landscape)
2H Byroid steppe
2I Open submerged meadows
2J Open floating meadows

3— Sparse vegetation or desert (plants so scattered that substratum dominates the landscape) :—
3A Desert forest (scattered trees, subordinate shrub or herb layers very sparse, or absent)
3B Desert scrub (scattered shrubs in an otherwise bare or only ephemerally-vegetated landscape, not here differentiated into shrub and dwarf shrub classes)
3C Desert herb vegetation (scattered herbaceous plants only)
3D Sparse submerged meadows

(*continued*)

CHECK-LIST FOR ENVIRONMENTAL DESCRIPTION—continued

6   Soil

Soil category (1/2/3/4a/4b/5a/5b/6a/6b) **	Notes

** See code for soil categories below

Code for soil categories

Soil category	**Example of soil groups in each category**

1   Saline soils   e.g. Solonchak, solonetz

2   High sesquioxide (ferritic) soils   e.g. Terra rossa, rotlehm, laterite, ferritic brown earth

3   Organic soils   e.g. Peat, fen, bog

4a   Well-drained, non-saline, non-ferritic soils with good profile development—calcareous surface or sub-surface horizons   e.g. Chernozem, terra fusca

4b   Well-drained inon-saline, non-ferritic soils with good profile-development—non-calcareous throughout profile   e.g. Brown ranker, brown earth podsol

5a   Poorly-drained non-saline, non-ferritic soils with good profile development—calcareous surface or sub-surface horizons   e.g. Calcareous gley

5b   Poorly-drained non-saline, non-ferritic soils with good profile development—non-calcareous throughout profile   e.g. Non-calcareous gley

6a   Soils with weak profile development controlled by climate   e.g. Serosem, burosem, desert soil

6b   Soils with weak profile development controlled by lack of time available for profile development   e.g. Recent alluvium

(*continued*)

CHECK-LIST FOR ENVIRONMENTAL DESCRIPTION—continued

7.1   General landscape (give brief description of geomorphological features):

7.2   Relief type

	Flat	Undulating 0–200 m.	Hilly 200–1000 m.	Mountainous more than 1000 m.	%
Sharply dissected					
Gently dissected					
Incised					
Skeletonised					
%					

7.3   List any special features of landscape:

8   Coast-line of HA Area—

8.1   Substratum % of coast:

Rock	Boulder beach	Shingle beach	Sand beach	Shell beach	Mud	Coral	Ice

(*continued*)

CHECK-LIST FOR ENVIRONMENTAL DESCRIPTION—continued

8.2   Physiography % of coast:
Cliffed (wholly or partially 'vertical' with at least some part inaccessible to land animals) : . . . . %
Sloping (cliffed coast-lines in which no part is inaccessible to land animals) : . . . . %
Flat (coast-lines which lack cliffs and sloping 'cliffs') : . . . . . %

8.3   Other features:

9   Freshwater within HA Area:

	Permanent	Intermittent
Swamps		
Ponds (less than 10,000 sq. m.)		
Lakes (more than 10,000 sq. m.)		
Cold springs		
Hot springs		
Rivers more than 5 m. wide		
Streams less than 5 m. wide		

(*continued*)

CHECK-LIST FOR ENVIRONMENTAL DESCRIPTION—continued

9.1   Other freshwater features:

10.   Salt and brackish water in HA Area:
      Salt lakes/estuaries/lagoons/salt pools/other (specify):
      (Delete those not present)

11.   Outstanding faunal featues:

	Species diversity	Abundance of individuals	Superabundance of individuals
Mammalia			
Aves			
Reptilia			
Amphibia			
Pisces			
Insecta			
Other (specify)			

11.1 Names of main species:

12.   Significant human impact:—

12.1 General: None in entire HA Area/None in part of HA Area/Impact on entire HA
      Area (delete where inappropriate)

(continued)

CHECK-LIST FOR ENVIRONMENTAL DESCRIPTION—continued

12.2 Particular:

	Past impact (pre-1900)	Present impact (post-1900)	Trend				NOTES
			Incr.	Decr.	No change	No information	
Cultivation							
Drainage							
Other soil disturbance							
Grazing							
Selective flora disturbance							
Logging							
Plantation							
Hunting							
Removal of predators							
Pesticides							
Introductions —plants							
Introductions —aminals							
Fire							
Permanent habitation							
Recreation and tourism							
Research							
Other (specify)							

(*continued*)

CHECK-LIST FOR ENVIRONMENTAL DESCRIPTION—continued

12.3 Additional details on each type of impact attached?: yes/no

13.1 List major biological/geographical references for the HA Area. Sheet attached?: yes/no

13.2 List main maps available for the HA Area.
List attached?: yes/no

13.3 Aerial photographs for the HA Area available?: for whole area/for part of area/none available.

14. Other relevant information:

Signature of investigator:.....................

(b)   Climatological description:

(i)   Routine meteorological observations should be obtained from local meteorological stations or existing records. Generally, such information will comprise the daily maximum and minimum dry-bulb temperatures, the relative humidity, rainfall, and possibly air movement. These data should be recorded in the appropriate section of the check-list given above.

(ii)   Direct observation:

Because of the paucity, and in many cases inapplicability of local meteorological data, the investigating team will need to set up its own climatological battery of instruments. At the present time, reliance has still to be placed on the traditional set of instruments, but active development is going on into the production of compact long-term recording systems (usually on magnetic tape) and an appropriate assemblage of sensors. One example of such a recording system is the 'Hy-Met' system, developed by The Plessey Company Ltd., Marine Systems Division, Ilford, Essex, England.

It samples at 5, 10, 20, 30 or 60 min. intervals and has an accuracy of 0.1 % Recording capacity is 82,500 measurements and the tape can be analysed in any form using standard Plessey translation units or the translation service offered to customers of the marine-systems division.

It is an automatic self-contained climatological station that can monitor such parameters as rainfall; humidity; wind speed and direction; air, soil and water temperatures; barometric pressure; pH; solar radiation and water level and flow during three months' unattended operation.

A family of stations has been designed to meet international requirements for remote hydrological and meteorological stations. The family includes hydrometeorological, climatological, water level, water quality and recording rainfall stations. Each may be arranged for automatic operation, the recorded data being telemetered to a control centre on demand.

The heart of each station is the Plessey Hy-met recorder. This sequentially samples up to eight sensors, recording their outputs in 10-bit binary code on standard $\frac{1}{4}$ in. magnetic tape. Using one, two, four or eight channels the recorder can accept outputs from both potentiometric and voltage sensors.

Alternatively a system of recording by dry and wet ventilated thermocouples, or thermistors, and by hot-wire anemometers, with appropriate potentiometer or bridge system could be employed. The Hy-met system is also suitable for recording the thermal conditions in any microclimate, e.g., a living or working-space, under bedclothes, etc.

For specifying the **thermal environment,** the four individual thermal factors—temperature, humidity, rate of air movement, and radiation from the surroundings—must all be taken into account. A cabinet of instruments for making these measurements should include:

> Whirling hygrometer
> 2 kata thermometers, silvered (130°–125°F)
> 2 kata thermometers, silvered (150°–145°F)
> 1 black globe, for globe thermometer
> 3 thermometers for use with black globe
> 4 surface contact thermometers
> 1 radiation shield
> 1 stop-watch
> 1 vaccuum-flask
> 1 polishing cloth for kata thermometers
> 1 bottle distilled water.

Many texts are available giving full details of the instruments and measurement techniques, e.g. Bedford, T., ' Environmental Warmth and its Measurement ', **Medical Research Council War Memorandum No. 17.** London, H.M.S.O. 1940, repr. 1961.

Instrument assemblies for rapid and continuous recording of air temperature, wet-bulbs, and globe temperatures, and air velocity have been described by Hosey and Mendenhall, **Amer. Indu. Hyg. Assoc. 20:** 121–130, 1959, (the ' Envirec ') and by Walters, J. D. (1968), **Brit. J. Industr. Med.** (in press). The latter instrument can be obtained from Light Laboratories, 10 Ship St. Gdns., BRIGHTON 1, Sussex, England.

For the measurement of **solar radiation,** a standard instrument for field use is the Casella bimetallic Actinograph.

The **ultra-violet spectrum** of sunlight is of importance in understanding the significance of variations in human skin colour (see **B11**), as this is linked with the protective value of melanin pigment against the erythematous and carcinogenic action of the shortest wavelengths of sunlight. This component of sunlight accounts for only a very small fraction of the total energy and is affected by such factors as the elevation of the sun, the state of the atmosphere, the position of the earth's surface, and the time of the year. It is therefore necessary to determine the integrated exposure over long periods as well as variation in the spectrum and intensity. To make comparable estimates of exposure in different localities it is essential to use a standardised instrument.

Magnesium tungstate detector equipment developed by Mr. Don F. Robertson in the Physics Department, University of Queensland, Australia, and tested in the field over 7 years has proved very reliable for comparison of exposure at different places. The response spectrum of the detector is reasonably close to the erythemal action spectrum. Units with the same spectral response can be produced, and the sensitivity remains constant over long periods. The electrical recording system is simple and very reliable.

The equipment provides its data on a register similar to those used in recording numbers of telephone calls. This has to be read by an operator— hourly, daily, or weekly, according to the minimum period over which it is desired to integrate the data. A printer can be attached if desired; this is not manufactured as part of the equipment, but information on its performance will be supplied. It represents a moderate peak load on the AC mains (order 2A at 240 V.)

If the instrument is required to be independent of AC mains, it will be necessary to design another form of power supply, either:

(a) a power pack operated from a car battery (e.g. 12 V.) or, (b) a power pack comprised entirely of dry batteries.

The cost of the components at the present time is approximately A$750.00 = approx. U.S. $750.00 per instrument, and purchasers would need to pay the freight charges from Australia (Brisbane). The cost of assembling the components will be nominal as the Department is anxious to see this equipment in use in different parts of the world.

Enquiries about this instrument should be directed to Professor H.C. Webster, Department of Physics, University of Queensland, St. Lucia, Brisbane, Australia.

For measurement of **altitude** in the field, a suitable instrument is the " Everest Pocket Altimeter ", manufactured by Revue Thommen Ltd.,

Waldenburg, Switzerland. This instrument is robust and fairly accurate. It has to be set at sea-level, and it is best to take a number of readings over a period, and use the average.

NOTE ON SECTION I
PSYCHOPERFORMANCE TESTS

A separate Handbook dealing with tests for psychological aspects of Human Adaptability is in the course of preparation under the editorship of Dr. S. Biesheuvel, based on the recommendations of an international working party meeting in London in September 1967.

This document will be made available as soon as it is ready to those teams which propose to include psychoperformance testing in their field studies.

In general, these tests are not easy to administer in the field, and should only be undertaken after basic multi-disciplinary studies have been carried out, and the demographic and social organisation of the community is well understood. Needless to say, a high degree of cooperation from the community will be essential to the successful prosecution of these studies.

The range of psychoperformance tests which might be undertaken is very large indeed, and the selection of a realistic and manageable battery of tests suitable for use in the field will depend on the nature of the study and on what is judged to be practical in the light of data obtained from the community investigated. It is more than likely that in many instances only the simplest of tests, previously found suitable for cross-cultural use, will have to be chosen. Information will also be provided on the precautions that have to be taken to obtain reliable and meaningful test data under a variety of cultural conditions, and on the ancillary information about both the community and the sample, which is required for valid interpretation of the results of the tests. Testing using the simplest procedures would therefore have to be chosen in the first instance.

The Section on 'Psychoperformance Tests' will deal with the following major topics and techniques:

(1) Psychophysiological measurement.
(2) Psychomotor performance (including tests of motor development).
(3) Tests of perception.
(4) Higher mental processes.

ACKNOWLEDGEMENTS

CONTRIBUTORS

The editors are deeply grateful to the under-mentioned for their help with and contributions to the Sections of the Handbook as listed below.

Abbie, A. A.
University of Adelaide, Department of Anatomy and Histology, Adelaide, South Australia.
Anthropometry and anthroposcopy

Adamson, G. T.
University of Technology, Loughborough, Leics., England.
Physical fitness tests

E. Asmussen,
Laboratory for the Theory of Gymnastics, The University of Copenhagen, Denmark.
Physical fitness tests

Barnicot, N. A.
Department of Anthropology, University College, Gower Street, London, W.C.1, England.
Genetic studies

Barrett, M. J.
Dental School, University of Adelaide, South Australia 5001, Australia.
Dentition

Beaven, G. H.
National Institute for Medical Research, Holly Hill, Hampstead, London, N.W.3, England.
Blood collection and sub-division

Bonjer, F. H.
Department of Occupational Medicine, Netherlands Institute for Preventive Medicine, Wassenaarseweg 56, Leiden, The Netherlands.
Work capacity studies

Brabant, H.
2 Place Constantion Meunier, Brussels, Belgium.
Dental studies

Brothwell, D. R.
Sub-Department of Physical Anthropology, Department of Palaeontology, British Museum (Natural History), Cromwell Road, South Kensington, London, S.W.7, England.
Anthroposcopy, particularly for photographic methods; Dentition

# 606 *Acknowledgements*

Brozek, J.
Nutritional Department, Lehigh University, Bethlehem, Pennsylvania 18015, U.S.A.
Growth and physique studies

Carlson, L. D.
School of Medicine, University of California at Davis, Davis, California 95616, U.S.A.
Climatic studies, particularly for "The Whole Body Cold Tolerance Waking Test"

Carter, C. O.
Clinical Genetics Research Unit, Institute of Child Health, 30 Guilford Street, London, W.C.1, England.
Genetic studies

Chambers, M.
C/o Division of Human Physiology, National Institute for Medical Research, Holly Hill, Hampstead, London, N.W.3, England.
Nutritional studies, particularly for food intake survey methods

Churchill, E.
Antioch College, Yellow Springs, Ohio, U.S.A.
Sampling methods

Clarke, C. A.
The University of Liverpool, Department of Medicine, Ashton Street, Liverpool 3, England.
"Detection of Foetal Red Cells in Maternal Blood"

Clarke, H. Harrison,
Professor of Physical Education, University of Oregon, Eugene, Oregon, U.S.A.
Physical fitness tests

Collins, K. J.
M.R.C. Environmental Physiology Research Unit, London School of Hygiene and Tropical Medicine, Keppel Street (Gower Street), London, W.C.1, England.
'Salt and water studies"

Corbett, J. L.
Department of Neurology, Churchill Hospital, Oxford, England.
"Salt and water studies"

Cotes, J. E.
Pneumoconiosis Research Unit of the M.R.C., Llandough Hospital, Penarth, Glamorgan, Wales.
Pulmonary function tests, particularly "Forced Expiratory Volume and Vital Capacity"

Crockford, G. W.
M.R.C. Environmental Physiology Research Unit, London School of Hygiene and Tropical Medicine, Keppel Street (Gower Street), London, W.C.1, England.
Multi-stress heat tolerance tests

Dahlberg, A. L.
Department of Anthropology, 1126 East 59th Street, Chicago 37, Illinois, U.S.A.
Dentition

Damon, D. A.
Harvard University, Department of Anthropology, Peabody Museum, Cambridge, Massachusetts 02138, U.S.A.
Anthroposcopy

Davies, C. T. M.
M.R.C. Environmental Physiology Research Unit, London School of Hygiene and Tropical Medicine, Keppel Street (Gower Street), London, W.C.1, England.
Work capacity studies, particularly measurement of maximum aerobic power

Davies, T. W.
Division of Human Physiology, National Institute for Medical Research, Holly Hill, Hampstead, London, N.W.3, England.
Blood pressure assessment

Durnin, J. V. G. A.
Department of Physiology, The University, Glasgow, W.2, Scotland.
Nutritional studies

Edholm, O. G.
Division of Human Physiology, National Institute for Medical Research, Holly Hill, Hampstead, London, N.W.3, England.
"Assessment of Habitual Physical Activity"

Fitheridge, A.
Department of Growth and Development, Institute for Child Health, 30 Guilford Street, London, W.C.1, England.
Growth and physique studies

Fox, R. H.
Division of Human Physiology, National Institute for Medical Research, Holly Hill, Hampstead, London, N.W.3, England.
"Controlled Hyperthemia Heat Tolerance Test"

Fujiki, N.
Chief, Division of Haematology and Genetics, Assistant Professor of Internal Medicine, Kyoto Prefectural University of Medicine, Japan.
Genetic and demographic studies

Garn, S. M.
Department of Growth and Genetics, The Fels Research Institute, Yellow Springs, Ohio, U.S.A.
Dentition

Goodwin, M. J.
Serological Population Genetics Laboratory, St. Bartholomew's Hospital, West Smithfield, London, E.C.1, England.
Blood group testing

Hamerton, J. L.
Paediatric Research Unit, Guy's Hospital Medical School, London, S.E.1, England.
"Cytogenetics"

Hammel, H. T.
Scripps Institute of Oceanography, La Jolla, California, U.S.A.
"Whole Body Cold Tolerance Sleeping Test"

Harrison, G. A.
Anthropology Laboratory, Department of Human Anatomy, South Parks Road, Oxford, England.
"Skin Colour Measurement by Spectrophotometer"

Hart, J. S.
Animal Physiology Section, National Research Council, Ottawa 2, Canada.
Cold tolerance studies

Healy, M. J. R.
M.R.C. (Clinical Research Centre), 172, Tottenham Court Road, London, W.1, England.
Sampling methods; demographic assessment

Heath, B.
5 Via Joaquin, Monterey, California, U.S.A.
Somatotyping

Hellström, B.
Institute of Work Study, Gydas vei 8, Oslo 3, Norway.
Work capacity studies

Henschel, A.
Physiology Section, Department of Health, Education and Welfare, U.S.P.H.S. Bureau of State Services, 1014 Broadway, Cincinnati 2, Ohio, U.S.A.
"Multi-stress Heat Tolerance Tests"

Hiernaux, J.
Centre de Biologie Humaine, Instituut de Sociologie, 44 Avenue Jeanne, Brussels 5, Belgium.
"Growth and physique"

Howell, M. L.
Faculty of Physical Education, The University of Alberta, Edmonton, Alberta, Canada.
"Tests with Dynamometers"

Acknowledgements 609

Hodgson, T.
Heat Mechanics Research Department, National Mechanical Engineering Research Institute, Council for Scientific and Industrial Research, Pretoria, South Africa.
"A Mobile Hot-Room for Field Use"

Hughes, P.
Department of Ergonomics, University of Technology, Loughborough, Leicestershire, England.
Radiography

Huizinga, J.
Instituut voor Antropobiology, Achter den Dom 24, Utrecht, The Netherlands.
Genetic studies

Hunt, T. J.
Division of Human Physiology, National Institute for Medical Research, Holly Hill, Hampstead, London, N.W.3, England.
Assessment of habitual activity

Ikai, M.
School of Education, University of Tokyo, Hongo, Tokyo, Japan.
Work capacity studies

Jarman, S.
Institute of Child Health, Department of Growth and Development, 30 Guilford Street, London, W.C.1, England.
"Growth and Physique"

Johnson, R. H.
Department of Neurology, Glasgow University, Glasgow, Scotland.
"Salt and Water Studies"

Kalmus, H.
The Galton Laboratory, Department of Human Genetics and Biometry, University College, Gower Street, London, W.C.1, England.
"P.T.C. Taste-testing in the field"; *"Colour-confusion Charts for Testing Colour Vision"*

Karvonen, M. J.
Physiological Department, Institute of Occupational Health, Haartmaninkatu 1, Helsinki 25, Finland.
Habitual physical activity

King, C. G.
International Union of Nutritional Sciences, St. Luke's Hospital Centre, Amsterdam Avenue at 114th Street, New York 10025, U.S.A.
Nutritional studies

Krog, J.
Department of Biophysics and Physiology, University of Kentucky Medical Centre, Lexington, Kentucky, U.S.A.
"*Whole Body Cold Tolerance Waking Test*"

Lakowski, R.
Psychology Department, University of Edinburgh, Edinburgh, Scotland.
"*Tests of Colour Vision by Anomaloscope*"

Lange-Andersen, K.
State School of Physical Therapy, Trondheimsveien 132, Oslo, Norway.
Work capacity studies

Leblanc, J.
Department of Physiology, School of Medicine, Laval University, Quebec, Canada.
"*Cold-induced Pressor Test*"; "*Cold-induced Vasodilatation Test*"

Lee, D. H. K.
National Environmental Health Sciences Center, P.O. Box 12233, Research Triangle Park, North Carolina 27709, U.S.A.
Heat tolerance studies

Lehmann, H.
Honorary Director, Abnormal Haemoglobin Research Unit, University Department of Biochemistry, Tennis Court Road, Cambridge.
Genetic studies

Lewis, S. M.
Royal Postgraduate Medical School, Ducane Road, London, W.12, England.
Haematological tests

Lourie, J. A.
Division of Human Physiology, National Institute for Medical Research, Holly Hill, Hampstead, London, N.W.3., England.
Skin-colour measurement by spectrophotometry; Tests with dynamometers.

Macnab, R. B. J.
Faculty of Physical Education, The University of Alberta, Edmonton, Alberta, Canada.
Physical fitness tests

Malhotra, K. C.
Postgraduate and Research Institute, Deccan College, Poona 6, India.
Morphological assessment

Malhotra, M. S.
Defence Institute of Physiology, c/o Madras Medical College, Madras 3, India.
Physical fitness tests

Mandel, S. P. H.
World Health Organization, Division of R.E.C.S., Geneva, Switzerland.
Sampling methods

Margaria, R.
Istituto di Fisiologia Umana, University of Milan, Milan, Italy.
Work capacity tests, particularly "Anaerobic Power"

McCance, R. A.
Sidney Sussex College, Cambridge.
Salt and water studies

McConnell, R. B.
Department of Medicine, University of Liverpool, Ashton Street, Liverpool, 3, England.
Tests on saliva and urine

Merriman, J. E.
University of Saskatchewan, University Hospital, Saskatoon, Canada.
Work capacity studies

Miller, D. S.
Department of Nutrition, Queen Elizabeth College, Campden Hill Road, London, W.8, England.
Nutritional studies

Morrison, J. F.
Human Sciences Laboratory, P.O. Box 809, Johannesburg, South Africa.
"Whole Body Cold Tolerance Waking Test"

Mourant, A. E.
Serological Population Genetics Laboratory, St. Bartholomew's Hospital, West Smithfield, London, E.C.1., England.
Genetic studies, particularly "Blood Collection and Sub-division"; "Transport of Blood Specimens"

Nadot, R.
Institut National d'Études Démographique, 23–25, Avenue Franklin D. Roosevelt, Paris, 8e, France.
Demographic assessment

Neel, J. V.
Department of Human Genetics, University of Michigan Medical School, 1133 E. Catherine Street, Ann Arbor, Michigan, U.S.A.
Genetic studies

Ohara, K.
Department of Physiology, Nagoya City University Medical School, Mizuho-Ku, Kawazumi-Cho, Nagoya, Japan.
Heat tolerance tests

Pariskova, J.
Vyzkumny Ustav Telovychovny, Prague 3, Ujezd 450, Czechoslovakia.
Skin-fold measurement

Peterken, G. F.
Monks Wood Experimental Station, Abbots Ripton, Huntingdon, England.
Environmental description

Pickford, R. W.
Psychology Department, Adam Smith Building, The University, Glasgow, W.2.
"Tests of Colour Vision by Anomaloscope"

Pinsent, R. J. F. H.
Research Adviser, The College of General Practitioners, 1 Mayfield Road, Handsworth, Birmingham, 19, England.
"Continued Morbidity Survey"

Pirie, N. W.
Rothamsted Experimental Station, Harpenden, Herts, England.
Nutritional studies

Polunin, I.
Department of Social Medicine, The University, Singapore.
General medical examination

Price Evans, D.
Nuffield Unit of Medical Genetics, The Department of Medicine, The University, Liverpool, 7, England.
"Testing for Acetylator Phenotype in the Field"

Ritchie, J. A. S.
Department of Human Nutrition, London School of Hygiene and Tropical Medicine, Keppel Street (Gower Street), London, W.C.1, England.
Nutritional studies

Roberts, D. F.
Laboratory of Human Genetics, University of Newcastle upon Tyne, 19 Claremont Place, Newcastle upon Tyne, England.
"Dematoglyphics"; *"List of Congenital Defects"*, *"Demographic Assessment and Related Socio-Cultural Factors"*

Rose, G. A.
Department of Medical Statistics and Epidemiology, London School of Hygiene and Tropical Medicine, Keppel Street (Gower Street), London, W.C.1, England.
Blood pressure determination

Schull, W. J.
Department of Human Genetics, The University of Michigan Medical School, Ann Arbor, Michigan, U.S.A.
Sampling methods

Seliger, V.
Department of Physiology, Faculty of Physical Education and Sport, Ujezd 450, Prague, Mala Strana, Czechoslovakia.
Tests of physical fitness

Shephard, R. J.
Department of Physiological Hygiene, School of Hygiene, University of Toronto, Toronto, Canada.
Work capacity tests, particularly measurements of maximum aerobic power

Shine, I.
Department of Genetics, University of Hawaii, Honolulu.
"List of Congenital Defects"

Sloan, A. W.
Department of Physiology and Pharmacology, Medical School, University of Cape Town, Observatory, Cape Town, South Africa.
Performance tests

Steele, P.
55A, Alpha Road, Cambridge, England.
Thyroid studies

Sunderland, E.
Department of Anthropology, Science Laboratories, South Road, Durham City, England.
Anthroposcopy

Sutter, J.
Institut National d'Études Démographiques, 23–25 Avenue Franklin D. Roosevelt, Paris, 8e, France.
"Demographic Assessment and Related Socio-Cultural Factors"

Tanner, J. M.
Institute of Child Health, Department of Growth and Development, 30 Guilford Street, London, W.C.1, England.
"Growth and Physique"

Thompson, B.
Medical Sociology Research Unit, Foresterhill, Aberdeen, Scotland.
"Socio-demographic Studies in Relation to Female Reproductive Performance"

Tills, D.
Serological Population Genetics Laboratory, St. Bartholomew's Hospital, West Smithfield, London, E.C.1, England.
Genetic studies, particularly blood collection and transport, and *"G6PDD Testing in the Field"*

Tobias, P. V.
University of the Witwatersrand, Medical School, Hospital Street, Johannesburg, South Africa.
Anthropometry and anthroposcopy

Turner, R. W. D.
Department of Medicine, The University, 12 George Square, Edinburgh 8, Scotland.
General medical examination

Walsh, R. J.
The University of New South Wales, School of Human Genetics, P.O. Box 1, Kensington, Australia.
Genetic studies

Walters, J. D.
Hospital for Tropical Diseases, 4 St. Pancras Way, London, N.E.1, England.
General medical examination

Ward, M. P.
15 St. Mary Abbots Court, Warwick Gardens, London, W.14, England.
Environmental description (altitude)

Webb, C. G.
Building Research Station, Garston, Watford, Herts, England.
Thermal comfort assessment

Webster, H. C.
Department of Physics, University of Queensland, St. Lucia, Brisbane, Australia.
Environmental description (ultra-violet radiation)

Weiner, J. S.
M.R.C. Environmental Physiology Research Unit, London School of Hygiene and Tropical Medicine, Keppel Street (Gower Street), London, W.C.1, England.
"Sweat-Gland Counts over the Whole Body"; *"Salt and Water Studies"*

Wenzel, H. G.
Max-Planck Institut für Arbeitsphysiologie, 46 Dortmund, Rheinlanddamm 201, Germany.
Heat tolerance studies

Whitehouse, R. H.
Department of Growth and Development, Institute of Child Health, 30 Guilford Street, London, W.C.1, England.
Anthropometry

Williams, C. G.
Human Sciences Laboratory, P.O. Box 809, Johannesburg, South Africa.
"Multi-stress Heat Tolerance Tests"

Williams, E. S.
Institute of Nuclear Medicine, Middlesex Hospital Medical School, London, W.1, England.
"Thyroid and Related Studies"

Wilson, J. O. C.
M.R.C. Environmental Physiology Research Unit, London School of Hygiene and Tropical Medicine, Keppel Street (Gower Street), London, W.C.1, England.
"Sweat Gland Counts over the Whole Body"

Wilson, O.
Department of Hygiene, Lund University, Lund, Sweden.
"Thyroid and Related Studies"

Wolff, H. S.
National Institute for Medical Research, Holly Hill, Hampstead, London, N.W.3, England.
Assessment of habitual activity

Wyndham, C. H.
Human Sciences Laboratory, P.O. Box 809, Johannesburg, South Africa.
"Measurement of Maximum Aerobic Power"; *"Whole Body Cold Tolerance Waking Test"*; *"Multi-stress Heat Tolerance Test"*.

HA CONSULTANTS

Growth and Physique Studies

Professor J. M. Tanner,
Department of Growth and Development, Institute of Child Health, 30 Guilford Street, London, W.C.1, England.

Respiratory Physiology Studies

Dr. J. E. Cotes,
Pneumoconiosis Research Unit, Llandough Hospital, Penarth, Glamorgan, Wales.

Work Capacity Studies

Professor K. Lange Andersen,
State School of Physical Therapy, Trondheimsveien 132, Oslo, Norway.

Cold Tolerance Studies

Professor L. D. Carlson,
School of Medicine, University of California at Davis, Davis, California 95616, U.S.A.

Heat Tolerance Studies

Dr. C. H. Wyndham,
Human Sciences Laboratory, Chamber of Mines Research Laboratories, P.O. Box 809, Johannesburg, South Africa.

Heat Tolerance Studies (Controlled Hyperthermia Technique)

Dr. R. H. Fox,
Division of Human Physiology, National Institute for Medical Research (Medical Research Council Laboratories) Holly Hill, Hampstead, London, N.W.3, England.

Studies on the Genetic Structure of Populations

Professor J. V. Neel,
Department of Human Genetics, University of Michigan Medical School, 1133 E. Catherine Street, Ann Arbor, Michigan, U.S.A.

Studies of Migrant and Isolate Groups

Professor F. S. Hulse,
Department of Anthropology, University of Arizona, Tucson, Arizona 85721, U.S.A.

Blood Group and Associated Surveys

Dr. A. E. Mourant,
Serological Population Genetics Laboratory, c/o St. Bartholomew's Hospital, West Smithfield, London, S.E.1, England.

Socio-Demographic and Population Dynamics Studies

Dr. J. Sutter,
Institut National d'Études Demographiques, 23–25 Avenue Franklin D. Roosevelt, Paris, VIIIᵉ, France.

Studies on Human Nutrition

Professor C. G. King,
International Union of Nutritional Sciences, Institute of Nutrition Sciences, Colombia University, 562 West 168th Street, New York 10032, U.S.A.

COMMISSION ON PHYSIOLOGICAL ANTHROPOMETRY OF IUPS
(1963–1968)

Chairman:	Professor J. S. Weiner	(UK)
	Professor K. Lange Andersen	(Norway)
	Dr. O. G. Edholm	(UK)
	Professor H. T. Hammel	(USA)
	Professor B. Metz	(France)
	Dr. L. G. C. E. Pugh	(UK)
	Professor J. M. Tanner	(UK)
	Dr. C. H. Wyndham	(South Africa)

U.N. AGENCY REPORTS

W.H.O. Monograph Series No. 53, 1966. Jelliffe, D. B. "The assessment of nutritional status of the community".

F.A.O. Nutritional Studies No. 18, 1962. Reh, E. "Manual on household food consumption surveys".

W.H.O. Monograph Series No. 56, 1968. Rose, G. A. and Blackburn, H. "Cardiovascular survey methods".

W.H.O. Technical Report Series No. 258, 1963. "Expert committee on medical assessment of nutritional status".

W.H.O. Technical Report Series No. 387, 1968. "Research on human population genetics".

INDEX